TO THE *Stutterer*

SPEECH FOUNDATION OF AMERICA

D0453308

Published by
SPEECH FOUNDATION OF AMERICA
Publication No. 9

First Printing—1972

Second Printing—1973

Speech Foundation of America
152 Lombardy Road
Memphis, Tennessee 38111

Additional copies of this booklet $1.00.

To the Adult Stutterer:

This is a remarkable book of therapy advice. Nothing like it has ever been published before. What makes it unique and unusual is that every article in this book has been written by men and women who have been stutterers themselves. Each one of them has been 'through the mill' and knows what it is to have experienced the fear, anxiety and despair which is so often the lot of the stutterer. They know your problem.

Also all of the authors of these articles are now or have been speech pathologists. This means that they are experienced and trained in helping others with their speech problems—and they have written these articles to help you eliminate your stuttering. On the next four pages we list their twenty-four names.

They represent a most distinguished array of authority and prestige in the field of stuttering. Included among them are sixteen who are or have been university professors of speech pathology, six who are or have been heads of speech pathology departments in such institutions, twelve who are or have been directors of speech and hearing clinics, and they include two psychiatrists, nine Fellows of the American Speech and Hearing Association and nine authors of books on the therapy of stuttering.

Although these writers do not all agree as to exactly what you should do to overcome your difficulty, there is a lot of uniformity in their recommendations and in their thinking. We believe that their ideas will help you. We are publishing this book in your interest and hope that you will make use of it. Good luck to you!

Malcolm Fraser

For the Speech Foundation of America
Memphis, Tennessee
September 1, 1972

Contents/Authors

Contents/Authors

Contents/Authors

Contents/Authors

Express Yourself Or Go By Freight

LON L. EMERICK

One score and seven years ago, in a desperate attempt to cure their son's chronic speech problem, my parents spent their meagre savings to send me to a commercial school for stammering. Alas, to their dismay and my deepening feeling of hopelessness, it was just another futile attempt. While I rode woefully toward home on the train, a kindly old gray-haired conductor stopped at my seat and asked my destination. I opened my mouth for the well-rehearsed "Detroit" but all that emerged was a series of muted gurgles; I pulled my abdominal muscles in hard to break the terrifying constriction in my throat—silence. Finally, the old man peered at me through his bifocals, shook his head and, with just the trace of a smile, said, "Well, young man, either express yourself or go by freight."

The conductor had shuffled on down the aisle of the rocking passenger car before the shock waves swept over me. Looking out the window at the speeding landscape through a tearful mist of anger and frustration, I felt the surreptitious glances of passengers seated nearby; a flush of crimson embarrassment crept slowly up my neck and my head throbbed with despair. Long afterwards I remembered the conductor's penetrating comment. For years I licked that and other stuttering wounds and nursed my wrath to keep it warm, dreaming that someday I would right all those unrightable wrongs. But in the end his pithy pun changed my life. The old man, incredibly, had been right.

Why indeed go by freight? Why carry excess baggage, endure endless delays, languish forgotten and rejected in sooty siding yards, be bombarded with countless jolts and unplanned stops? Why let your journey through life be dictated by the time table of stuttering? Perhaps you too are searching for some way out of a morass of jumbled box cars and the maze of tracks that seem to lead only to empty, deadened spurs. Although it is difficult to give advice without seeing you and identifying your particular situation, I do know there are several things that have helped me and many other stutterers. May I extend this challenge to you: I invite you to do something difficult but with a sweet reward—to change the way you talk. The pathway to better speech is fraught with blind alleys, dark frightening tunnels and arduous climbs. Beware of any treatment that plumes itself in novelty and promises no pain; deep inside you know this cannot work. May I show you the trail?

The first thing you must do is admit to yourself that you need to change, that you really want to do something about the way you presently talk. This is tough but your commitment must be total; not even a small part of you must hold back. Don't dwell longingly on your fluency in the magical belief that someday your speech blocks will disappear. There is no magic potion, no pink pill that will cure stuttering. Don't sit around waiting for the right time, for an inspiration to come to you— *you must go to "it."* You must see that the old solutions, the things you have done to help yourself over the years (and those cover-up suggestions from well-meaning amateur therapists, "Think what you want to say," "Slow down," etc.) simply do not work. Ruts wear deep, though, and you will find it difficult to change; even though the way you presently talk is not particularly pleasant, it is familiar. It is the unknown from which we shrink.

You must be willing to endure temporary discomfort, perhaps even agony, for long range improvement. No one, except perhaps the quack, and there are still a few around, is promising you a rose garden. Why not take the time and effort now for a lifetime of freedom from your tangled tongue? How can you do that? You break down the global problem of stuttering into its smaller parts and then solve them one at a time. It's *simple*. No one said it was *easy*. Shall we begin?

1. Are you acquainted with your stuttering pattern? What do you *do* when you stutter? What can you *see, hear* and *feel*? Where are the triggers for those sticky blocks or runaway repetitions? How does your moment of stuttering progress from the first expectation you are going to stutter until the word is uttered? How do you release a block . . . an extra surge of energy, a sudden jerk of your head? I am asking you to observe closely what you do when you stutter; you can use a mirror, a tape recorder, your finger tips to search for areas of tension. A friend or relative whom you trust can also help you make a careful inventory. Stuttering is not some mysterious beast that

takes over your mouth—even though it may appear that way because it seems to occur so automatically. Stuttering is a series of activities that you *do*. It is your way of talking for now. Before you can change what you do, obviously you have to spend some time cataloging precisely what it is you do. Here is how one stutterer described his stuttering pattern:

Can tell when I'm going to stutter . . . at least three words ahead. Tense my lower jaw. Purse my lips tightly . . . even when trying to say the /k/ sound! Blink my eyes shut and turn my head down and toward the right. I push harder and finally utter the word, "kite," by jerking my jaw forward.

2. Now, when you have a good idea of what you do when you stutter, set up a program of change. Take all the elements —the excess baggage—that make up your stuttering pattern and consciously and deliberately attempt to *add* (exaggerate), *vary* (instead of jerking your head to the right, jerk it to the left) and *drop* (stutter without that one mannerism) the separate aspects, one at a time. Start in an easy situation—alone, perhaps—and gradually increase the difficulty. Here is a chart that will help you organize your practice time:

head jerk	*Add*	*Vary*	*Drop*
	Monday, read aloud for 15 minutes.	Wednesday, read aloud for 15 minutes.	Friday, read aloud for 15 minutes.
	Exaggerate head jerk to the *left*.	*Exaggerate* easy head jerks to the *right*.	*Stop* use of head jerk.

(Follow this same plan for changing the other elements of your stuttering pattern; lip tensing, eye blink, etc.)

But, you say, I want to *stop* stuttering. Sure! But first you need to break up the habit pattern that you have built up over the years and this cannot be done instantly. The habit is powerful, because at the end of all the tension and struggle, the word does usually emerge. In a sense, then, stuttering works—so you persist in using the rituals that allow you to escape from stuttering. To break up a habit, you must alter its stereotyped nature.

3. When you are familiar with the various elements comprising your stuttering pattern and can alter them, then try to stutter more *easily* and *openly*. In a very real sense, the best

advice I can give you is that you must learn to stutter better, with a minimum of tension and hurry. Instead of pushing so hard, try to ease out of your blocks by sliding into the first syllable of the word; start the *movement* and *sound* flow at the same time and glide into the word. Use strong movements of your lips and jaw and *feel* the shifts in those structures as you move *forward* through a word. Much of the agony and consequent social punishment of stuttering comes from tensing and. holding back. Here are some instructions we gave to a stutterer recently who was learning to turn his stuttering on and off:

> When I raise my finger, you increase the pressure
> —to a real hard block. Then, as I lower my finger,
> slowly let the tension come out. That's right. Now,
> go back and forth on your own: increase and
> decrease the tension. Learn to play with your
> blocks this way; get the *feel* of coming out of those
> hard fixations.

4. Now I am going to ask you to do a strange thing: *to stutter on purpose*. I know, it sounds weird but it works. Why? Because it helps to drain away the fear (what have you got to hide if you are willing to stutter on purpose?) and it provides a lot of experience practicing the act of stuttering in a highly voluntary and purposeful manner. The more you stutter on purpose, the less you hold back; and the less you hold back, the less you stutter. We once worked with a young exchange student who almost completely extinguished her stuttering in one week by doing negative practice. We were enmeshed in doctoral examinations so we gave her a hand-counter and told her: "There are 100,000 people living in Lansing; see how many you can talk to and. show your stuttering." When I saw her seven days later she was haggard and worn but grinning broadly and not stuttering. Having taken us literally she had worked around the clock. Incredibly she had confronted 947 listeners! And she was totally unable to stutter involuntarily.

5. You must sharply reduce or eliminate the avoidances you use. Everytime you substitute one word for another, use a sound or some trick to get speech started, postpone or give up an attempt at talking, you make it harder for yourself. Instead of diminishing when evaded, fears incubate and grow. The avoider must maintain constant vigilance and continually devise new ways to elude the dreaded words, listeners or situations. It's like

pouring water into a leaking cask. Make a list of all your avoidances: What types do you use (starters, delaying tactics, etc.)? When, in what contexts do you use them? How frequently do you resort to evasion? In other words, prepare an avoidance inventory. Then, systematically vary and exaggerate each one; use the avoidances when you don't need to in a highly voluntary manner. Finally, when you find yourself using an avoidance involuntarily, invoke a self-penalty; for example, if you avoid the word "chocolate," you must then use that word several times immediately thereafter. One of the best penalties is to explain to the listener the avoidance you have just used and why you should resist such evasions.

6. No stutterer is an island. Peoples' reactions to you and your interpretations of their reactions have, as you know, a profound effect upon your speech. You need to go out and renew your acquaintance with listeners; you need to talk to all kinds of people in all kinds of situations. Set up daily quotas or challenges for yourself; enter those tough speaking situations and demonstrate to yourself that you can, even though stuttering, get the message across. Any adventure is more fun when shared with congenial and helpful companions. Fortunately, there is a group, the Council of Adult Stutterers with chapters in many parts of the country, that can provide information and support especially in this important aspect of altering old attitudes about your speech problem.*

7. Strange as it seems, you may find it difficult to adjust to more fluent speech. For years you have been laboring from block to block, you have been speaking a stuttering language. And, if you have used stuttering as an excuse or crutch, you may feel naked and exposed without it. The best antidote is to practice your new fluency until it becomes familiar to you. Plug your ears and read aloud, feeling the flow of words; shadow-talk along with speakers on radio or television; enroll for a speech course in your local area.

Licking the problem of stuttering, mastering your own mouth, takes time; it cannot be accomplished overnight. How long it will take you I cannot say, for no two stutterers approach the challenge in the same way or move at the same rate but all have in common a beckoning mirage luring them ahead. Here then are the foundation blocks. Can you create from them stepping stones? Don't go any farther by freight. Express yourself!

*Write to Professor Eugene Walle, The Council of Adult Stutterers, Catholic University of America, Washington, D.C. 20017.

Stuttering: What You Can Do About It

Margaret Rainey

I deeply wish that I could reach every stutterer in the world to tell the story I am about to tell here. Last evening, as a speech clinician, I gave a speech to a large group of people who were vitally interested in stutterers and in the nature of stuttering. This morning as I sit drinking my coffee, and while the memories and experiences of last evening are vivid, I want to share my feelings and my knowledge with as many stutterers as possible.

It is interesting that I had no fear of that audience. I had no dread of the monsters of fear that once reared their ugly heads and choked off my words and even my thoughts. Yes, I am a stutterer, and I hope that it will help any stutterer who may read this to know that I was such a severe stutterer that I could not put two meaningful words together until I was twenty-four years old. Do I still stutter? Oh, I call myself a stutterer because I still have small interruptions in my speech now and then. But there's another more important reason why I call myself a stutterer. *I'm not trying to hide the fact anymore!* I learned long ago that the harder I tried to camouflage my stuttering, the more severely I stuttered. It was a vicious circle and I wanted out. So I got out! How? I stopped stuttering severely with much less effort than I once used in trying in the wrong way to stop. And the wrong ways were to try to run from it, hide from it and forget it. I made the mistake of using every trick in the book to pretend to be a normal speaker, but none of the tricks worked for long. Failures only increased, and after years of agony I finally discovered that it was finally time to make an about-face. Why try to avoid and camouflage stuttering any longer? Who was I trying to fool? I knew that I stuttered, and so did my listeners. I finally took time out to ask myself why I should continue to fight the old, destructive feelings in the wrong way. I began to look at these feelings, and as I began to accept them and my stuttering, success in speaking began. It is interesting that the old ways of struggling were so difficult to give up. It felt as though I had an angry tiger by the tail and dared not let go.

I talked to the hearts of that excellent audience last evening and didn't pull my punches. Nobody should ever pull their punches when talking about the problem of stuttering. The problem is too vital to be treated in any other manner than with the truth. After the session was over I was gathering my notes together when I looked up and in front of me stood a young man in the throes of trying to say something. We shook hands and I listened and waited. A severe stutterer he was—so severe that apparently he dared not introduce himself. We sat down so that we might be as comfortable as possible, and in his unique pattern of speech, he asked some pertinent questions about himself and his stuttering.

The young man's first question had to do with whether there might be a physical cause for his stuttering. He explained that he was five years old when he was hit by a car and said that the scar was still on his neck. He wondered what other reason there could be to prevent him from saying his words fluently. To be struck by a car is a traumatic incident indeed, but I told this young man that his real scars were psychological ones and that the physical one on his neck was only skin deep. He was anxious to know what those psychological scars were and I was anxious to tell him that *he* knew better than *I*. "The answers lie in your looking closely at your stuttering pattern and at yourself."

This sincere young man asked a gut level question which all stutterers ask, "What do people think of me?" He said that he was weary of laughter and ridicule. I tried to explain that to a great extent he was putting the cart before the horse, the most important question that he should investigate is *what he thinks of himself*. I strongly suggested that he was by far his worst critic and that he had been living for years being his worst critic. But I also told him that he had lived most of his verbal life upon the judgments and misjudgments of others.

"It's your job," I emphasized, "to help other people understand. There's nothing like understanding that makes for the acceptance of differences. Help normal speakers to understand that what they are doing to stutterers is well-meaning, but wrong." I explained to him that we both knew that stuttering is indeed behavior which *is* different and that realistically we should not expect a person who has never had the problem to know what to do about it when he sees and hears it in another person.

I went further with this explanation because he was listening so intently. "When your listener looks away from you, it is because he thinks that you *want* him to look away. Ask him not to do it. It's as simple as this! When a listener laughs out of embarrassment, it might be tremendously helpful to realize that the embarrassment is the listener's, not yours. Don't borrow trouble, you've got enough of your own!"

We both agreed that the stutterer's listener should react to him just as though he is a normal person with an interesting kind of speech difference. That's how stutterers *want* to be treated, but they never request it. As a matter of fact, I had to tell him that *I* would feel more comfortable if he would look at me while we talked, and it was interesting that as he began to look at me he struggled less and less.

Now it was my turn to ask a question and I asked whether or not he thought that he had suffered long enough in feeling himself to be inferior. I indicated that his world of agony did not hinge solely upon his stumbling speech. His attitudes about himself, his listener and his speech were important. Hadn't he struggled long enough, and in vain, to pretend as best he could that he was not a stutterer? Be done with swinging at these straw men! They were *his* ghosts, not his listener's. I told him that his fear of stuttering is the greater part of the reason that he stutters. He seemed to understand.

It was my turn to ask still another question. "When was the last time you discussed your stuttering with anyone?" He said that he had never talked about it with anyone. "You know," I replied, "just as eye communication during speech is one of the most important ways to tell the other person that you have something to communicate, so is open discussion of your stuttering and your feelings about it." One of the biggest mistakes that stutterers and normal speakers make is to consider this problem to be a verboten, hush-hush subject.

I explained to this handsome young man (who had described himself as being repulsive) that no two stutterers stutter alike. Yet, every stutterer possesses two very strong and incapacitating feelings in common: *Fear* and *Anxiety*. Herein lies the heart of his problem. If the fear of stuttering can be reduced, then certainly stuttering itself can be reduced.

He wanted to know whether or not there would ever really be a cure for him. All stutterers search for the magic pill. I told him that a "cure" is rare, but not impossible. "But this doesn't mean that you have to live the rest of your verbal life in struggling. Why wrestle with those words so hard? You're even struggling between words," I pointed out to him. "You must be very tired!" He agreed that he was. Then I told him something else that gave him pause: "Don't make the mistake of trying to compete with others. Compete with yourself—from day to day, from speaking situation to speaking situation and from word to word. Competing with yourself means that you learn to understand *and cope with* the fears that surround your speech.

The young man told me that he knew of no place to go for help and some relief from his stuttering. I answered that it would be ideal if he could find some place and named a few university clinics where highly qualified speech clinicians with deep and intuitive understanding, work with stutterers. But I also emphasized to him that he could become his own speech clinician. He didn't get this idea right away, so I gave him some concrete suggestions.

"When a problem exists," I explained, "the first thing to do is to examine it carefully with the hope of discovering what was wrong." I told him that one of the most constructive things that he could do for himself was to observe himself several times a day in a mirror as he talked. Although it is a tough row to hoe at first, there is nothing as therapeutic as self confrontation. "Be as objective as possible," I found myself almost pleading with him. "Look and listen closely and discover just what it is that you are doing when you stutter. And after you make these discoveries, *refuse* to make them again. Easier said than done? Yup! But it's well worth every effort that you put into it. When you begin to *really* accept yourself as the stutterer you are, you're on your way to much easier speech and most certainly to greater peace of mind." I also suggested that he get himself a tape recorder and listen to himself with long ears. He'd soon discover that 90% of his stuttering consists of behavior that has made his stuttering more severe, not less severe.

The job is to think and work in a positive manner. The job involves coming to realize that those head jerks, eye blinks, tongue clicks, postponements on feared words, substituting non-feared words for feared ones, and the thousand and one ways in learning "how not to stutter" are not helping to get those words out. They are preventing the words from being said strongly, aggressively and fluently.

"Those blocks may look and sound like monsters to you now, but you can turn them into straw men. Attack them! You must *refuse* to allow your words and fears to control you. Remember that one failure leads to another and you're really trapped if you're caught in the web of misunderstanding the dynamics of your stuttering symptoms." He was listening intently.

"Know and remember that success begets success and self pity will get you nowhere!" Yes, he was still listening intently and was seeming to absorb the messages. Does working on yourself take guts? You bet it does! Does using your guts pay off? You bet it does!

My parting words to this young stutterer, in whom I hoped a wise investment had been made, were "Try it! You'll like it! . . . and let me hear from you."

And now, five cups of coffee later, I hope again that I have touched and helped another stutterer to help himself.

Desirable Objectives and Procedures For an Adult Stutterer

Wendell Johnson

I believe that as a "representative adult stutterer" you should look upon your "stuttering" as certain things which you have learned to do—not something that is "wrong with you" or that "happens to you." You should strive to substitute the normal speech behavior of which you are basically capable for the undesirable ways of reacting that you have learned.

Here is one basic method you can use. At a time when you feel that you "are stuttering" pay very close attention to what you are doing. A clinician can help you do this by asking you— or you can ask yourself—precisely what you are doing. You should answer this question in descriptive detail, and when you have done this you should ask yourself why you were doing what you were doing. Did you think you had to do these things? For what physical or other reasons? What good evidence do you have for the reasons you give? What did you hope to accomplish by doing those things? Did you think you had to do them in order to say what you wanted to say? Or "to keep from stuttering"? Would you talk better or worse if you did not do those things? If you did not do those things would you do more or less of something else, or nothing at all, that you would classify as "stuttering"? Would you be able to speak satisfactorily without doing those things? If not, why not? If so, why do you do them at all?

By means of this "practice in being clear about what you mean and how you know what you are talking about" you tend to find out that the doubts, fears, tensions, and related reactions that make up your "stuttering" are unnecessary and pointless, and that without them you speak all right. You tend to develop the conviction that what you call your "stuttering" is something that you do that you do not have to do and had better not do. It is made up of things you do trying not to do what you call "stuttering"—but they are themselves the "stuttering" you are trying not to do. In other words, "stuttering" is what you do trying not to "stutter" again. Why try to keep from doing something that you won't do at all if you don't try to keep from doing it?

On the basis of this conviction that your "stuttering" is made up of the things you do trying to keep from "stuttering" and that you can talk all right if you don't do these things, you become able to persuade yourself more and more effectively "to go ahead and talk." With this conviction, moreover, you will tend to regard the doubting, fearing, and tensing which you continue to do as error rather than abnormality. You will tend to think of these things as mistakes to be calmly taken in stride while you are making them, but not as mistakes that you can never stop making.

On this basis, you will be prepared to benefit from speaking as much as possible to more and more persons and in more and more situations. Meantime, you should continue to put yourself through the "what are you doing—why are you doing it—what else could you do if you didn't do it?" routine as often and for as long as you feel you benefit from it. In these ways you can develop more and more thoroughly the beliefs and feelings and reactions of normal speech.

You will achieve your objectives most readily with a qualified clinician who can help you obtain the information you need and discuss it with you; assist you in making the most of your practice activities and your observations of your own speech behavior and that of other persons; enable you to take part in individual and group learning experiences; listen sympathetically and understandingly when you want to talk about your problem and your feelings about it; and give you the advantage of any instruction and counseling that you may need.

Message to a Stutterer

Joseph G. Sheehan

If your experience as a stutterer is anything like mine, you've spent a good part of your life listening to suggestions, such as "relax, think what you have to say, have confidence, take a deep breath," or even to "talk with pebbles in your mouth." And by now, you've found that these things don't help; if anything, they make you worse.

There's a good reason why these legendary remedies fail, because they all mean suppressing your stuttering, covering up, doing something artificial. And the more you cover up and try to avoid stuttering, the more you will stutter.

Your stuttering is like an iceberg. The part above the surface, what people see and hear, is really the smaller part. By far the larger part is the part underneath—the shame, the fear, the guilt, all those other feelings that come to us when we try to speak a simple sentence and can't.

Like me, you've probably tried to keep as much of that iceberg under the surface as possible. You've tried to cover up, to keep up a pretense as a fluent speaker, despite long blocks and pauses too painful for either you or your listener to ignore. You get tired of this phony role. Even when your crutches work you don't feel very good about them. And when your tricks fail you feel even worse. Even so, you probably don't realize how much your coverup and avoidance keep you in the vicious circle of stuttering.

In psychological and speech laboratories we've uncovered evidence that stuttering is a conflict, a special kind of conflict between going forward and holding back—an "approach-avoidance" conflict. You want to express yourself but are torn by a competing urge to hold back, because of fear. For you as for other stutterers, this fear has many sources and levels. The most immediate and pressing fear is of stuttering itself and is probably secondary to whatever caused you to stutter in the first place.

Your fear of stuttering is based largely on your shame and hatred of it. The fear is also based on playing the phony role, pretending your stuttering doesn't exist. You can do something about this fear, if you have the courage. You can be open about your stuttering, above the surface. You can learn to go ahead and speak anyway, to go forward in the face of fear. In short, you can be yourself. Then you'll lose the insecurity that always comes from posing. You'll reduce that part of the iceberg beneath the surface. And this is the part that has to go first. Just being yourself, being open about your stuttering, will give you a lot of relief from tension.

Here are two principles which you can use to your advantage, once you understand them: they are (1) your stuttering doesn't hurt you; (2) your fluency doesn't do you any good. There's nothing to be ashamed of when you stutter and there's nothing to be proud of when you are fluent.

Most stutterers wince with each block, experiencing it as a failure, a defect. For this reason they struggle hard not to stutter and therefore stutter all the more. They get themselves into a vicious circle which can be diagrammed as follows:

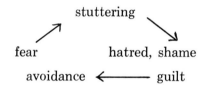

Stuttering is a lonesome kind of experience. Possibly you haven't seen too many stutterers and those you have seen you have avoided like the plague. Just as there may be people who know you or have seen you or even heard you who don't realize that there's anything wrong with your speech, so those who have a speech handicap similar to yours keep it concealed. For this reason few realize that almost one percent of the population stutter, that there are more than a million and a half stutterers in the United States today. That many famous people from history have had essentially the same problem, including Moses, Demosthenes, Charles Lamb, Charles Darwin, and Charles I of England. More recently, George VI of England, Somerset Maugham, Marilyn Monroe, and the T. V. personalities, Garry Moore and Jack Paar have been stutterers at some time in their lives. In your speech problem you may not be as unique or as much alone as you had thought!

· Each adult stutterer has his individual style, made up usually of tricks or crutches which are conditioned to the fear and have become automatic. Yet they all suffer from basically the same disorder, whether they choose to call it stammering, a speech impediment, or something else. *How* you stutter is terribly important. You don't have a choice as to whether you stutter but you do have a choice as to how you stutter. Many stutterers have learned as I have learned, that it is possible to stutter easily and with little struggle and tension. The most important key in learning how to do this is openness: getting more of the iceberg above the surface, being yourself, not struggling and fighting against each block and looking your listener calmly in the eye, never giving up in a speech attempt once started, never avoiding words or ducking out of situations, taking the initiative in speaking even when doing a lot of stuttering. All these are fundamental in any successful recovery from stuttering.

You can stutter your way out of this problem. As long as you greet each stuttering block with shame and hatred and guilt, you will feel fear and avoidance toward speaking. This fear and avoidance and guilt will lead to still more stuttering, and so on. Most older therapies failed to break up the vicious triangle because they sought to prevent or eliminate the occurrence of stuttering which is the result of the fear. You can do better by reducing your shame and guilt and hatred of stuttering which are the immediate causes of the fear. Because stuttering can be maintained in this vicious triangle basis, there are many adults who could help themselves to speak with much less struggle if they would accept their stuttering, remain open about it, and do what they could to decrease their hatred of it.

Some individuals, given a start in the right direction, can make substantial headway by themselves. Others need more extensive and formal speech therapy or psychotherapy in clinics.

Because you stutter, it doesn't mean you are any more maladjusted than the next person. Systematic evaluation of objective research using modern methods of personality study show no typical personality pattern for stutterers, and no consistent differences between those who stutter and those who don't. Because you stutter, it doesn't mean you are biologically inferior or more neurotic than the next person. Maybe a little fortification with that knowledge will help you to accept yourself as a stutterer and feel more comfortable and be open about it.

If you are like most of the million and a half stutterers in this country, clinical treatment will not be available to you. Whatever you do you'll have to do pretty much on your own with what ideas and sources you can use. It isn't a question of whether self-treatment is desirable. Clinic treatment in most instances will enable you to make more systematic progress. This is particularly true if you are among those stutterers who, along with people who don't stutter, have personality and emotional problems. Every stutterer does try to treat his own case in a sense anyway. He has to have a modus operandi, a way of handling things, a way of going about the task of talking.

I have tried to set down some basic ideas which are sounder and more workable than the notions that most stutterers are given about their problem.

You might go about it this way. Next time you go into a store or answer the telephone, see how much you can go ahead in the face of fear. See if you can accept the stuttering blocks you will have more calmly so that your listener can do the same, and in all other situations see if you can begin to accept openly the role of someone who will for a time stutter and have fears and blocks in his speech. But show everyone that you don't intend to let your stuttering keep you from taking part in life. Express yourself in every way possible and practical. Don't let your stuttering get between you and the other person. See if you can get to the point where you have as little urge for avoidance and concealment in important situations as you would when you speak alone. And when you do stutter—and you will—be matter of fact about it. Don't waste your time and frustrate yourself by trying to speak with perfect fluency. If you've come into adult life as a stutterer, the chances are that you'll always be a stutterer, in a sense. But you don't have to be the kind of stutterer that you are—you can be a mild one without much handicap.

Age is not too important a factor, but emotional maturity is. One of our most successful recoveries on record is that of a 78-year-old retired bandmaster who resolved that before he died he would conquer his handicap. He did.

In summary, see how much of that iceberg you can bring up above the surface. When you get to the point where you're concealing nothing from your listener, you won't have much handicap left. You can stutter your way out of this problem, if you do it courageously and openly.

Helping Yourself Overcome Stuttering
Dominick A. Barbara

Speech is a fundamental aspect of the whole personality. Its function is not only to communicate verbally but also to express relationships. The stutterer never stutters when he sings or is in certain relaxed social situations. Instead, he has difficulty speaking whenever he comes in contact with certain forms of authority, or gets into situations where he feels his inner psychic balance and security are threatened.

If a stutterer wants to help himself stutter less, he must arrive at some understanding of *what* he is feeling and *what* he is meaning to convey to his listener, rather than *why* he is blocking. For example, when a stutterer says, "I'm stuck on a word, I can't go on talking," it isn't sufficient just to take this expression at face value. At this level it appears the person is having difficulty speaking, feels helplessly stuck, and can't seem to get past a particular feared or bugaboo word. However, upon closer examination, and at a deeper level, the stutterer can discover that the reason he blocks and continues to do so is that his fear of showing weakness or displaying verbal disruption is an embarrassing and humilating condition. Through stuttering he also reveals that his imagined omnipotence as a "flawless speaker at all times" is threatened; this ultimately leads him into potential failure and disapproval as a speaker.

Encouraging yourself to "speak up" or "to speak slowly" alleviates the problem only temporarily. You may attempt to control your stuttering by sheer will power, learn better devices for avoiding bugaboo words, or speak in a rapid manner in order to race through the possibility of stuttering. Only when you approximate inner balance with a healthy coordination of feelings and action can you rid yourself of your stutter and ultimately achieve relaxed and spontaneous speech. At first this may appear to be a difficult and impossible task, but with some degree of tolerance and self-discipline you can achieve at least the initial breakthrough to your inner problems, and to an ultimate resolution of stuttering.

The stutterer has a *Demosthenes Complex*. He makes demands upon his speech and his intellect which are excessive and impossible to achieve. This verbal perfectionism creates unnecessary inner chaos and turmoil. The person who tends toward stuttering feels he should *always* speak calmly, *never* appear ruffled, and *constantly* be in control of his listener. When he speaks he demands of himself the ultimate and the impossible. He feels he should be the master of his words and have a reservoir of everflowing facts and ideas. He should speak in a clear and concise manner, pause at the right time, never run ahead of his ideas, and be continually spontaneous and interesting when talking.

On the whole, people who stutter are highly intelligent and capable. Yet there appears to be a discrepancy between their realistic capacities and potentialities and what they unrealistically expect of themselves. Although there are many areas of productivity through which an individual can express his capacities and earn a comfortable living, I have found that many stutterers seem to be drawn toward jobs or professions where the use of verbal communication is paramount. It is not uncommon to find people who have difficulty speaking attempting to become salesmen, lawyers, psychologists, and radio announcers. There is no serious objection to this endeavor provided stuttering does not interfere too greatly. As a stutterer you can become successful in most jobs or occupations. However, to attempt to become a trial lawyer, where you would have to plead your case in court and be able to use your words in a forceful and astute manner, would be sheer folly for an active stutterer. The law profession offers many opportunities outside the courtroom for the use of abilities, knowledge and potentialities in the preparation of briefs, or other equally satisfying legal capacities, where speaking plays a minor role.

There are some "Do's and Don't's" that might help you work on your stuttering problem:

1. Since speaking is a healthy and volitional form of self-expression, the stutterer should encourage himself to "speak up" and "speak with others," not as a performance task, but as a means of arriving at social communion and communication. At first this will appear embarrassing and difficult, but the more you accept your shortcomings and the less you put emphasis on your impediment, the more relaxed you will become and the greater interest will you develop in self-expression.

2. Instead of depending on his natural resources for speaking, the stutterer generally resorts to various learned maneuvers,

evasions, substitutions, and magical rituals. He substitutes an "easy word" for a "feared word," adds extraneous words to help him over difficult spots, postpones the utterance of a sound by the use of "ah-ah," or even changes the entire context of what he is saying. These devices help the stutterer break through a hesitation or block, but they are basically artificial in nature and actually intensify the stuttering itself.

Get rid of these artificial devices! This may seem impossible or difficult at first, but depend upon your own natural resources and you will find that in the final analysis you will be greatly rewarded. Of course when you first attempt to relinquish these devices your stuttering will get worse; but if you have the patience, tolerance and courage to survive the initial blows, your spontaneous and normal speech will ultimately win over. Practice this a few minutes each day with your spouse, your parents or a trusted friend and you will be amazed at the results.

3. The stutterer is strongly dependent upon the reactions of his audience. What he fears depends to some degree on how he feels he will perform in the act of speech itself, and to a large extent, upon the response he expects from his listener. The stutterer is in constant need of the approval, praise, recognition and reassurance from other people. He feels that since he stutters he can make claims on other people for absolute understanding, sympathy, consideration and attention. Because of his heightened sensitivity to coercion, criticism, rebuff, or even the slightest denial, his listeners become constant threats to his particular problem. The more threatening his audience appears the greater the amount of rejection he will experience from others. The use of these claims upon others, based solely upon one's stuttering, is unrealistic and can only lead to frustration, repressed anger, and to perpetual entrapment.

To avoid this dilemma make your expectations more reasonable. Don't expect everyone to approve or accept everything you say. If more than half of what you say is accepted or agreed upon, you are running a good average. Don't expect everyone to blindly accept, love or admire you. Most people have problems of their own and may not have the capacity of becoming involved with you. Also remember that we listen to only 50 per cent of what we hear, and comprehend only 25 per cent. If you are operating within this range you are doing well. Finally, as you feel more confident and accept yourself and others more realistically, the less you will have the need to stutter.

4. One of the most important things for a stutterer to remember is get his feelings out into the open. There is plenty of room in discussions for agreement and disagreement, providing it can lead to productive communication.

Accept yourself! This is the key word to your verbal success. Accept both your assets and your limitations. When you feel important to yourself and equal to others, you no longer experience your speech as foreign, but as coming from somewhere inside of you.

When you feel yourself stutter, interrupt your speech, take control of yourself, and find a good balance within yourself. Forget that you have just had some difficulty and attempt some honest or jovial remark about it. Now you can start all over again with greater inner confidence and your chances of stuttering a second time are greatly reduced.

Do not become overwhelmed by a feeling of disaster. The embarrassment and humiliation you experience comes mainly from within yourself, and the feelings you think your listeners are experiencing are mostly fabrications of your own. Most listeners are interested in *what* you are saying, and should you stutter, they usually have compassion for your difficulty and overlook it in the face of continuing the relationship.

Finally, do not live through your words alone. You need not depend upon your words as your sole means of communication. The spoken word is merely a symbol of something else and does not carry with it an effect of dread or fear. Do not be afraid to use your words with courage and conviction. A careless word does not cause a calamity. The speaking situation should not be experienced as an arena of combat where one can emerge the victor or succumb to the mercy of others. In the final analysis, speaking should be considered as a means of verbal exchange with plenty of room for individual and mutual expression of thought, wishes, ideas and feelings.

Once you feel that you are in command of your own speech you will no longer feel hopelessly caught in its grip. Only then will you feel that you have a choice in whatever you are saying. Once you grow within yourself, the more courageous and confident you will feel as a human being. Finally, the less conflict you experience the more you will discard anything that is disturbing within yourself, including your stuttering. Energies which are utilized in the process of keeping your stutter alive are now freed to be used toward healthy growth and self-realization. You will become more relaxed, spontaneous, alive and productive. Speaking will now be used for the sole purpose of communicating and relating, and not as an area of testing.

Overcoming Fear and Tension
In Stuttering

JAMES L. ATEN

Most people talk without much difficulty most of the time. It's true that people hesitate and stumble over words at times, especially when under stress or fatigue, but they show little concern over such mistakes. What, then, makes your speech different and what can you do to help yourself? Invariably, the person who stutters overreacts to his mistakes. He fears they will occur, becomes tense and feels helpless. During the time that tension is so high, the flow of speech stops or will not start. As you continue to have these tense moments that become different from what normal speakers experience, fear increases to higher and higher levels. You come to dread and perhaps avoid speaking. Many stutterers learn that their greatest enemies are *fear* and *tension*. If the battle with stuttering is to be won, fear and tension must be gradually eliminated. Let's look at some battle plans that have helped quite a few stutterers conquer the majority of their fears, eliminate excessive tensions, and find that speech in most situations can once again come easily.

Conquering Fear. We have all probably heard that the way to eliminate fear is to "just face up to it." We have learned all too slowly that for some stutterers, fear may actually increase rather than decrease if they continue to face fear situations and fail. They may experience the same old tension, and fail to get the word out, while attempting to "just go ahead and face their fears." For most of you, fear grew because of repeated failure and the resulting embarrassment over that failure. Your *hope* is that fear can be unlearned by handling hard words and situations better. Performance builds *realistic confidence* that can become a substitute for fear. Here's one way: *Substitute Positive Planning for Fear and Anticipated Failure.*

Stuttering (the fear and tension build-up part) usually begins much earlier in time than you normally think. When the phone rings, you may get into a tense and helpless state while going to answer it. The trouble doesn't suddenly begin as you start to say "Hello." You have learned that tricks such as delaying or rushing often let you down and so your fear spirals upward. When told that you have a job interview in two days, you often begin worrying about how you'll do and expect failure. Having failed last time, you probably will again unless you plan a new approach to the task:

1. Picture yourself approaching the person who will be interviewing you. Take a breath, then *let* it all go. This feels good and for the first time you experience the condition your speech musculature should be in if words are to come out without tension.

2. Imagine extending your hand slowly to shake hands. Your body movements are slow and confident ones. This reduces the tendency to rush or force speech. Mentally you are calmer. The employer says "Hello, I'm John Wood. You must be . . ." Just thinking about answering this with your first and last name fills you with fear and you feel your breath tighten.

3. *LET GO* of that tight breath. Think about the easy movements you could make in answering "Hi, I'm Ed Jones." At first just picture the movements, then after that initial surge of fear subsides, try answering with a kind of easy, half-sigh-like *"Hi"*—Pause—easy again—"I'm *Ed"*—Pause again—let tension go—easy onset—"Jones."

As you rehearse this, several things begin to happen. First, you begin to see that there is less to fear if you don't jump and answer with your first name, which is usually very hard for you. Second, as one stutterer in our field has said, "Time must become your Friend." You will learn that "haste makes waste," even though a few times in the past it has worked.

Fear won't go away by just waiting or going slower; you have to do some positive planning and desensitizing yourself to the employer's presence and request. You must practice the introduction many times *and* not just alone but with someone. After you have experienced success alone, ask your wife or friend to be the employer and rehearse. First answer silently, then softly, then in a normal voice. Whether you stutter during the interview or not is of lesser importance. The chances are you will approach the situation easier than you have in a long time and that your actual stuttering will be less severe. New approaches to handling the feared situation bring gradual improvement by reducing fear. This comes through hard work, not magic, pills, tricks, or waiting until you "feel better." The same type of practice and rehearsal can be used in preparing to say "Hello" on the telephone. In fact, you may find the phone less fear-inducing and want to try it first, or, perhaps just greeting someone casually. As one stutterer said, "I try not to go out and put myself into a very difficult situation at first, where I know I'm going to fail." He had learned to approach some situations, though obviously not all of them, by thinking about responding the new easier, relaxed way and with practice found that he had lost much of his fear. Less fear means less tension in speech.

Conquering Tension. You must learn to substitute easy, slower, more relaxed movements for rushed, tight, forced movements. Typical tension sites are your chest and breath, your throat and vocal cords, jaw, lips and tongue. The practice suggested here can make for success in reducing the fear that follows from blocked movements, so think of these as stages of therapy that you can "put together" for greater effect.

Choose some words that begin with sounds that you think of as being hard—those on which you often stutter. Speech normally begins with a relaxed, unconscious flow of breath. Practice sighing and letting voice come easily. You don't make voice, it just happens if you will *let* it. The same is true of sounds you make with tongue and lips. Feel yourself gently close the lips for the "P" or move the tongue to form such sounds as "T" and "K", then go ahead and say the rest of the word. Notice how little effort speaking takes. Fear has resulted in too much forcing to get words out. You must learn what 'not forcing' is, and practice until easy movements become habitual. First, practice at a very soft, almost silent level, then gradually at a normal voice level. Practice the movement gently to make the difficult word begin easier, then work on other words that begin with that same movement. Assuming that you engage faithfully in daily practice, try a different sound each week. Fear of words lessens as you repeatedly prove to yourself you have a new, easy way of producing them that is becoming automatic. As you practice, be sure not to let the tongue, lips, vocal cords, or breath become tight or touch too hard. No word or speech movement requires conscious effort. Feel the relaxed easy movements into and out of words. *Stop* and begin the easy movements again for the next word series. Now, you are talking in phrases that are short and that you have confidence you can initiate, if you remember to use the easy beginning you have practiced. Remember, speech sounds better in short phrases with frequent pauses.

By conquering fear-arousal through learning to plan your approach, and then using the easy movements which keep tension from making you feel helpless, you are beginning to control stuttering rather than letting it rule you. Certain speaking situations become easier. At this point you must begin to integrate your success. That is, you are not just *having* good and bad days, you are creating some successes out of potential failure. That's what building confidence is all about—and stutterers say time after time, "I talk better when I'm more confident." When you have created a better performance, you can realistically feel more confidence. The model is then begun for turning 'bad cycles' into good ones. You are then able to turn your attention to fluency rather than frequent expectation of stuttering. One of our adult stutterers who successfully went through the above said, "Now I think more about my fluent successes, and does that ever help!"

You appreciate most in life those things you do for yourself. Getting over stuttering takes tremendous self-discipline and desire. We have found that just practicing easy movements without trying to reduce fear is not too successful, since high fear keeps you from remembering the new easier speech movements at the time when you most need to use them. Also, just trying to reduce fear without giving you something to do that is new— *and that works*—may simply allow fear to creep back into the situation very quickly. We have seen that the majority of the stutterers we work with, using the above procedures, achieve a significant degree of fluency in most situations.

Toward Freer Speech

FREDERICK P. MURRAY

Before embarking on the path of endeavoring to improve your speech, I suggest that you do some preliminary work along the lines of constructive and positive thinking. Motivation directed toward the goal of better speech is of the utmost importance if you are to move successfully along the road to better fluency. I would encourage you to tap whatever sources you have within you or might attain from religion, friends, or books, and utilize them toward this aim. Belief in yourself and cooperation with others are vital necessities as you undertake your task.

Do not expect the solution to years of confirmed stuttering to be rapid. Many stutterers have mistakenly believed that if only the "cause" could be found, a fast cure would result. Will the fire that is consuming a house extinguish itself merely because the match that started it has been discovered in an adjacent field? Stuttering in its advanced stages is self-perpetuating, much like a fire. It feeds on itself; fears of words and speaking situations act as cues to intensify it. Clearly, there will be a need for you to face up to, confront, and work upon your problem. This will call for active efforts on your part because strongly conditioned motor responses are changed by *action*, not by thought.

Many of you have heard about the wonders of hypnosis and may look to this technique to provide a quick answer. Rest assured that this has been tried throughout the years, but almost invariably with only temporary and fleeting success. It does not serve to build up the necessary resistance to the innumerable threats that now haunt you with regard to your oral communication. The ability to cope with these factors will come about only gradually as you change both your speaking behavior and personal attitudes, and as you adjust yourself to the new self-role that improved speech will thrust upon you. It is similar to an enormously fat man attempting to lose a hundred pounds. To do this safely he must do so at a rate that his heart and body can tolerate. If it occurs too rapidly, deep wrinkles will appear, and in extreme cases, he may collapse from the rapid change that his organism has undergone. The body needs a chance to integrate itself to each successive level of improvement in weight reduction. So it is with the stutterer who must adjust himself to better fluency. Therefore, I urge you to have tolerance with yourself as you proceed along the way. Do not demand the impossible at first! There is no law that states you must pick up the heavy end of the log everytime.

At this point it is appropriate to mention something about the likely dimensions of a recovery from a long standing bout with stuttering. It is highly improbable that you will ever be conscious of the month, or perhaps even the year, during which you master most of your difficulty. Specific steps of accomplishment along the way are hard to measure. You will, however, be able to cite a few key situations in which you surprised yourself by good performances and these will act as catalysts to your overall progress. Judging from my personal acquaintance with several dozen stutterers who have achieved a good recovery, I note there is not one who would claim to be completely fluent at all times. In other words, each one admits to occasional moments of disfluent speech or residuals of stuttering. However, persons who have not stuttered say that their speech fits approximately the same description. Some stutterers have arrived at a point where their overall speaking skill surpasses that possessed by the average speaker. So keep your head high!

Your ultimate goal, no matter how it may be reached, is to convince yourself that you are capable of speaking in oral communication situations. This is the opposite of saying to yourself that you cannot succeed in these situations because you cannot talk. The important thing, however, is that the conviction is thorough enough that it reflects itself automatically via your emotions and feelings. Remember, our speech is a mirror of how we feel at any given moment in time.

To help you in your goal the following guidelines are offered to provide information that should assist you.

Perhaps the first concrete step you should take is to acquaint yourself with your stuttering behavior. Odd as this may seem, few severe stutterers know what they are doing that interferes with the forward flow of speech. In order to carry this out effectively, you must first learn to keep in touch with yourself during your moments of stuttering. This is in direct contrast to attempting to run away from yourself and doing everything possible to try to avoid the occurrence of stuttering. Feedback of various types will assist you in this self-study endeavor. For example, you can look at yourself in a mirror and assess what you are doing while you make a phone call likely to elicit stuttering. Is it possible to record your speech in a communicatively stressful situation, then play the tape back for the purpose of careful analysis? Painful as this may seem, it is one good way to bring yourself to grips with your problem. If you can achieve a sufficient number of these behavior-exploring experiences you will discover that your stuttering is not a constant and fixed behavior; rather, it is something that varies greatly and is composed of some parts that are *not* handicapping. Regardless of the severity of the longer, highly abnormal blockages, each and every stutterer has some degree of easy moments of stuttering in his speech. These miniature stutterings represent goals in themselves. If you can learn to whittle the others down to similar proportion, more of your scoreable difficulty will have disappeared. This leads to the realization that there are countless ways in which to stutter. Even though you may have no choice as to whether or not you will stutter, you do have the choice of *how you stutter*.

It is also necessary to develop an awareness of the feelings you have in connection with your stuttering. Often your speech difficulty may seem to overwhelm you so much that you are unable to evaluate objectively the emotions that are intimately tied with it. Anxiety, guilt and shame are usually linked to severe speech blockages. Clearly, there will be a need to make some degree of separation between these compulsive forces. Success in accomplishing this should deprive the stuttering of some of its most powerful maintaining factors. Your fundamental task is twofold: alter your speech behavior, and bring about positive changes in your self-perceptions and feelings. A longstanding psychological principle states that one way to influence emotions and bring about a change in feeling is to deal directly with the outward behaviors that are associated with, and are the chief symptoms of, these inner states. If you can modify the severity of your more grotesque speech interruptions by substituting more relaxed forward-flowing speech movements, you will be putting this psychological principle into action. One excellent way to encourage this is by carefully planning certain speaking experiences. Your immediate goal should be to allow yourself to *stutter openly* and without tension and struggle. Do not try to speak as fluently as possible! By deliberately permitting yourself to prolong the initial sounds of many of the words you use, you will be taking the psychological offensive. You will be providing yourself with new outlets through which much of the built-up anticipatory fear can be dissipated, rather than steadily mounting up inside you. In addition, you will be giving your neurophysiological system an opportunity to work in better harmony rather than having one component counteract another. You will be confronting rather than avoiding your problem; the habitual avoidance of speech situations and feared words will get you *nowhere* in the long run. The sooner you are able to give up your holding-back behavior, the better! The following guidelines can serve to help you along the path of recovery from stuttering:

1. The handicap of stuttering consists mostly of learned behaviors. These can be unlearned.
2. Stuttering behaviors can be changed. Remember, you can choose how to stutter even if you cannot choose not to stutter.
3. A person can stutter in many ways.
4. Emotions can be altered by modifying symptoms associated with them.
5. Fear and avoidance lessen as confrontation is increased.
6. Long lasting improvement is unlikely to occur in a scientific laboratory setting. Learn to assemble your own portable laboratory and use it in the real world.
7. Recovery is probably going to be a long and gradual process. Have patience with, and respect for, yourself.

This summarizes and highlights what I have found to be an effective means of fostering improvement in speaking behavior, and maximizing the possibility of attaining a workable solution to your problem. Good Luck!

Change: Potential Qualities Become Actualities

Joseph G. Agnello

I stuttered very severely from the age of 3 years until the age of 28. What occurred during those 25 years with regard to my speech problem is another topic, but what brought on some of the miraculous changes in my speech and personal characteristics can be attributed to my therapist. However, the therapy under him did not bring on a great deal of immediate change in my speech performance. I still had repetitions and the forcing of syllables, but even so I was extremely satisfied when therapy was terminated. I felt I could *move forward in my speech.* I could speak whole sentences and phrases without getting severely hung-up on a syllable. This in itself was very satisfying to me and at that time was as good as being cured. Many of my peers and teachers did not understand how I could stutter so severely and yet talk on, almost oblivious of the tremendous amount of hesitations and blockings. What they failed to recognize was that I could now move forward in my speech. I was free to express all kinds of thoughts. I could even order a chocolate soda without being traumatized by the whole damn incident.

Prior to therapy I had many *preconceived and false ideas about why I stuttered.* Since so much advice is given so freely, and since none of the advice ever appears to do much good, one doesn't really feel there is much that can be done about stuttering. Some of the advice I received was good but I was not ready to make use of it, and consequently, I rejected it. Advice that one cannot act upon to bring about change is usually discarded forever, and in many respects this is too bad.

There are certain feelings and attitudes about stuttering that seem to perpetuate the problem. Most of them have little basis in fact. Some of the feelings and attitudes that plagued me during my early years were: I will always have this inability to talk; I stuttered because there was something wrong with my mind, because I was mentally slow, because nobody really liked me, because my father was a drunkard and was mean to me, because I masturbated, because I could not face up to my stutterings; I stuttered because I stuttered, because I was so nervous, and because I thought faster than I could talk, etc.

On the other hand, when I didn't stutter I thought it was

due to certain positive traits about me. Some of these were that I was a good athlete, was intelligent, had a good sense of humor, and was friendly. All of the "becauses" don't really make much sense. They don't offer any sensible explanations. For instance: Why those moments of severe stuttering? Why times of less stuttering? Why *any* fluency? WHY? To dwell on the "becauses" and "whys" only circumvents the reality of the problem.

After resolving some of these preconceived notions about my stuttering I felt free to try different things with my speech. I no longer felt bound to my old pattern of stuttering. I now felt a new ability to move forward and the feeling of personal freedom to explore and plan my own course of action. It was *self-confrontation to questioning that eventually brought on insights.* Questions such as How serious is my stuttering? Is my problem just stuttering or is it maybe not knowing how to relate to people? Do listeners really care if I stuttor or is it the way I react to my stuttering that determines how they will react? What do people really think about my stuttering? Maybe I have a problem of listening? How do other people talk and listen? How do I listen to myself? Do I really hear my stuttering? Do I seriously attend to the meaning of words? Can I change?

Most people are kind, gentle and usually mean well. Usually people are interested in what you have to say. It is a big job to talk *with* people. The fact that you get stuck on words is another issue. Even if you didn't get stuck on words you would still have an awesome responsibility in learning how to explain things clearly. *Speech is a public affair.* You must work on speaking forthrightly and clearly, and on establishing verbal relationships with other people. Think clearly of how you are going to say what you want to say and plan how you will organize your discourse. Think critically about your listener. What is his background? Does he understand what I mean? Am I going too fast for him? Is he afraid of me, or am I afraid of him? Why does he appear not to be listening to me? Is it my manner of talking? What can I do to make the listener more relaxed?

As a researcher I have spent many hours observing other stutterers and have made acoustical and physiological analyses of "how stutterers stutter." This was helpful to me because it forced me to examine my own stuttering very critically. I was fascinated by the peculiar ways I approached certain words and how I moved from one syllable to the next. Observations of my own stuttering and hard experimental work have led to what I think is the most universal feature concerning the basic problem stutterers exhibit with regard to the motor performance of speech production.

Timing is most crucial for on-going forward-moving speech. Voicing has to be precisely terminated and initiated at some point during the production of speech. Voicing must interact in a precise manner with articulatory movements and this is the likely site of difficulty. The glottal signal excites the oral cavity and an articulatory gesture must act to facilitate, check or terminate the glottal pressure. Any action that emphasizes or enhances *smooth transitions* from sound to sound, syllable to syallable, or word to word will be beneficial for on-going speech. Beyond the matter of word transition there is another form of stuttering that may be prevalent but not so obvious. This is stuttering on organization of thoughts. One thought concept must have organization with a transitional phase into the next thought. These thought units generally are encompassed within phrases. Any effort that disrupts, discourages, or fails to assist smooth transition will generally be identified as stutterings or eventually evoke a poor pattern of on-going "free speech."

I found the following practices to be helpful in my efforts to improve my speech:

1. Practice speaking in rhythm to a definite beat.
2. Practice speaking in the style of a famous speaker. Carl Sandburg spoke slowly, prolonged vowels and had long pauses. He was my model.
3. Fake stuttering. Make an effort to relate to some of the questions previously mentioned (Do I really hear my stuttering? and, How serious is my stuttering? etc.) When you fake stuttering with some objectives and questions in mind, you must assume responsibility both for yourself and for your listener. If the "fake stuttering" becomes "real" or you fail to be objectively critical about your stuttering, then you are most likely not being truthful to yourself and the listener.
4. Talk slowly and deliberately. Stutter slowly and deliberately.
5. Listen to recordings of your speech.

6. Use "loose pullouts" after getting stuck on a syllable. Come out of stuttering in an easy manner without the sudden jerks and plosive efforts.

7. Speak honestly to others about stuttering.

In summary, I feel the following developments were most instrumental in my acquiring what I consider to be "cured stuttering."

1. Giving up efforts to explain my stuttering and its causes. Too many "becauses" and false ideas about "why" I stuttered had only confused me and made things worse.

2. Organizing what I wish to say and organizing my manner of saying it so I can *move forward* in my speech, even if there is some stuttering.

3. Answering some very pertinent questions about my speech and myself through some serious self-confrontations.

4. Assuming the responsibility for talking and remembering that there is another person in the conversation, too. Learning to restrain myself and reserving judgments about myself and others. Learning to pause, to sit quietly, and listen attentively.

5. Working on actual speech exercises, tasks and assignments that were aimed at developing smooth articulatory co-ordination (motor planning) and transition from sound to sound, syllable to syllable, word to word, phrase to phrase, and thought to thought. Doing these tasks both alone and in real speaking situations.

Suggestions For Self-Therapy For Stutterers

Margaret M. Neely

Dear Fellow-Stutterer: If you are an adult who has stuttered most of your life, you have probably tried many ways to cope with the problem. So have I. As a stutterer and a therapist, my observation is that each person finds his own way. There are a multitude of approaches to the correction of stuttering. The procedure I suggest is not necessarily the "best" approach; it is simply an approach that has been effective for me and for most of the individuals with whom I have worked. It is a direct attack on the speech and it involves effort. Many people resist the work aspect and want easier ways to overcome the problem. The feelings of anxiety that accompany stuttering have become so over-whelming that the stutterer reacts by wanting a simple way with immediate results. Drug therapy to relieve anxiety and mechanical devices to block your own hearing or to supply you with rhythmic patterns are easy methods which seem immediately beneficial. I believe that nothing succeeds on a long term basis like hard work on the speech itself, an idea that may be due to the very personal viewpoint of anyone who is both a therapist and a stutterer. My own experience has been that nothing "cures" an adult stutterer but one can effectively manage stuttering so that it ceases to be a significant problem throughout one's life.

Why does this approach require work? Because speech, like walking and other body functions, is acquired early in life and becomes habitual long before school age. Those of us who stutter have learned both fluent and stuttered forms of speech which have become automatic. You, as a stutterer, must study your speech patterns in order to become aware of the differences between stuttered and fluent speech. Stuttered forms of speech can be changed in various ways, just as handwriting can be modified. It is this changing of an established habit that requires work.

Several psychological problems confront the stutterer as he tries to alter his speech. These problems include a lack of confidence in his ability to do anything with his stuttered speech because of previous failures, an inability to cope with feelings of resentment and loneliness about having this problem (why me?), and worry and concern about the effect of his stuttering on other people and their possible resulting opinions of him. In addition, the stutterer struggles with the idea that because he can say his words fluently some of the time, he should be able to say them fluently all of the time. He may believe some psychological problem needs to be removed and this belief results either in periodic over-worry about his speech or complete disregard for it. These feelings which have become automatic, as has the stuttering, usually are the painful part of stuttering. This is why you may feel the need to first work on eliminating the feelings you experience when you stutter. However, it is easier to work on the speech first, and the feeling next, because much of the accompanying emotion disappears when you have gained control of your speech.

How do you start?

Your goal should be to find a way of speaking that is comfortable for you. You will need to eliminate the abnormality of your stuttering and try to find an easier way to talk which is under your control.

Study your speech. Learn to change the habitual form of stuttering to a more controlled pronunciation of the word. Change your speech to include fluent speech, pauses and the controlled saying of words, as well as occasional stuttering.

To study your speech, analyze how you say words both fluently and in a stuttered form. You may think of a word as being a unit or "lump" of sound; actually a word is composed of separate sounds, much as a written word consists of separate letters. To say a word you must move from sound position to sound position with your speech articulators shaping the air that carries the voice. Learn to be aware of the feeling of muscle action as you move through a word. When a word is said fluently these muscular movements are coordinated, loose and easy.

When you stutter, you will notice that there is a great deal of tension in the speech muscles used to say the beginning sound. Much of the abnormality of stuttering is your automatic reaction to the feeling of the sudden muscle tension that you experience as a "blocked" feeling. You try to fight the blocking by pushing harder, rather than by releasing the tension and moving to the rest of the word. As you say an isolated word beginning with a B or P, for example, concentrate on the feeling of movement as you bring your lips together and as they move to the next sounds. In the habitual stuttering pattern the muscles will either tighten and then release to bounce back to the same position, or will jerk forward to the rest of the word. This is in contrast to a fluent saying of the first sound which will have loose contact of the lips and a smooth shift to the next sound position.

Study your conversational speech. You may stutter more in connected speech than when you say single words. Such factors as the speed of speaking and word position in a sentence can influence how a word is said, and can precipitate stuttering. Stutterers have a good deal of fluent speech as well as stuttered speech. Learn to be aware of the feeling of fluency and the sensation of fast, easy movement of the muscles involved in speech. These movements are interrupted only to take a breath, or to pause for meaning. When a pause for stuttering occurs, you may notice that the rate of speech increases after the block as if to "make up" for lost time. Sometimes this increased speed produces a rapid, jerky speech pattern that is difficult to understand. Stutterers usually hurry in their speech more than normal speakers do. You may want to consider changing the rate of both your fluent and your stuttered speech.

How do you practice changing the habitual form of stuttering to a controlled pronunciation of words?

Begin with single words. Watch in a mirror as you place your mouth in position to say the first sound of the word. Move slowly and gently from sound to sound through the word. Practice this silently, whispering, and then aloud as you learn to feel the sensation of relaxed movements of the lips, tongue, and throat. Through awareness of muscle movement you can control your speech production even when talking to other people and are unable to use a mirror.

Read aloud to yourself. Say each word in the sentence as if it were an isolated word. Be highly conscious of the feeling of movement through the word.

Practice saying words directly using a talking-and-writing technique. Write the first letter of the word as you begin to say the word and prolong the first sound until you have completed the written letter. This slow first movement of the word will train you to combat the excessive muscle tension which automatically occurs at the beginning of stuttered words.

Try to learn a new speech pattern which can be used in

every day speaking. You may have noticed that one of the important factors which influences the amount of stuttering in your everyday speech is your feeling of inner stability. This feeling is what you experience as self-confidence, calmness and self-control. Many influences from the environment, or from your physical state, can affect your equilibrium. Most of these environmental influences are beyond your control. However, you can change to a speech pattern that is under your voluntary control, rather than responding to the pressures with habitual tense and stuttered speech. This pattern should consist of your fluent speech, which you refuse to hurry, and your careful, relaxed, controlled speech. By using your awareness of muscle movement to guide your lips, tongue, and throat from sound to sound throughout the word, much as in writing, you can reduce much of the abnormality and tension that occurs in a stuttered word. Use of this controlled pronunciation on some of the fluent words as well as the stuttered words can keep a smooth speech pattern. This takes work, but can become habitual in many situations. Your over-all goal is to find a way of speaking that is comfortable for you. This should include the following ideas:

1. Acceptance of the idea that you are a "controlled" stutterer rather than a fluent speaker.
2. Awareness of the "feel" of shaping words fluently.
3. Mastery of the panic of stuttering will occur when you accept, as normal for you, the pauses and moments of tension that occur in your speech. By reducing the struggle of stuttering you relieve yourself of embarrassment, but you cannot hurry when stuttering.
4. Self-discipline in daily practice.
5. Humor as you look at your mistakes in speaking. Many things about stuttering can be funny.

Stuttering is a life-long problem which improves with age. As a stutterer you can gain great satisfaction in watching yourself acquire better and better control of speech as you work on it.

Self-Improvement After Unsuccessful Treatments

Henry Freund

Like most adult stutterers in this country you have probably been subjected to some form of therapy at one time or another. This therapy was either totally ineffective or resulted in only temporary improvement. Maybe it even resulted in a "cure," only to be followed by a relapse. Such an experience may have provoked in you an attitude of pessimism as far as the possibility of a more effective treatment is concerned. Or, it may have strengthened your desire for the "miracle," the perfect cure which would eradicate every trace of stuttering. Both these attitudes are unjustified.

For those who are pessimistic about the possibility of help it may be encouraging to learn that some stutterers have been able to help themselves either in spite of, or possibly because of, repeated and unsuccessful treatments. Some of the contributors to this book will give you specific and practical advice about what to do in times of trouble. I want to give you a short description of my own attempts at self-improvement, after many unsuccessful treatments, and the principles on which they were based. This is my own strictly personal way of helping myself and should not be considered as a blueprint to be followed rigidly. Each individual must go his own way.

For those who are overly optimistic a few words of caution are needed. I am intentionally talking only about *improvements* and not about *cures*. I am of the opinion that for the adult stutterer the best we can expect is long-term, even lifelong improvement, which renders him a less unhappy and less socially withdrawn person. This is not a perfect cure. Traces of the disorder usually remain and relapses occur. This applies equally to those who were treated by others and to those who treated themselves. It seems to me that those "former stutterers" who really don't have any trace of stuttering left did not recover as a result of planning and conscious efforts but actually outgrew their disorder without knowing how and why. Their cure is, as we say, a spontaneous recovery and not the result of therapy.

I was definitely a severe stutterer and was treated unsuccessfully by leading European authorities during my elementary school and high school years, as a student in medical school and even after graduation. Without the knowledge I acquired as a result of all these futile attempts at therapy, however, I probably never would have succeeded in helping myself overcome the worst of my stuttering. As an eight year old child I experienced a short-lived and almost miraculous improvement by using a smooth, melodic manner of speech with prolonged syllables; sentences were uttered as units. It was a manner of speech akin to singing. I noticed that I could apply this method in front of strangers with perfect ease and confidence when accompanied by my therapist. But he accompanied me only rarely, and never made any systematic attempt to enlarge the range of situations I could master. I returned home as "cured," only to relapse quickly. The next two authorities conducted therapy strictly within the walls of their office. The first one, after many tricks and much logical persuasion, finally stumbled upon rhythmic speech; again I felt an almost miraculous ease, but no attempt was made to help me apply this in front of others. The last therapist totally rejected my request to accompany me into real life situations. He wanted me to have the courage to do it alone. My numerous attempts to approach people alone and to conquer my fear of stuttering all ended in failure and my stuttering grew worse. From bitter experience I learned how futile it is to make demands upon the stutterer without giving him a helping hand. What I needed was not an authority but a friend and collaborator genuinely interested in me and ready to help me. I was fortunate to have a brother who could be this friend.

At age 35 I gave up my practice as general practitioner of medicine and moved from Yugoslavia to Berlin for postgraduate training and specialization. My shyness to approach people had reached a point where something had to be done about it and I was now given an opportunity to make a new start and my chances for a successful attempt at treating myself were favorable. Not only had I accumulated an extensive knowledge on stuttering, but through my many unsuccessful treatments in the past I had developed definite ideas of what was necessary to do to bridge the gap between theory and practice. I tried to follow these main principles.

1. I determined to make full use of the opportunity to devote myself completely to the task of self-improvement. The

chances of success would be better if I were able to live completely for this one task. I had to make full use of a new environment where nobody knew me as "stutterer" and where nothing reminded me of my past defeats and humiliating experiences.

2. I knew by now that I possessed a normal ability to speak. Speaking is an automatic act and most of the time I did speak normally. I knew that stuttering occurred situationally, that it resulted from fear and the expectation of failure and that this lead to an inhibition or stoppage of the voice. I talked under the illusion that speech sounds are difficult and that an enormous amount of force was necessary to overcome my self-created obstacles. Talking was a highly emotional experience which gave me a feeling of helplessness, failure and defeat. But I also knew that the method I used as a child which stressed all the positive aspects of speech (the stream of breath and voice, the unity of the sentence as a whole, the singing-like, melodic aspects of speech) was in the past prone to draw my attention away from the dreaded speech sounds, tended to calm and relax me, and rendered my speech more pleasurable. As a first step I would now start again to use this method with those persons closest to me and regain my old confidence in it. I could use this as a steppingstone to contacts with others.

3. I would discuss with my brother my daily predicaments, fears, doubts, successes, defeats and other personal problems. After establishing a good and trusting relationship I explained my strategy. He should accompany me wherever and whenever I needed his help; he should remain silent when I was sure of myself but should take over when I stumbled; or he could start to talk and then I could gradually take over. In this manner I could slowly expand the variety of people and situations where I could talk methodically, calmly and confidently.

4. After establishing a greater degree of security and confidence I would be able to reduce and finally discard the need for my brother to accompany me. I would be on my own and would expand the range of situations I wanted to master. I would do this gradually and would not ask for too much too soon. In times of trouble, I should not be too proud to discuss my problems with others.

5. Having widened somewhat the range of situations and

people that I could handle without fear I had to secure my newly won abilities by preparing myself for the inevitable reversals. Relapses would be unavoidable and had to be expected for there would be no foolproof method to eliminate them. In the past relapses were prone to shatter my belief not only in a certain method, but also in ever being able to overcome my stuttering. This would not happen again if I were prepared to meet them in the right spirit. Situations and circumstances would arise when the magical power of any method would be overpowered by old fears and self-doubts, and when some outposts of the liberated area might get again lost. The right spirit to meet relapses and reversals is a philosophy of self-tolerance, of the acceptance of your own weaknesses and limitations, and of a greater objectivity toward self and others. This results in a lessened sensitivity. Here, too, an open discussion with an understanding person sometimes helps to clarify issues which subjectively you are unable to see clearly.

I followed these and other similar guidelines. The breakthrough occurred when, after a period of preparation and accompanied by my brother, I for the first time dared to approach a stranger for the purpose of experimenting on him. In spite of a panic-like fear and desire to run away, I heard myself asking him a question in a surprisingly calm and methodic fashion. This first breakthrough shattered the walls of fear and avoidance. It was a positive emotional experience of strong impact; it created a new confidence and opened up new vistas. The world became a friendlier place to live in and I felt closer to other human beings. Many similar positive experiences followed. My liberated verbal territory became too big to ever again fall prey to the demons of fear and doubt. For the next six years I spoke practically without conscious fear of stuttering and was able to engage in activities like counseling, lecturing and teaching as head of several speech clinics. These tasks I could not have possibly performed before. Then minor relapses, especially during exceptionally difficult life-situations, started to occur. While traces of the disorder have remained, and while with advancing age I have again become slightly more socially handicapped, the disorder never again assumed the severity it had prior to age 35. But even now, 40 years later, I still not only continue to study myself but also to treat myself. I still work to normalize my relationship to others and on my life-philosophy. For me, this is a lifelong task.

This is my story of self-improvement after unsuccessful treatment. Maybe there are some ideas which will prove helpful to you. I hope so!

Some Helpful Attitudes
Underlying Success in Therapy

HAROLD L. LUPER

It's been more than twenty-five years since I first entered the speech therapy program which proved effective in significantly reducing my speech problem. Much has happened in speech pathology since that time. Although there have been few completely new techniques, the manner of programming these techniques and the manner in which they are applied to persons have continually been improving. Speech pathologists are constantly seeking better ways to help the stutterer and what's considered best today will probably be replaced in the future with something better. For this reason, I shall not dwell as much on the specific techniques and activities that helped me as upon the general attitudes and principles which seem to underlie successful stuttering therapy.

The Power of Constructive Assertiveness. A few years ago, Norman Vincent Peale popularized a set of attitudes in his book, *The Power of Positive Thinking*. One of the principles that I found of most value in changing my stuttering problem might be called *constructive assertiveness*. Like many of you, one of the most common and most debilitating characteristics of my problem was my habit of avoiding. I continually searched for ways to get around saying words on which I expected to stutter. There was almost no limit to what I would do to avoid situations in which I feared my stuttering would embarrass me. Going to a party would be an extremely tiring event because the entire evening would be spent trying to stay alert for words on which I might stutter and finding ways to avoid saying them.

Fortunately, even before I began active therapy, I found out that avoidance only makes the fear worse. While serving in the army, I had written a speech pathologist asking for help. He informed me he would be glad to see me after I was out of the service and gave me a few suggestions as to what I could do in the meantime. His most important suggestion was to begin to lick the problem of avoidance. He suggested I go ahead and say those words on which I expected to stutter and to go ahead and enter those situations which I normally avoided. I began to try it. It was hard, but soon I found that the temporary discomfort of struggling through a difficult word was far better than the constant vigilance and search for the easy way out. Through the years, I have found that this is still one of the best ways to reduce my anxiety and to improve my speech when I again begin to have trouble.

Being assertive means being aggressive. You don't need a therapist to harness this power. Search for those words or situations that are beginning to bug you rather than hiding them until they build up to giant fears. If you stutter on a particular word, you can deliberately use the word again in other conversations until the fear is gone. If a certain situation makes you tense so talking is difficult you can go back into similar situations until you feel more at ease. Where you used to avoid, search for positive constructive ways to reduce your fear and struggle. At times, it means bearing some temporary embarrassment while you stick it out on a hard word, but overall you'll find that your fear, tension, and struggle are less when you practice constructive assertiveness.

Exploring the Dreaded Unknown. Early in my therapy program, I made a startling discovery. Although I had stuttered for years, I really did not know much about what I did with my speech apparatus as I stuttered. Like many other persons who stutter, I had been so embarrassed when I was stuttering, that my total attention was drawn to trying to "get out of" my seemingly helpless struggle against an unexplainable "block." In therapy, my clinicians helped me learn to study my speech behaviors and to analyze what I was doing at those moments when I was struggling. Many of the things I was doing interfered with fluency more than they helped. Although in the past, I'd repressed awareness of my stuttering behaviors, I now found that much was to be learned from encountering and analyzing them. You, too, can explore the unknown. When you do, you may find that you push your lips together too hard or jam your tongue against the roof of your mouth. You may notice that as you start to say a word, you build up too much tension. Once you begin to see what you are doing that makes talking difficult, you find that much of this behavior is controllable. Concentrate on changing what you do when you stutter by doing differently some of the things that seem to interfere with your fluency. Stuttering will then lose some of its magical powers and become only those things which you do. Eventually you should make a very important discovery; that is, that you are not completely helpless at the moment you are stuttering.

Defining Realistic Obtainable Goals. Another helpful attribute that ties directly into the changes we've just been discussing is to set for yourself realistic and definable goals. Many of you will have, as I did, a rather perfectionistic attitude toward speaking. I wanted complete fluency with absolutely no stuttering. Anything less was a failure.

When you realize that all speakers have some hesitancy and disfluency in their speech, and when you realize that it is unrealistic to expect to change completely and immediately a problem you've lived with for years, you will be able to get satisfaction from small gains and to have greater tolerance for those difficulties you still encounter. Rather than hoping for complete fluency in each situation, work towards more realistic goals of improvement in certain specific behaviors, such as reduction of excessive lip tensing.

Reducing the Importance of Stuttering. One of the hardest things for me to learn was that the problem of stuttering is not the worst thing that can happen. For years I had felt stuttering was the biggest problem in life and this affected my entire self-perception. I was definitely handicapped because I was a member of the small minority that stuttered. Getting older has many disadvantages but it had the advantage of helping me put things in perspective. As I encountered other persons with other problems, I eventually realized that there are many difficulties worse than stuttering. One can still do most of what he wishes even if he does stutter.

Putting stuttering in a more realistic perspective may reduce some of your tension and make it easier for you to work on it. You should feel less embarrassed when it does occur, and you can stop thinking of yourself as a handicapped individual and thus improve your overall self-confidence.

Maintaining Improvements. Many of you who stutter have had the experience of getting better during therapy only to find yourself having trouble again when therapy is discontinued. This event, sometimes called a relapse, frequently leads to demoralization and the failure complex—a feeling that there's little use in trying to change your stuttering since it will probably return.

Frequently the person who has had this experience over-reacts to the return of struggle behaviors. He may well forget that even the amount of trouble he is having now is not nearly as frequent nor as severe as it was formerly. The fear of stuttering suddenly reappears and avoidance and struggle behaviors soon follow. Rather than accept this defeatist attitude, it's far better to go back to the basic principles; that is, determine what specific things you're doing and start again to do those things which you've found make talking easier.

Too many persons who stutter stop too soon after gaining some fluency and losing some of the fear. They fail to realize that stuttering behaviors have been learned on a complex reinforcement schedule over a long period of time. They fail to do those things which will maintain the new speaking behaviors. In all kinds of learning we normally go through three stages: (1) establishment of the new habit, (2) transfer of the habit to different situations, and (3) maintenance of the new behavior. If, after making some positive changes in your speech behavior, you revert to those attitudes and practices that originally were a part of the problem, you may find that the problem reappears.

To maintain the progress you've made in therapy it's wise to enlarge your speaking horizons. Now's the time to take that course in public speaking you've always dreaded or to begin to accept more invitations to social events where you know you'll have to meet a lot of people. Just as it's difficult to imagine maintaining recently learned swimming skills when you don't continue to go swimming, it seems pretty hard to imagine maintaining newly acquired attitudes and behaviors in speaking if you don't continue to enter a lot of speaking situations.

I hope some of my experiences will be helpful to you. Before ending, however, I must express a sincere debt of gratitude to the two persons who served as my clinicians some twenty-five years ago. They know who they are. I probably could have made many of the changes I've made without them, but I'm convinced they helped change my life for the better.

What You Can Do About Your Stuttering

J. DAVID WILLIAMS

You can do quite a bit if you really want to. You should begin by facing and describing those feelings and behaviors that make up your overall stuttering problem. Unless you know your problem in detail you won't know what you're working on or how much progress you've made. As honestly as you can, try to observe yourself and write down your observations. Then you can look at your own words. You may want to revise them later. Here are some questions you might try to answer.

Exactly what are your *feelings* about yourself as a stutterer and how do they affect your day-to-day relationships with other people? How do you feel when you know you're going to have to speak in various situations, how do you feel when speaking (during stuttering as well as not stuttering), and how do you feel afterward? What problems can you *really* blame on your stuttering? What are your stuttering *behaviors*? Use a mirror and a tape recorder to analyze yourself (this can be tough!). How much do you tense up and struggle when you start feeling "blocked" on a word? Do you compress your lips or hold them wide open, jam your tongue in certain positions, hold your breath, shut your eyes, or what? In which speaking situations do you do these things with the most tension? When *don't* you do them? During how much of your speaking time, or on about what percentage of your words, do you *not* stutter? To that degree you are a normal speaker. Keep that in mind! Your job is to change your feelings and behaviors so that you will speak *more* of the time the way you now speak some of the time. Quite possibly you're more of a nonstutterer than you are a stutterer.

You do not like your stuttering and its real or imagined social consequences, so it is natural to try to avoid it. At times you may totally avoid stuttering by choosing to be absent, by withdrawing from a speaking situation, or while speaking you may substitute a non-feared word (one on which you do not expect to stutter) for a feared one. This allows you to escape for the moment, but increases your worry about future situations.

What happens at the actual moment of stuttering and how do you react to the sudden feeling of blockage or paralysis? You may have a fairly simple, straightforward pattern of stuttering, or you may instantly swing into a tense performance of struggle behaviors. Can you determine what they are from your self-observations? You are struggling to be fluent and to avoid stuttering. Ironically, these struggle behaviors are what other people see and hear as your stuttering! You have sabotaged and double-crossed yourself. Your pattern of stuttering behavior consists chiefly of the things you are doing to avoid stuttering. That's a pretty basic idea. Mull it over a bit.

Instead of tense, out-of-control struggles, you need speech behaviors that don't try for impossibly perfect fluency but which do lead to good feelings of control, confidence, self-respect and decreased anxiety and frustration. These interfere less with communication and are more acceptable to you and your listener. So here they are! No tricks, gimmicks, secret recipes or instant cures; just voluntary modifications of your speech behaviors that will help you do what needs to be done.

Slow Stuttering. Do *not* change your usual rate of speaking unless you really speak too fast to be understood (very few people do). Leave your non-stuttered speech alone. But when you start to tense up and stutter, *at that instant* shift into slow motion. Don't give up your speech effort, but try to do everything easily, gently and slowly. Relax and let go; keep your lips, tongue and jaw moving without jamming. Don't panic. Take all the time you need; keep things moving slowly. Keep your confidence and don't buckle. Keep going forward slowly but positively. Totally resist any feeling of hurry or pressure. Let 'em wait. At some critical point in time (a second or less, two seconds, ten seconds or more) you will suddenly know you're over the hump. You'll feel your tension drain away as your confidence surges back. Simply finish that word and keep talking along at normal speed until you start to tense up for another bout of stuttering. Then you instantly shift into slow motion again.

Many stutterers who originally had very tense, complex patterns of stuttering have worked themselves down to this easy, simple, slow stuttering with little tension or interruption in their speech.

Sometimes a moment of stuttering seems to catch you by surprise, and you find yourself holding your mouth wide open or jamming your lips together as you feel the sudden surge of tension that leaves you frozen with panic and frustration. *Stop struggling* at that instant. Don't try to change your lip or tongue position. Hold everything as is until you feel your tension start to fade. Either keep the sound going, or gently re-initiate the sound you wanted to make; make absolutely no effort to finish the word until you can do so with complete ease. Then finish the word naturally and keep on talking. In this way you are deliberately taking control of the situation and are manipulating the behavior that has always seemed to be out of control.

Deliberate Repetition of Initial Sound or Syllable. At the first feeling of tension and struggle say only the first sound or syllable of the word easily and lightly, repeat it a few times until you feel relaxed and confident, then finish the word. "Please pass the sa-sa-sa-salt." If you start to tense up while repeating the sound or syllable, try to relax and let go again; keep the repetition going until all tension drains away, then perhaps toss in one or two more relaxed repetitions just to show yourself that you're in control before you finish the word. Remember, this is not real stuttering which is tense, struggling, out-of-control behavior. This is calm, relaxed, controlled, deliberate disfluency, and is a means of dissipating your tense, panicky feelings of impending stuttering.

Deliberate Repetition of Entire Word. Occasionally when you stutter on a word, really mess it up, and don't seem to be able to do anything about it at the moment, go ahead and stutter your way through it. After you complete the word, *stop!* Resist the tremendous urge to keep talking and pretending that your stuttering never happened. You need to confront the fact that it *did* happen. Go back and say the word over again, and again, and again, and more times if necessary until you say it easily and naturally with no tension. *Then* keep on talking. This leaves you with a feeling of success for having done something positive to conquer your fear and avoidance of stuttering.

In learning and practicing these behavior modifications, as in everything you do to work on your stuttering problem, you should proceed from easier tasks and situations to harder ones. Begin by practicing each of these techniques a few minutes daily in the easiest, least-threatening situation for you—either when alone or with someone else, and if possible with a mirror and tape recorder for visual and auditory "feedback." Approach doing them with calm confidence and relaxation. These behaviors may feel strange at first, but keep in mind *why* you are doing them, and with continued practice you will do them more easily, naturally and successfully. Always resist the urge to hurry or to pop the word out as quickly as possible. Panic, tension, and an overwhelming urgency are the hallmarks of stuttering; they are what you must overcome. Sooner or later you will begin to decide which of the behaviors best serve to give you a feeling of ease and confidence in speech, and reduce your tensions and your urge to fight your stuttering.

I would recommend the almost constant use of a tape recorder. There's nothing like being able to hear your own speech in order to judge what you do and don't like about it, and to decide what changes to make as you practice. Try to record your speech in different speaking situations. A small battery-powered recorder may be used in "real life" situations.

On separate index cards, list various speaking situations in which you fear stuttering. As you gain confidence in your modified stuttering techniques, try them in one or two of your least feared situations. When you have successful experiences in them move on to a slightly more feared situation, and so on. This gives you a guide to progress in self-therapy.

Above all, keep in mind that the less you struggle in your efforts not to stutter, and the less you avoid feared words and situations, the less you will stutter in the long run. You do not become fluent by fighting desperately to be fluent. This is what stutterers spend a great deal of time and energy doing, and this is probably the biggest reason why they continue to stutter. In this sense, fluency comes in the back door. It is a by-product of your really not caring whether you are fluent or not. You will steadily improve in the desired ways as you carry out your new speech behaviors in more and more situations, so they become increasingly automatic and integrated into your day-to-day living.

It's not a matter of luck. You make your own "luck." You can get there!

From One Stutterer To Another

SPENCER F. BROWN

We stutterers all know the feeling of panic of a tough block. To some of us this feeling is frequent and painfully familiar. At such moments the thing to do, hard as it may be, is to cool it. I have found that it helps to remember the words of a collect from the Episcopal Book of Common Prayer: "O Lord . . . who hast safely brought us to the beginning of this day."

In other words, you've come this far, you've come to *this* stuttering moment. You have survived all your former troubles including your speech problem. You've been in all sorts of agonizing situations before, and you've managed to get through them. At a moment of near panic you can't be expected to tell yourself at length what I've just been saying, but you can compress it into thinking, "I'm still here. Cool it!"

Besides telling yourself this, what do you do to handle a terribly tense block and the seeming impossibility of uttering the word you're trying to speak? First, stop trying to say the word. Then immediately try to ease it out. This is a technique taught by some of the most effective speech therapists. It would seem to be an obvious way of dealing with those ghastly blocks, yet few stutterers seem to discover this technique by themselves.

I'm now going to make a suggestion that will bring me angry letters from some speech pathologists and even, perhaps, from some stutterers. I suggest that you follow what is the almost universal practice of stutterers and on occasion use an easy word in place of a hard one. When you're having a particularly difficult time I see nothing wrong with this common practice of word substitution. I am well aware of the theory that holds that substitution of easy words for feared words increases the stutterer's fear of nonfluency. It is said that if you don't meet head-on the challenge of the fear of stuttering on a certain word, your fear of that word, and of stuttering in general, will increase. This is supposed to increase and perpetuate your problem. I'll admit that this reasoning makes good sense, but I know of no clear scientific proof of the theory.

Theory aside, the fact remains that only with expert clinical guidance can a stutterer learn to avoid substitution on a day after day, month after month basis in all speaking situations.

Furthermore, in my acquaintance with speech pathologists who are themselves stutterers, I have detected substitutions in the speech of each one. Although not frequently, those people whose clinical theories condemn substitution sometimes use substitutions themselves. Why not make life a bit easier for yourself once in a while? Don't make a habit of substitution, but don't feel guilty about using it now and then.

We stutterers have to learn to accept with as much tranquility as we can the fact that we stutter. This is not the same thing as "being resigned to it." Passive resignation never helped anyone. This resigned attitude implies an over-valuation of the importance of fluency. You don't resign yourself to having a hang-nail. You resign yourself only to something you regard as a great misfortune. If you think fluency of speech is the most important thing in life, maybe you should reconsider your priorities. One of the most successful and widely loved men of our era was Eisenhower. During press conferences he was hesitant, repetitive, and often failed to make sense. Many of his interruptions were exactly like those disfluencies people call stuttering. The important difference is that Ike wasn't distressed by his nonfluent speech. We can learn to overlook our own disfluency. Sometimes my wife will say to me, "You're stuttering a lot today." Often I'll reply that I wasn't aware of it. I'm happy when this occurs, for it indicates that I am more interested in the person I'm talking with and what I'm saying than in whether or not I'm being fluent.

If you're not able to find a speech therapist to help you, other kinds of people can often be of great assistance. My high school chemistry teacher, a former stutterer, gave up his lunch hour twice a week to talk with me about my speech. He didn't pretend to be a therapist. Since he didn't know exactly how he had gotten over his stuttering, he wisely refrained from making any specific suggestions. Rather, he listened and occasionally asked questions that helped me analyze what I was doing. My stuttering didn't cease, but I felt a lot less concerned about it and much better about myself.

Perhaps you can find this kind of sympathetic friend who will listen while you talk about your stuttering. Let him know you don't expect advice. You don't expect him to be a clinician, just a friend. I shouldn't say "just," for this sort of friend is priceless and hard to find. If you know another stutterer probably both of you can profit from talking about speech problems, provided you don't try to give each other advice.

Don't expect that psychotherapy will help your stuttering much. A psychiatrist or psychologist is trained to deal with emotional and neurotic problems. If you have severe emotional problems, by all means get the sort of help a psychiatrist or psychologist is trained to give you; but remember, "nervousness" is common to all people. Don't expect him to improve your stuttering appreciably. Learning how to deal with your other problems will doubtless make life easier, and sometimes this has an indirect effect on stuttering. But, beware the well-intentioned amateur who thinks he can "help" even though he has no training.

So you're cut off from qualified professional help? Well, you've got plenty of company! Most of the other people in the world who need any given type of specialized help, such as speech therapy, counseling, medical or dental care, never get it either. But somehow they mostly manage to make do. Professional therapy is great, but if you can't get it, don't bewail its absence. After all, fellow stutterers, there are strengths and resources within each of us. Only through these can we ever really accomplish anything.

Reducing The Fear of Stuttering

WILLIAM D. TROTTER

In order to reduce the amount of stuttering you do you must reduce your fear of stuttering. One way of reducing your fear is by increasing the amount of speaking you do, particularly in situations that you customarily avoid. The more speaking you do the more you will find out that stuttering isn't as fearful as you think. In general, the penalties attached to stuttering are not as great as you might imagine them to be.

You can get a good estimate of your speaking time by keeping a *speaking time record*. Carry a small notebook with you and two or three times a day jot down the persons with whom you have spoken and the approximate amount of time in minutes and seconds that you spoke to them. With a little practice it is relatively easy to estimate the amount of time you have spent talking with a person. At the end of the day just add up your total amount of talking time. Although there are wide individual differences, the average speaking time of a person who stutters is about 24 minutes; the average for a person who does not stutter is 44 minutes. It would probably be a good idea if you tried to speak as much as the average person. In general the amount of improvement you make will depend on the amount of talking you do, especially if you do this talking in situations you ordinarily avoid. In order to determine what kinds of speaking situations you avoid, keep a *speaking time record* for a week and classify situations such as talking to strangers in face-to-face speaking situations, talking to friends or acquaintances in face-to-face speaking situations, telephone calls to strangers, telephone calls to friends or acquaintances, speaking in discussion groups, speaking in class, and speaking to a member of the family, etc.

If you find that you customarily avoid the telephone, as many stutterers do, you will find it helpful to make some telephone calls every day. One way of getting over a fear is by doing the thing you're afraid of and finding out it is not as fearful as you had anticipated. Maybe you will find this record helpful to you.

Another way of helping yourself with your stuttering is to read while looking into a mirror. You do this in a place where you can be heard by at least one person, otherwise you probably won't stutter. After you have looked at yourself stuttering in the mirror for several hours your stuttering will be less frightening to you; this seems to carry over into your everyday speaking. Watching yourself stutter in a mirror makes you more objective and less emotional about your stuttering. Try to do this mirror work for at least fifteen minutes a day.

Listening to yourself stutter on a tape recorder is another good way of helping reduce your fear of stuttering. You should time your stuttering blocks and count the number of times you stutter. You will probably find that your blocks are not as long as you thought they were and that you actually stuttered about half as much as you expected you would. Learn to be more realistic! By listening to yourself stutter you accustom yourself to the sound of stuttering; when you are in a real speaking situation and you hear yourself stutter you're not as likely to panic.

You will feel better about your speech if you reduce the number of times you substitute non-feared words for feared ones. To test this out make five telephone calls and keep an account of the number of times you substituted non-feared words for feared ones. Then make five more telephone calls in which you try to make as few substitutions as possible. You should feel better about your speech when you are not substituting words or switching phrases to avoid stuttering You may find that your fear of stuttering is actually *more* of a problem than your stuttering.

Stuttering on purpose or "faking" at the beginning of a conversation might help you stutter less severely and less frequently throughout the rest of the conversation. To see if this idea is of any help to you fake some stuttering (any kind of stuttering may be used as long as it is clearly recognizable to the listener as stuttering) in ten conversations. Try ten more conversations without faking. See if there is a reduction in the frequency and severity of your stuttering when you faked stuttering at the beginning of the conversation. You might find that when you do this imitation stuttering you rarely experience real stuttering. This is because when you stutter on purpose you will feel little or no tendency to be anxious about whether you are going to stutter. When you go ahead and stutter on purpose you're not apt to become as tense or bothered about whether or not you're going to stutter. At first you may not be very successful in stuttering on purpose in more difficult speaking situations; gradually, you might become more successful in those where you ordinarily stutter severely.

Most people are somewhat tense talking to stutterers because they do not know how to react. Perhaps they believe that the stutterer is very sensitive about his problem and are afraid they will say or do something that will hurt his feelings. One way to make your listener feel at ease about your stuttering is to tell an occasional joke about it. If you are in a bad block and just can't get a word out you might say, "Well, if I don't get this word out soon we might be here all night." It's a good idea to have a healthy sense of humor about your stuttering. You might try one or two of these jokes on your friends to see if it puts them a little more at ease when talking to you.

Sometimes it is helpful to explain something about your stuttering to people who are important to you. This person might be a parent, teacher, friend, employer or a fellow worker. You might explain, for example, how you would like to be treated by your listener when you are stuttering. The purpose of this is to make you and the people you speak with more relaxed concerning your stuttering. If you feel that a person understands your stuttering you are likely to stutter less to that person. An open and honest attitude is healthy for all people involved.

You might find it helpful to adopt a more simple way of stuttering. This could consist of an easy prolongation of the first sound or syllable of the word. Listen to your own recording of this on tape and watch your performance of it in the mirror. After you have arrived at the point where you are adept and at ease using this pattern of stuttering on the tape recorder you should introduce it into your easier speaking situations; later, introduce it gradually into your more difficult speaking situations.

During the past twenty-five years there has been much interest in the effect of masking noise on stuttering. For two and a half years I used a portable masking noise generator. Whenever I felt I would stutter or was in the middle of a stuttering block I would turn the generator on and instantly hear a 90 to 100dB low frequency masking noise in my ears. I used this aid in all types of speaking situations, especially those in which I had most difficulty such as telephoning or giving a lecture. When I used the aid I had about one-fourth the number of stutterings and only an occasional one would be longer than one second in length. Although there was a reduction in both the frequency and duration of stuttering, the stuttering was never entirely eliminated. Whether or not such a device would help you would be difficult to predict.

I have also used an instrument that delivers a masking noise whenever you speak. This instrument is turned on automatically by the sound of the voice by a microphone attached to your throat. Or, you might find an electronic metronome useful; the beat of the metronome is fed into the ears through a cord from a small container carried in the pocket.

If you are like most stutterers you will probably not be too enthusiastic about using any of these electronic devices to help your stuttering. Although I have tried these instruments with a great number of stutterers, I have never found a stutterer who would wear one for anything but a short period of time. Perhaps the reluctance to use such aids is regarded as a sign of weakness. I do not think you should buy an electronic aid until you have had a chance to try it for several weeks. Neverthless, research has shown that such devices do improve fluency. As fluency improves the fear of stuttering decreases and as the fear decreases the fluency improves still further.

Several novels feature stutterers in important character roles. It would be valuable for you to read these books because after reading them you will have to conclude that a stutterer can be respected despite his stuttering. Respect, I think, is what the stutterer most longs for and finds hard to obtain because of his speech. In *Two Hours on Sunday* by Joseph Pillitteri one of the three or four principal characters is McHaney, a professional football coach and a stutterer. Brian Moore's *The Revolution Script* features as a kidnapper a stutterer known as C.T. (Jacques Cosette-Trudel). One of the two principal characters in Joseph Hayes novel *Like Any Other Fugitive* is Laurel Taggart, a girl stutterer who is on the run from her father. Herman Wouk's novel *The Winds of War* describes a fictional meeting between Somerset Maugham, the English author and stutterer, and President Roosevelt during World War II.

Advice To People Who Stutter

John L. Boland, Jr.

Stuttering in children can often be relieved through counseling and psychotherapy in working with the child and his parents, but as you probably already are aware, nobody knows how to 'cure' stuttering in adolescents and adults. However, you can work with your speech difficulties so as to help yourself feel less victimized by your stuttering.

It is important that you learn as much as possible about how you stutter and what you do when you stutter so that you can modify your symptoms in ways described by VanRiper, Sheehan and others. This knowledge of symptom modification techniques should help. It is possible, however, to worry too much about symptoms and ways of controlling them. Stutterers are usually too inhibited already and symptom modification procedures can be another kind of inhibition. Symptom controls, at best, are an uncertain aid and the stutterer should be aware that they are not sure and certain answers to his problem.

Stutterers come in all sizes and shapes but most of the stutterers I have known have characteristic personality problems. Most are perfectionistic. They tend to be too guilty—too anxious —too worried—too indecisive—and too inhibited. They have trouble getting along with themselves comfortably and working effectively with other people.

Most stutterers have trouble enjoying themselves. They tend to visualize themselves as always competing with other people trying to decide who is best on one ladder or another. They are engaged in a long-term 'identity crisis.' They would have these personality difficulties even if their stuttering symptoms were somehow miraculously removed.

You can learn something about your particular symptoms and you can modify them. However, in my opinion, your biggest struggle will be involved with changing your personality problems. You need to communicate more openly and easily with other people including being frank about your stuttering. You need to be warmer and more loving, to be more spontaneous and flexible, to be a more truly 'human' being. These are worthwhile goals for everybody but particularly for a stutterer.

You should start right away working on these problems with

someone who is knowledgeable about stuttering and is a competent psychotherapist. He may be a speech pathologist, a psychiatrist, a psychologist or possibly a social worker. Most all stutterers need to continuously work on changing their outlook on life—a lifetime goal.

Message To Adult Stutterers

Gerald R. Moses

As a person who has stuttered for some time you have probably been more preoccupied and perplexed about this troublesome problem than any other aspect of your life. You have found that your stuttering interferes with and complicates even the most basic relationships with other people. Your expectations and hopes for personal, social and professional success have been limited by your feelings of being an inadequate talker.

You have found that concern for what others think of you has made you feel trapped and frustrated. You have wondered why you can talk freely in one situation and not at all in another. Most of all, you have asked, "Why me? Why do I stutter and my friends do not?" You have tried to follow suggestions given by others. "Slow down, think what you are going to say, whistle, etc." You have even invented some of your own techniques for preventing the occurrence of stuttering. Most of these suggestions have had some foundation in distracting your attention from stuttering. Some of them have even worked for awhile. But temporary relief due to distraction has not solved your difficulties.

You have found much of what you have read and heard about stuttering to be confusing and embarrassing. While some writers feel that you stutter because you are physically different from people who do not stutter, others seem convinced that your stuttering lies in an emotional problem. Actually, persons who stutter seem to fall within the same range of physical and emotional characteristics as persons who do not stutter. The real difference between those who stutter and those who do not seems to be that stutterers stutter.

As the problem of stuttering develops, easy repetitions and prolongations are replaced by struggled attempts to say words. Embarrassment and the avoidance of words, situations and certain listeners occurs and a degree of emotionality is injected which complicates and compounds the problem. Penalty reactions by listeners convince you that your speech is unpleasant. This leads to further desperate attempts to prevent the occurrence of stuttering by whatever means available; struggle and avoidance are among the most commonly used.

During periods of crisis or conflict alternative ways to cope with and resolve problems present themselves. The range of alternatives is extreme. On the one hand we find flight or avoidance. On the other hand we find fight or struggle. Depending on the occasion either extreme might be appropriate, but a reasonable compromise seems to be more healthy, more effective and more generally used. When extreme measures become the rule the original problem has been compounded. On one hand, the problem becomes a struggle problem; on the other, an avoidance problem. The problem of stuttering develops or worsens when extreme reactions become learned as routine responses to what was once a more simple problem of speech disfluency.

Crucial to this point is the fact that struggle and avoidance *worsen* a problem of stuttering. Easy repetitions of sounds become hard repetitions with tension and facial contortion when force and hurry are added to them. Audiences react negatively to the struggle, and this convinces you that you must "try harder" so you increase your struggle. Similarly, penalty reactions to your stuttering prompt you to avoid or conceal your stuttering. Your speech becomes cautious and backward-moving. Your attention is directed to planning escape from stuttered words rather than to planning your thoughts. Avoidance strengthens your need to be fluent. The most evil part of this development is the subtle way in which struggle and avoidance become a part of you. They become involuntary and you do not recognize when you use them.

If you are serious about working to resolve your stuttering problem then it is time to change your approach to the problem. Easy ways out of difficulty are momentarily convenient, but in the long run they reinforce the problem. Although a step-by-step approach to solving a problem of stuttering does not account for individual differences among those who stutter, the following suggestions are placed in the order of their importance.

Reduce Avoidances. Determine to reduce your use of avoidances. Try to stutter openly and audibly. Let your stutterings be heard and seen rather than continue to conceal them by hurry and quiet. Try to keep your stuttering forward-moving and purposeful rather than postponed and half-hearted. Try to maintain eye contact with your listeners. Looking away severs the communication link with your audience and convinces them that you are ashamed and disgusted with the way that you talk. When you present yourself in an embarrassed and uncomfortable way you are more likely to receive negative audience reactions than if you stutter openly and severely. Deliberately enter previously feared situations. Judge your performance on the basis of the degree to which you approached the situation rather than on the basis of how much you stuttered or how fluent you were. Begin to recognize yourself as you are and as you want to be rather than as you think others want you to be. All of us need to be loved by, and in close contact with, other people. However, too much "human respect" makes us prisoners of what we think others want us to be.

Stutter in an Easier Way. When you are openly tackling the majority of your moments of stuttering you can try to change their form. Look at your stutterings objectively rather than emotionally. Study them by holding on to them longer than it would have taken to stutter-out the troublesome word. Resist the impulse to get the stuttering over with quickly. Although it is difficult to become less emotional about what you do, you need to become more realistic about yourself. For awhile, you must place greater emphasis on recognizing how you talk rather than on what others think of you.

Experiment with different ways to stutter for the purpose of learning how you stutter and the strength of your stuttering. Recognize and specify what you do when you stutter. Begin by listing the struggle behaviors that you use which are not a part of the act of speaking. Become aware of head or arm movements, eye blinking, other movements or body rigidity, lip-smacking or other noises, puffing of the cheeks or pursing of the lips. You will seek to eliminate these behaviors by increasing your awareness of them and separating them from your attempts to talk. Practice their use and insert them voluntarily into your speech when you have moments of less stuttering. Show yourself that they are not required for talking by using them independently of real and severe moments of stuttering.

Other behaviors which characterize your stuttering can be changed and normalized. Make an inventory of speech related struggle that accompanies your stuttering. Factors such as hurrying the utterance, tension in the lips, face and throat, and unusual preformations of sounds should be noted.

Normalize your attempts to say stuttered words. Normal speech is easy and forward-moving. Movements are released effortlessly. Try to prolong the first sound in a troublesome word until you feel you can release the rest of the word easily. If prolongations are uncomfortable for you, try an easy repetition of the first *syllable* of the word. Maintain the prolongation or repetition *out loud*. Make your approach to the word purposeful and straightforward. Your task is to learn to approach your stutterings openly and honestly and to eliminate the effort and hurry associated with previous attempts to talk. Judge your performance based on the degree of approach (stutter loud enough and long enough to examine what you are doing) and the degree of ease of release.

This is strong medicine! It is contrary to what you have improvised and learned. The emphasis is upon controlled *exhibition* of your stuttering, not upon inhibition. The number of times that you have previously inhibited your stuttering should suggest that many exhibitions will be needed to change significantly your manner of talking. Comfort in the use of normalized stuttering will follow only after much exercise. You may wish to select a friend or confidant with whom you can discuss your successes and failures, your heroics and flops. Your goal is not perfect speech, but rather the reduction of concern about your speech and the normalization of your attempts to talk.

Recognize and Tolerate Normal Disfluency. Normal speech contains disfluencies of many types. Easy repetitions of words and phrases, revisions, and incomplete phrases are a few types of normal disfluency. When these occur, and as long as they are *not* used as avoidance devices, they should be recognized as normal and not as symptoms of stuttering. Intolerance of normal disfluency causes you to try to talk with perfect fluency, an unattainable goal for anyone. Listen to these breaks in fluency in the speech of nonstuttering talkers. When the same kind of disfluencies occur in your own speech, they should be accepted and viewed as normal.

Again, these suggestions are strong medicine. I appreciate how difficult they seem. I encourage you to give them a fair trial. Finally, accept my best wishes for success and my respect for your determination to approach and resolve your problem of stuttering.

No Stutterer Is An Island Unto Himself

Gary N. LaPorte

When are you going to start doing what you are supposed to be doing? This question, like many others, is asked and the usual reply is, "I'm trying but I just don't seem to be getting anywhere." "Why?" To examine some of the common things that stutterers use to help themselves several stutterers were asked for a brief list of things they use. Perhaps some of the things they use to help themselves are things which you have used. If so, ask yourself the question, "Have they given me long lasting relief from stuttering, or merely temporary relief?" Here is the list: (1) Substituting another word for the word I feel I will stutter on, (2) using the syllable "uh" to get through a word, (3) laughing to get the word started, (4) talking slowly, or with a ryhthmical pattern of speech, (5) snapping my fingers to get the word started, (6) stopping and attempting to start over again, and (7) counting on someone else to say the word for me.

These devices, tricks or whatever you wish to call them are but a few of the many ingenious ways that stutterers have discovered to combat their day to day fight with communicative difficulty. Are they useful, or are they useful only temporarily?

We should realize that these tricks serve two purposes; to either prevent, or to get through, a feared word. Most stutterers feel they need some ways to cope with their stuttering, but these may not be as helpful in the long run as they first appear to be.

Unfortunately, these devices all serve to help maintain the problem of stuttering and result in the avoidance rather than the confrontation of stuttering. Avoidance can be defined as a process of shying away from the responsibility of facing your problem. You may say to yourself, "I do stutter, I know I do, so I am facing it." This is not true because although you recognize you stutter, you still continue to try to hide it. Facing your stuttering means (1) Saying 'I stutter' and discussing it openly with as many people as you can, (2) Learning some more positive ways of assisting yourself through your moments of stuttering every day. (3) Giving up your old tricks, and (4) Admitting to yourself that your stuttering presents a real problem. The following suggestions may help you to work on your stuttering.

What should you talk about when you discuss your stuttering? Whenever you have an opportunity to discuss your stuttering with someone, do it! Talk about such things as their feelings toward someone who stutters or the things you have done in the past to hide your own stuttering. Discuss why you have tried to hide your stuttering and the problems you have had finding a job. This will be difficult for you to do, I know, because I experienced this myself. But after forcing myself to do this many times it became easier and well worth the effort. The more frank you become about your stuttering the more you will enjoy talking about it and the less you will try to hide it.

What can you do to make your stuttering come out easier, and with less tension and struggle? Deliberately stutter! Yes, stutter on purpose in as many situations as possible, but stutter in a different way. Use a bounce and repeat the first syllable one, two or three times in this manner: "ta-tent" or "Da-Da-Diane" or "ska-ska-ska-school." Use the short "a" vowel because this is usually unlike the real vowel that goes with the word; it is easier to go from a syllable that has a vowel unlike the first vowel in the word. For words which have a short "a" like "car" maintain this short "a" because switching to another vowel would sound awkward.

What should you do when you find yourself stuttering on a word? Don't hide your stuttering. Instead stutter obviously. Stop what you are saying and say that same word over and over again before you continue. If you have difficulty saying it again use the bounce pattern. It may sound like stuttering, but it will be easier stuttering with a lot less frustration. For example, suppose you stuttered on the word 'tomorrow' in the sentence, "I'll call you tomorrow." Stop after 'tomorrow' then say 'tomorrow' over by bouncing and then continue the rest of the sentence. Face your problem, don't hide it. With practice, this will help you stutter more easily and with less frustration.

What should you do if you feel you will stutter on a word? Say to yourself, "I am going to say that word even though I may stutter on it, but I'm going to say it with a bounce." Or you might want to prolong the first sound in much the same way you would hold onto a note if singing. If you can say the word fluently, this is fine, but I would advise you to use some deliberate form of stuttering as noted above. Otherwise, you may become too sure of yourself and have a tendency to use fluent speech too soon. This might result in more stuttering at first because you have no means for dealing with your blocks. Later you can use more fluency if you like.

What can you do when you are stuck on a word? Concentrate on the *next* sound in the word and then go on to that sound, and then to the next sound, and so on until you have moved progressively through the word. For example, if you're stuck on the "b" in birthday, concentrate on the next sound "ir" and then "th," "d," and "ay" thus moving through the word. If you prefer, you can also stop after you have moved through the word and say it over again using one of the bounce patterns.

These suggestions for helping you face your stuttering by discussing it openly with other people and by deliberately stuttering in an easier manner will show that you are not afraid to stutter and can stutter in front of other people in any situation.

Perhaps all of these suggestions have interested you, and you might even try one or two of them. Merely trying, however, will not be enough. You will have to make yourself do these things and this will not be easy. You will need much courage. All I can say is that these suggestions helped me, and I feel they will help you. If you are willing to take responsibility and put these suggestions into practice, then you may find you need to modify them to fit into the work schedule you have determined for yourself. Be careful, however, not to modify them to the point where they cause you to go back to your former habits of avoiding. Always keep the idea of facing your stuttering foremost in your mind; do not avoid.

"No Stutterer is an Island Unto Himself." You must come to the realization that you must communicate with people as much as you can. You must not hide your stuttering, but bring it out into the open and work on it.

Finally, a speech pathologist can be of assistance and should be consulted if at all possible. He may be able to provide advice and suggestions that will help you deal with your communication difficulties.

A Therapy Experience

Hugo H. Gregory

The story of my stuttering therapy that I would like to tell here began when I was fifteen years old. Fortunately, I like to browse through periodicals, and one day while doing so I read about an institution 1500 miles away from my home in Arkansas that offered help for stutterers. At this center I was shown that I could modify my stuttering by prolonging vowel sounds and making lighter consonant contacts. This approach brought great relief and hope that I might, after all, aspire to become a lawyer and take part in politics. This method seemed to be "the way" to break the habit of stuttering.

Although I was conscientious and practiced using my manual of words and sentences beginning with all the vowels and consonants, a few months after I returned home I began to slip; the vicious circle of increased fear and stuttering began to return. However, I never again struggled as much with my speech as I had before this initial therapy.

I returned to the program the following year and began to learn some of the important lessons that have helped me to speak with increased freedom and versatility each year. I had previously focused too much on "controlling" my stuttering and had been willing to do anything (prolong the vowel, or use "light contacts") to keep from stuttering. I began to realize that I was concentrating too much on the *speech* aspect of therapy and was missing the part which had to do with *attitude*. I recall that the clinicians had talked about the way in which stutterers, in fact all people tend to overemphasize what they perceive as a problem. Stutterers tend to become very sensitive about the fluency of their speech. This is easy to understand, but it is not easy to change! As I examined my attitude I began to see that if I stuttered in a situation I was very hard on myself and considered myself pretty much a failure. Later on, after I was in college, Wendell Johnson's ideas helped me to understand that I should not attempt to evaluate myself as "either-or," (*either* I am a stutterer *or* I am not a stutterer.) I began to view myself as a person who sometimes stuttered as I talked and that I was going through a process of changing. This process involved evaluating what happened when I stuttered, modifying the way I talked, evaluating again, changing again, etc. It also involved changing my attitude of wanting to "beat" stuttering rather than studying it and changing it. It helped me learn that others did not think about my stuttering nearly as much as I did.

During my first two years in college I began to see more clearly that a stutterer has to take responsibility for making others feel comfortable in his presence. If he can be less sensitive about his stuttering those around him will be more comfortable, this will make him more at ease, he will stutter less, and so it goes; the vicious circle will be put into reverse. Since I was doing something constructive about my speech, I could smile about difficulty more. I could even feign some voluntary disfluency. The writings of Van Riper influenced me to be willing to *stutter on purpose*. I have always been fascinated by the idea of experimenting with all of the obvious or subtle ways I can be disfluent. In addition to studying what occurs when I speak that, as Williams puts it, interferes with the flow of speech and learning to change that pattern, I made a game of playing with my speech pattern, "do-do-ing th-i-i-is or tha-a-t." In this way the fear of speaking has melted away. I can speak differently, and of course I can communicate better, but it has been very important to me to be willing to be disfluent voluntarily. For me, this counteracts the rather deeply ingrained desire to be perfectly fluent and keeps the fear "doused."

Between the ages of fifteen and twenty I worked rather intensely on my speech and gradually realized that I would need to work on situations of increasing difficulty by planning, experiencing and then planning again, etc., until I became more and more confident. For example, during my freshman year in college I worked on introducing myself. After working to keep eye contact with my listener, I worked on modifying my speech and using some voluntary disfluency when saying "I'm Hugo Gre-Gregory." By the end of the year I never avoided introducing myself or making introductions.

Another general philosophy of my therapy has been that by tackling situations of greater difficulty, others which were once hard become easier. Thus, in my junior year in college I felt ready for public speaking. Sure, I stuttered when making a speech, but conversations with one or two people became much easier. Eventually getting up to speak before a group became easier, too!

At about this time I began my training as a speech pathologist and embarked upon a career, as my wife and children tell friends, of being a "professional stutterer." By the way, I've always noticed that when my wife tells some person "Hugo is a professional stutterer," the person looks somewhat perplexed as if to say, "Does he stutter?" or, "Why do you mention it?" The point is that we are very open about my stuttering. I found out very early that this attitude is an important ingredient in therapy.

Do not get the impression that I am advocating being anything but realistic about stuttering. Apprehension about saying certain words and the dread of stuttering in a situation are very real social and vocational handicaps for a stutterer. I know it has been easier for me as a stutterer during my adult years to be in speech pathology and to be working with stutterers. Coping with a fear-associated problem such as stuttering is difficult. Still, when we have such a problem we have to enter into activities, preferably with the help of a speech pathologist, that enable us to make realistic change and improvements. Reducing the fear and increasing the comfort when communicating can be very rewarding!

I also found, in working on my speech, that one makes many discoveries that can be applied advantageously to daily living. From the time I began therapy I have realized that I must take responsibility for my behavior and the way in which others evaluate me. In addition, I became aware of the tendency to lean on my stuttering as an excuse for not participating in some activity or for not being as successful as I might strive to be.

I continue to learn. I have practiced relaxation procedures as one approach to modifying the muscular tension involved in stuttering and to diminishing emotional arousal during speaking. Relaxation has been generally useful when I have needed to be more calm during a crisis.

As a speech pathologist working with adult stutterers I have found that the most important factors that determine progress are (1) that the stutterer have a goal that requires better speech, and (2) that he form the habit of working consistently and steadily to accomplish his purpose. Someone once told me that the price of better speech is keeping steadily at it. Many stutterers can have a speech pathologist to help them evaluate their problem and guide them in therapy. To those who cannot have this help in therapy I say "Find out whatever you can whenever you can, and then work steadily." At the end of every week, those having therapy and those not having therapy should ask as I always have, "What have I learned about my speech this week?"

Four Steps to Freedom

RICHARD M. BOEHMLER

As an adult seeking advice for your stuttering it seems to me four basic problems must be solved:

A. *Identifying* the specific nature of your stuttering,
B. *Developing* an effective therapy program,
C. *Successfully carrying* out the therapy program,
D. *Maintaining* success in the future.

Now these four problems can be solved. Stuttering is not the mysterious dilemma it was years ago. Although the nature of stuttering varies from individual to individual, it can be understood. Effective treatment methods have been developed, but to be effective the treatment must be appropriate to *your* specific stuttering pattern. The first step is to *identify* yourself.

A. Knowing that you "stutter" is not enough. If it were, advice for treatment would be much simpler. However, your stuttering is probably not the same as mine was, did not have the same causal history, and would not necessarily respond to the same treatment. Your stuttering is unique to you and its uniqueness must be identified.

Self diagnosis is a difficult task at best, so you may need professional help. If help is not available there is a great deal you can do on your own. You can start by describing exactly what you do or do not do when you wish to speak. Be as specific as you can. Describe specific movements, feelings and actions. If the speech production mechanism is blocked, describe exactly which muscles do not move in the appropriate fashion. Describe ways in which your communication patterns differ from those of your friends, or from your own patterns when you are communicating freely and successfully. It would be helpful to divide your observations into five categories:

1. *Involuntary Fluency Breakdowns:* Breaks in the flow of speech which you did not intentionally produce and which you find undesirable;

2. *Interfering Hypertension:* Specific muscle tensions which make speaking difficult. For example, tensions in your arms do not effect speech production, but excessive vocal cord tension would if this tension interfered with vibrations;

3. *Speech Patterns Used to Avoid:* Breakdowns such as deliberately starting over, using a pause, talking slowly, and substituting a word synonym when a breakdown has occurred or is anticipated;

4. *Patterns Used to Cope with a Breakdown:* Speech and non-speech behaviors used after the flow of speech has stopped such as increased air pressure against the "blocked" articulatory position (forcing the lips apart), or releasing the "block" by increased tension in non-speech muscles (foot stomping), or relaxing the muscles involved in the "block," etc.;

5. *Self-Concept as a Communicator:* Thinking of how you will speak rather than what you will say, or remembering "stuttering" as the highlight of the conversation and imagining yourself a speaking failure, etc.

An unlimited number of examples of questions would need to be presented to cover all potential patterns of communication covered by "stuttering." Chapters 6 and 7 in Van Riper's *The Nature of Stuttering* would provide helpful background reading for increasing your ability to do this step well.

Two words of caution! First, a perfect flow of language formulation and speech production is a rare skill. Most of us have errors in formulation and imperfections in our speech production. Include these in your analysis but be sure to distinguish between those patterns, including breakdowns, which are acceptable and those which are not. Compare what you do against what your friends do. They also repeat sounds, words and phrases, interject "uh" or stop while saying a difficult word. Therapy should lead toward acceptable, free flowing speech but not *perfect fluency*. Second, objectivity is a serious problem in self-analysis. In the absence of a speech clinician to aid you, ask your spouse, friend or teacher to point out what they see and hear you do as you communicate. This will aid you in obtaining specific descriptions of your stuttering. The use of a tape recorder will also help.

If a clinician were to make the above analysis I would expect him to spend several hours in most cases. Expect no less and even more from yourself. A thorough job of self-identification is critical to proceeding or moving ahead successfully.

B. Many therapies have been developed to deal with "stuttering." The ideas presented by other contributors to this booklet include many of the possibilities and are quite adequate for dealing with most advanced stuttering behaviors; restatements and extensions of these points are not necessary. Your task is to select those ideas which most closely fit *your specific* problem.

Breakdowns from *excess tension* may reflect an inappropriate articulation rate, poor formulation of thoughts, anxieties about blocking, anxieties about speaking situations, or more general anxieties about yourself. A clear understanding of the nature of stuttering can lead directly to the appropriate therapy. Common sense, past experiences with therapy and reading the suggestions of various authors may be adequate for you to proceed at this point, but professional help may be needed in selecting the appropriate therapy.

One note of caution. None of us, whether stutterer or clinician, can be 100% correct. Our diagnosis of ourself or of others is subject to error. Selection of the appropriate therapy is based on our most educated opinion after careful study. Likewise, in diagnosing your own problem, don't hesitate to evaluate the effectiveness of the therapy if it is not helpful. Continuing ineffective therapy is not only expensive but a waste of precious time. Select what seems to be the most appropriate therapy and put it into practice. If it doesn't work within a reasonable time, try to evaluate why and then change it accordingly.

C. Making a therapy program successful involves a great deal more than correct identification of the problem and the selection of appropriate therapy. It requires consistent, devoted and thorough application of the therapy program. Whether you are working by yourself or with the aid of a speech clinician, the success of therapy is primarily up to you. This is not a cop-out on my part. No one but myself improved my speech. Others have helped me by providing information, giving emotional support, identifying bias, etc., but the dirty work of therapy is, and always has been, *my* responsibility. Likewise, I have not changed the communication skills of any of my clients. I have only helped them to help themselves. They did the job if the job was done. Even in other helping professions the clinician only helps; he does not do the basic job. Your body heals itself, the surgeon only helps the process. Just as the body cells must do the major part in healing a wound, you must do the major part in changing behavior patterns, in developing communication skills, and in obtaining freedom to communicate. Many failures are due to the individual spending too *small* a portion of his talking time learning new ways of behaving, and too *large* a portion of his communication time practicing old patterns. This just doesn't work! Therapy must be practiced full time to be highly successful. You must feel that you are on the right track and you must be committed to putting the program into practice. Plan your work well, then work your plan harder than you have ever worked before. Success will follow.

D. Relapses into old stuttering patterns are the rule, not the exception. Follow through: provide for maintenance and reinforcement of success. Whether the changes you make involve your self-image, decreasing blocks, coping better with blocks, more fluent speech, or greater freedom to communicate, the change will not maintain itself. Patterns of life which have been established and maintained for many years cannot be changed in a few months and then continued spontaneously on their own. Therapy must be continued until new patterns are as automatic and as much a part of you as was your old stuttering. Not continuing to maintain the results of your therapy program will not only make a relapse practically inevitable, but will also require some degree of starting over and going over the same ground again to bring back the success you earned. Remember how you improved, and keep the improvement going.

Stuttering is no longer the dilemma of the communication disorders. It can be changed. If freedom to communicate is not yours because of stuttering, it is my advice that you develop a very specific understanding of *your* communication patterns. Based on your understanding choose the most appropriate therapy program you can, and work at the program with more consistency, devotion and energy than any other task you've ever tackled. As success is obtained, maintain it with equal vigor. I believe that most therapy has failed because of poor diagnosis, inappropriate therapy, halfhearted application of therapy and poor follow-through. Don't make these mistakes! Identify, plan, work, and then follow-through!

Guidelines

PAUL E. CZUCHNA

By the time most stutterers become adults they have become profoundly frustrated in their efforts to speak fluently, and irritated at themselves for their failure to do so. They feel that they have at least average intelligence, but have endured endless labor and energy expended during their efforts to communicate. They feel helpless about mastering their stuttering and wonder what is wrong with them. As a result, they fear stuttering more and more and enjoy speaking less and less.

For years most adult stutterers have received well meaning suggestions that have been directly or indirectly aimed at stopping the stuttering altogether. These suggestions imply miraculously quick cures and fluent speech. "Take a deep breath before a word on which you may stutter, then say it without stuttering." "Think of what you're going to say before you say it, and you won't have any trouble," etc. You, like every other stutterer, have heard such prescriptions that imply and instill within him the belief that it is "wrong" to stutter. In his efforts to speak fluently, the stutterer becomes more and more fearful of being unable to cope with the intermittent stuttering that may occur. The more he struggles to avoid possible stuttering or attempts to hide or disguise the stuttering that cannot be avoided, the more he denies that he has a problem.

There appear to be two main types of stutterers: (1) the *covert* stutterer who attempts to avoid contacts with feared words and situations that might identify him as a possible stutterer to his listeners and (2) the *overt* stutterer who struggles laboriously through word after word as he communicates. The remaining types are varying combinations of these two. Which one are you?

Let us look at some of the communicative behavior of the *covert* stutterer and some of his associated feelings. Covert stutterers scan ahead during their utterances and continuously look for any expected word difficulty that might result in stuttering. They must be fully and constantly prepared for any emergency so they can avoid these words and not unmask themselves. When they anticipate possible stuttering they attempt to avoid direct contact with feared words. They postpone words they must say by various means until they feel they might be able to utter them more fluently. Or, at the precise moment they must utter a particular word, they use various timing devices such as eye blinks, quick body movements or gestures. Rather than endure any obvious struggle that might be interpreted as stuttering, they may attempt to get others to fill in these "key words" for them or completely give up their intent to communicate. Covert stutterers have learned which kinds of speaking situations tend to produce unavoidable stuttering and they have become masters at avoiding these situations (i.e., walking a mile or two to talk to someone rather than use the telephone; sending others on errands which involve speaking, etc.). Do you do these things?

In contrast, the more *overt* stutterer seemingly "barrels on through" words and sounds quite directly when he expects difficulty during his communication. He may not like his struggling efforts, but he has learned to endure them. At the same time he may have a minimum of word and situation avoidance since he expects to stutter anyway. He may, however, postpone word utterances and do some avoiding of his more obnoxious behaviors *during* moments of outward stuttering. These stutterers sense the penalty they receive from listeners who become impatient due to the amount of time it takes to communicate. Yet they still like to talk and do so. They resent other people filling in words for them or attempting to complete their utterances. These stutterers are often profoundly frustrated in their efforts to increase their rate of speaking, yet at the same time they exhibit many kinds of struggling behaviors that really interfere with accomplishing this. They stutter harder than they need to! They do things that actually prevent them from saying their words easily. Perhaps you do, too.

Stutterers do not need to learn how to speak fluently. They already know how to do this even though they rarely pay any attention to their fluent utterances. They may have to learn more about how to respond to the fear or experience of blocking, but they do not have to learn (as something new) to say words fluently. Some of the intense frustration comes from knowing how to say words fluently, yet finding themselves stuck and unable to do so. Stutterers need to learn what to do when they do stutter if they are to eventually reduce the fear and frustration involved. As a tentative reachable goal to shoot for, they must learn to move more easily through stuttered words rather than recoiling from them. They need other choices of ways to stutter when they expect to stutter as well as other ways of completing word utterances after they block. In short, they first need to learn a better way of stuttering, one which will interfere very little with communication. Do you know how to stutter fluently?

Most stutterers initially react with revulsion and rejection to the thought of learning to stutter differently with less struggle. After all, they have spent many years attempting either not to stutter at all, or attempting to hide stuttering when it does occur. The more *covert* stutterer may respond with extreme fear and panic even to the thought of trying to learn to stutter fluently, for he has spent considerable time and effort developing his many tricks to avoid ever being discovered as being a stutterer. The *overt* stutterer may have grave doubts that he can ever learn to stutter more effortlessly, yet recognize that this would provide some relief for him. Nevertheless, the thought of learning to stutter more fluently, as an intermediate goal to shoot for, begins eventually to become a possibility. They would prefer to have a quick cure; perhaps if they could learn to be fluent even when they do stutter, it wouldn't be so bad. How do you respond to this?

The *covert* stutterer has a longer way to go than does the more overt stutterer. The covert stutterer must first literally rediscover what he is fearful of doing by deliberately stuttering more overtly when he anticipates stuttering. To do so, he must resist using his old avoidance tricks when he expects to stutter. He must learn to endure by experiencing what he is usually only guessing he might do. The *overt* stutterer, on the other hand, must learn to examine and tolerate more and more of what he actually does when he stutters rather than deny the existence of his obvious stuttering behavior. Both overt and covert stutterers must come to know vividly what is to be changed and get a fairly clear picture of the procedures that will create a more fluent kind of stuttering. They must then learn to build solid bridges to fluency rather than repeatedly trying to jump to fluency and falling and failing. Do you know how to get out of the mess where you now are?

The following crucial experiences, which you must seek

again and again, are the basic building materials and equipment needed to build a bridge from where you are now to where you want to be in the future:

1. You are basically responsible for your own behavior, including your stuttering.
2. Stuttering can be deliberately endured, touched, maintained and studied.
3. Avoidance only increases fear and stuttering, and must be reduced.
4. Struggling, hurried escape from stuttering blockages, and recoiling away from expected or felt blockings, make stuttering worse than it need be, and tends to make it persist.
5. It is possible to release yourself voluntarily from blocking or repeating prior to completing a word utterance.
6. When a moment of stuttering occurs it can be studied, and its evil effects erased as much as possible.
7. Attending to your normal speech and adopting short, forward-moving, effortless moments of stuttering reduces more severe stuttering.
8. The self-suggestion of incoming stuttering can be resisted and words can be spoken fairly normally.
9. It is possible to build barriers to destructive listener reactions that tend to precipitate stuttering.
10. Ambivalence, anxiety, guilt and hostility can be decreased.
11. Every effort should be made to build up your ego strength, self-confidence and self-respect.
12. Society in general rewards the person who obviously confronts and attempts to deal with his stuttering.
13. It is more personally rewarding to stutter fluently than to stutter grotesquely, and it is fun to be able to talk anywhere even if you do stutter.

Will you merely read this list and then forget it? Or will you consider each item carefully and see if you can find some way to use it to help yourself?

These experiences which the stutterer must repeatedly undergo may be difficult to devise or to carry out by the stutterer alone. The stutterer feels in enough lonely isolation with his stuttering problem as it is. Therapy for stutterers ordinarily requires having a competent speech therapist available as a

guide, one who can share experiences with the stutterer throughout the course of therapy. The companionship of a competent
speech therapist is usually essential for therapy success. Get
help if you can, but if none is available, help yourself. Others
have done so!

Face Your Fears

Sol Adler

My youth, as is the case with so many stutterers, was filled with alternate hope and despair as I hungered for some relief from my stuttering. This of course is not unique; most stutterers have had similar feelings. But have you ever asked yourself what it is that really bothers you, what it is that causes despair? Is it your stuttering or is it your fear of people's reactions to your stuttering? Isn't it the latter? Most stutterers have too much anxiety about what they think people might say or might do as a result of the stuttering. These anxieties can be lessened.

I remember well these feelings of worry, anxiety, and despair. If you can learn to dissipate some of these terrible feelings—you will be able to help yourself as many other stutterers have done.

There is one effective method you can utilize to achieve this goal. Face your fears! This advice is easy to give and admittedly difficult for many of you to take; however, it is advice that has helped many stutterers and it can help you.

Learn to face your fears of stuttering in different speech situations. My involvement in such "situational-work" during my early career created peace of mind for me. It was a slow process; I didn't achieve such freedom all in one day or week or month; and it was hard work. But I did it, and others have done it, and so can you.

Somehow you must learn to desensitize yourself to the reactions of others and refuse to let people's actual or imagined responses to your stuttering continue to affect your mental health or your peace of mind.

This is easier said than done but it can be accomplished. I found that by facing my fears gradually I was able to achieve such a goal and I have known other stutterers who have "thrown" themselves into similar confrontations. Use whatever pace that best suits you but get involved, one way or another, in these confrontations with your "speech fears." There will be times when you will be unable to face the fears inherent in different situations, but persevere. Don't give up! Continue facing your fears as often as you can. Besides the peace of mind that develops, you will also become more fluent in your speech. You will find yourself manifesting lesser amounts of stuttering and that stuttering will never be as severe as it was previous to your confrontation.

You will find that as you grow older you will develop more ability to do these things. With growing maturity we can generally face our fears more frequently and more consistently. But how long do you want to wait?

List all the speech situations in which you fear stuttering. These are pretty standard situations; for example, most stutterers fear using the telephone. They experience much distress when they are called upon to answer the telephone while it rings incessantly, or conversely, when they must place a necessary call. I remember well how often I "played-deaf" when the telephone would ring. Sometimes, unfortunately, I might be standing not more than a few feet from that ringing telephone, and my protestations regarding "answer what telephone?" would be of no avail. Face this fear by making many telephone calls each day to different persons—people whose names are unknown to you. Practice stuttering while you speak to them. Stutter in different ways. For example, I once had a patient make such a call and the party on the other end turned out to be a preacher. The patient had been told he must ask for J - J - J - J but to never complete the name. The preacher was an extraordinarily kind person and evidently with some time to spare. He continually urged the patient to "take it easy" and assured him that he wouldn't hang up. For two or three minutes the patient continued repeating the initial "J" until, in sheer desperation, the preacher said, "Son, there is no "J" here. I'm sorry but I have to go," and with that he hung up. What do stutterers learn from this and similar experiences? Not to be as afraid of answering the telephone since the worst possible thing that could happen to him would be for the party to hang up on him, or to say something derogatory to him. In either case, his world doesn't end. By such experiences you will find yourself getting toughened caring less about how people might respond to you and, finally, you will be able to use the phone with lesser amounts of fear, anxiety, and stuttering.

Another classic situation most stutterers fear is asking questions of strangers. I suspect that this bothers you too. What I did, and have my patients do, is to stop people who are walking somewhere, or are in stores, and ask them questions concerning the time, directions, the price of some object, etc. All student clinicians who have trained under my supervision have been asked to do first whatever they ask the patient to accomplish. Thus they too had to first ask such questions of strangers. But since they were not stutterers they had to feign stuttering and they were required to do it very convincingly. These normal speakers discovered, as you well know, that much anxiety is experienced when asked to perform as indicated. But anxiety becomes reduced and dissipated if you engage in these kinds of situational experiences rapidly, one after another, almost without pause. For example: ask ten or fifteen people about their views regarding the cause of stuttering. You will find that after the eighth or ninth person has responded you will no longer possess all the fears you did when you initiated this exercise. Also, as a bonus, you might be surprised to find yourself actually listening to and arguing with your respondents. and actually enjoying the exercise.

To argue about and/or to discuss effectively with anyone the causes or nature of stuttering means that you have to have some relevant information about stuttering. Do you know what this speech disorder is all about? If not, you should. You should learn as much about it as is possible. If your library does not contain sufficient information, write to the editor or publisher of this booklet for additional information or, write to the American Speech and Hearing Association in Washington, D.C. for information. No longer tolerate the false information from your parents, friends, teachers or others who are interested in you, and want to help, but who are probably very ignorant about stuttering. Educate them! But educate yourself first!

I discovered also that by talking to other stutterers I received indirectly the benefits of their therapeutic experiences. Find other stutterers! It may surprise you to find out how many fellow stutterers are available. Form groups! In this way you can help each other. It will be so much easier for you when you can find someone in whom you can confide and who understands your problem. Work up your own situational assignments. Alternate as clinician and patient with the proviso that the "clinician" must first do whatever he asks the "patient" to do. Watch people closely! See how they react to your stuttering. Do you see facial grimaces or indications of shock or surprise on their faces? Occasionally you may but often you may not. You will find that when you both become objective enough to observe these people carefully, and to compare notes regarding their responses, you may even begin to enjoy the exercise. Your group should also try to obtain the services of a competent and sympathetic professional person who can guide you in discussions regarding those factors involving personality development. If not, discuss them yourselves. This kind of introspection—or self-analysis—helped me a great deal. It made me look at myself to see what made me tick. I began to realize that much of the behavior I disliked in myself was motivated by my fear of stuttering.

In summary I have suggested two matters of great importance to you regarding your stuttering: (1) Learn all about stuttering; read everything you can regarding this disorder; there is much literature available. (2) Face your fears as often and as consistently as you can. Do not give up if and when you backtrack; try to meet "head-on" these feared situations. When you can do so with some degree of consistency, you may find a new "life" awaiting you.

Some Suggestions For Adult Stutterers Who Want to Talk Easily

Dean E. Williams

For purposes of this paper, I want you to assume that I am meeting with an adult group of stutterers for the first time and that you are a member of that group. My purpose will be to suggest what I think you can do to improve the ways you talk. The major points presented in this paper are those that would be discussed and elaborated and experienced during the subsequent weeks of therapy. It is important to point out that I am talking to you as a *group;* for any one person in the group, I would direct my attention toward his own special feelings, viewpoints and needs. Because this discussion is directed toward a group, it will be necessary for each of you to think through the comments made and to apply them to your own individual problem.

. . . . . .

In working to solve a problem such as stuttering, you must first ponder the various ways that you think about the problem for they affect, in good part, what you do as you talk. They affect the observations you make, the ways you react inside, and the ways you interpret the success or failure of what you have done. Furthermore, they determine, in the main, what you will do the next time you talk.

Think about your stuttering problem. *How* do you view it? *What* do you do that you call your stuttering? *Why* do you think you do it? *What* are the most helpful things you can do when you stutter? *How* do they relate to what you believe is wrong? *What* does not help? Why? When one begins to ask questions about what he is doing, it can stimulate him to make observations about his behavior. This, in turn, encourages him to become *involved* with the ways he feels, with the ways he thinks, and with what he is doing as he talks. This is necessary! You cannot solve a problem by acting like an innocent bystander waiting for someone else to answer questions that you never thought to ask. It is *your* problem and you must face it. Perhaps I can help stimulate you to consider your own beliefs by relating examples of how a few other stutterers of different ages have viewed their stuttering. In my opinion, the ways they talk about the problem change in relation to the number of years they have attempted to cope with it.

The seven-to-nine-year-old stutterer is apt to be confused and bewildered by the ways he talks and by people's reactions to it. One second grade boy reported that when he was in kindergarten and first grade he had repeated sounds a great deal. People called it "stuttering." Now, he tensed and "pushed" to get the words out so he wouldn't "repeat," or "stutter," as he understood the meaning of the word. Now, people were calling the tensing and pushing "stuttering." He was confused!

A 9-year-old typically held his breath, blinked his eyes and tensed his jaw. This, to him, was his stuttering. One day he began taking quick breaths and then blurting the word out quickly. He reported that he was doing this so he wouldn't do the holding of breath and other behavior mentioned above. People were still reacting to that as "stuttering." He was bewildered. The children were doing certain behaviors in order to "help them get the words out," and those behaviors were called stuttering. When they did something else in order to not do those behaviors, people also were calling that stuttering too. Their only recourse, then, was to do something else so they wouldn't do what they just did. Does this sound confusing? It was confusing to the children too! Yet, one can observe the same behavior in adults. When was the last time that you did something similar, for example jerking your head backwards, so you would not tense your jaw and prolong a sound?

Children in their early teens often report more magical beliefs about stuttering than do the younger children. When some 12 or 13-year-olds were asked to discuss the question "What is stuttering like?" one 13-year-old boy reported that it is like trying to ride an untamed horse. He worried about when it (the "stuttering horse") would shy away from a word, would balk at the sight of a word or would begin to "buck" on a word. He felt that the only thing he could do was hang on as hard as he could, keep a tight rein on the horse and just "hope" that the horse wouldn't be too violent. Another 13-year-old reported that talking was like Indian wrestling. He constantly had to strain and to struggle so that his opponent (his stuttering) didn't get the best of him. As he talked, he tried to overpower it. The children talked as if they had to fight *against* their "stutter." Their "stuttering" was an adversary with a mind of its own, and in most instances, they were afraid that it was stronger than they were. With this viewpoint, then, it is quite natural for the child to feel that he has to tense, to struggle, and to use his muscles to fight the "stutter." It has been my observation that adults who stutter generally do the same thing, although they may not explain so vividly the reasons for doing it.

As adults, you probably have stuttered for many more years than the children just discussed. Whereas they still are actively trying to "explain" to themselves the reasons why they tense and struggle, you may have forgotten to ask "Why?" anymore. You no longer question the necessity or helpfulness of doing the tensing or head jerking or eye blinking that you do. You just accept it as part of what you, as a stutterer, *have to do* to talk. This is unfortunate because then you do not direct your attention toward observing, studying, and experimenting with what you can do in order to talk without the tensing and struggling. Yet, you *can* learn to talk easily and effortlessly.

There is nothing inside your body that will stop you from talking. You have the same speaking equipment as anyone else. You have the ability to talk normally. You are doing things to interfere with talking because you think they help. You tense the muscles of your chest, throat, mouth, etc., in an effort to try and fight the "stutter." Yet these are the same muscles that you need to use in order to talk. You can't do both at the same time because you only have one set of muscles. Therefore, it is extremely helpful to begin studying what normal speakers do as they talk. This is what you want to learn to do. Observe carefully the way they move their mouth, lips and jaws as they are talking. Then, sit and talk in a room by yourself, or read in unison with someone else and study the feeling of movement as you talk. There is a certain "just right tensing" that you do as you move your jaw and tongue and lips. Study it! This is what you want to do when you talk. Now begin to look at what you do to interfere with talking when you do what you refer to as your "stuttering." If you begin to hold your breath or tense your jaw, for example, you cannot move as easily as you must do to talk the way normal speakers do. In short, you need to develop a sharp sense of contrast between what you are doing that you call "stuttering" and what you do as you just talk easily. Use a mirror or a tape recorder to help you observe what you are doing. Above all, get a feeling deep in your muscles of the movements involved in easy talking. Then you can become much more alert to what you are *doing* (not what's "happening" to you) as you tense and interfere with talking.

After careful observation and practice of what you do as you talk easily and on-goingly, as opposed to interfering with talking by tensing, stopping, or speeding etc., enter a few speaking situations that are not so threatening that you cannot observe your behavior. It has been my experience that ordinarily the person observes that he gets scared, or he gets a "feeling" that he was going to stutter, and he tenses. What is this feeling? Work to be able to tolerate it so you can observe it carefully. Enter more speaking situations. Answer some questions. To what is the feeling similar? Does the feeling *alone* make you unable to talk? Or, do you tense when you begin to experience the feeling? When you start to talk do you pay attention to what you want to do (the movement you want to make) or are you attending to the "feeling" waiting for it to tell you whether you will be able to talk or not? Study the feeling. If you study it in various situations as you are talking you will become aware that it is a feeling that is in no way special from any other feeling of fear or embarrassment, etc. It is very normal. However, it is a feeling to which you have learned to react by tensing, or by speeding or slowing your rate. Essentially, you react to it by *doing* extra muscular activity than is necessary to do in order to talk. When you become aware that the struggling behavior you call stuttering is something that you are *doing* as you talk, and not something that magically "happens to you," you are in a very good position to begin to change what you are doing as you talk so that you can talk easier. Then, you can begin to talk by starting to move easily, being willing to experience the feelings that you may feel, but to continue moving easily. You can tolerate a few bobbles as you do this. Then, you can begin to see that there is a way out of this jungle. There is a reason to become optimistic because it is within your ability to do it. It's essentially a problem of learning to just "let yourself talk." You have learned to do too much. You do things to interfere. Learn by observing and experimenting that these things do not help. Talking is essentially easy ongoing movement of the jaw, tongue and lips, etc. Tensing unnecessarily only gets in your way. Your success in countering the excessive tensing as you talk will depend upon two factors. The first involves the thoroughness with which you come to understand that there is no "stuttering" to be *fought, avoided* or *controlled*, other than the tensing you, yourself, perform. Once you understand this as you talk, your own tensing becomes a signal for you to begin reacting constructively by immediately easing off on the tensing and attending to the easy on-goingness of talking.

The second involves practice. You must practice talking easily as you would practice typing or playing the piano easily and on-goingly even though you had a feeling in your stomach or chest that you might "goof" it at some point. Then, expand your speaking situations—and practice—until you can talk comfortably at any time you choose to speak.

This is the beginning of therapy for you. From now on, it is up to you!

Do-It-Yourself Kit For Stutterers

Harold B. Starbuck

Dear Sir or Madam: In reply to your letter of complaint about our Do-It-Yourself Kit for Stutterers, I apologize for not including the instructions. However, the kit was supposed to be empty! You don't need any gadgets to correct your stuttering. You already have all the tools and equipment you need. As long as you've got your body, complete with movable parts, you're set to begin. Don't ever forget that even though you went to the most knowledgeable expert in the country, the correction of stuttering is still a do-it-yourself project. Stuttering is your problem. You stutter in your own unique way. The expert can tell you what to do and how to do it, but you're the one who has to do it. You're the only person on earth who can correct your stuttering. Here are your instructions:

The first thing you must become is an honest stutterer. By that I mean you've got to stop trying to be fluent. You have to stop struggling with your feared words. Go ahead and stutter on them. Let your stuttering come out into the open. Hit the block head on and let it run its course. Start by stuttering aloud to yourself. Stutter on every word you say. Stutter two or three times on every word. Get used to it and notice that as you stutter freely you can eliminate all those retrials, avoidances, and half-hearted speech attempts. Practice on your family and friends. They won't mind and will be rooting for you. This is a tough step, but do it in every speaking situation until you are stuttering freely. Don't try to talk fluently without stuttering.

Now that you are able to stutter openly and without fear or shame, you can begin to answer the question, "How do I stutter?" You've got to examine and analyze the act of speaking to see what errors you're making. You must be making mistakes somewhere or you would be speaking fluently. What are you doing wrong that makes your speech come out as stuttering? Speech is, after all, just a stream of air we inhale, reverse, and push out our mouths while we shape and form it into speech sounds. One must realize that you can't have speech unless you have the air coming out your mouth. Examine your speech breathing. Are you inhaling a sufficient amount. After the air is in and you're ready to talk, are you reversing it smoothly and starting an outward flow, or are you holding it in your lungs? Are you blocking it off in your throat at the level of your vocal folds? (This happens on most vowel blocks.) Are you humping your tongue up in the back of your mouth and blocking it there, as on K and G? Is the tip of the tongue jammed against your gum ridge blocking the air on T and D? Have you jammed your lips together so no air can flow out on P and B? No air flow means no speech, and hard contacts between any two parts of the speech mechanism result in a blocked air stream. Now examine yourself a little more closely. Examine the muscular movements, stresses, and strains you use in producing those hard contacts. Examine the muscular tensions and pressures. Is it any wonder you stutter? Speech is an act of almost continuous movement, and when you stop that movement you're in a stuttering position. In order to say any speech sound, you have to move into position to say that sound, move through it, and then move out of it into position for the next sound. Find out what and where your blockages and stoppages are, and what muscular tension causes them.

Is there a solution? There is to every problem! What you've got to do now is to correct every problem or error you've analyzed. We call this the *Post-block Process of Correction*. Here's how it works:

Stutter on a word. When the word is completed, stop completely and analyze all of the errors you made while all the tensions and pressures are still fresh. Now, figure out a correction for each error. For example, suppose the air was blocked off in your throat on a vowel sound. The correction is an open throat. You will have to concentrate on the throat area so no muscular action jams the vocal folds closed. Concentrate on keeping them open the way they were when you inhaled. Reverse the air stream slowly, start the sound, and say it.

Suppose that the lip muscles had jammed the lips shut into a hard contact which allowed no air to pass. The correction would be a light contact or, better, no contact at all between the lips. Concentrate on controlling the lip muscles so that the lips just barely touch, or almost touch, and air is able to flow between them. An important aspect here is movement out of the sound, so you have to control the lip muscles in their movement out of the sound as well as into it. The air flow must be coordinated with the lip movement so that the sound is produced as the lips form the sound.

Figure out a correction for every error as in the above examples. When you have all the necessary corrections figured out, you are ready to try the word again. Exaggerate your corrections at first when you say the word, paying more attention to how the word feels rather than to how it sounds. The sounds may be slightly distorted and prolonged at first. That's good. The prolongation is the result of slow careful muscular movements as you move into, through and out of the sounds. The distortion is the result of light loose contacts. Feel the controlled air flow; feel the controlled muscle movements as you move fluently through the word with no stoppages.

Do a good job on the Post-block Process of Correction. This is where speech correction takes place. Don't just say the words over again fluently after you stutter. Say them carefully, concentrating on the feelings of muscular action as you coordinate the breath stream with the formation of sounds. Concentrate on the feelings of movement and fluency.

In the above step, we worked on the stuttering after it happened. Now we're going to move ahead a bit and work on it while it's happening. To do this you still have to stutter. While you are stuttering (which means you've got to keep the block going longer than the average), you must analyze what is happening incorrectly. When the errors are analyzed, you can start making corrections such as stopping a tremor, loosening a contact, and getting rid of tension until you are producing the stuttered sound in a stable, correct way. Then you can initiate movement out of the sound and complete the word. We call this step the *Block Process of Correction*. You go through the same process as you did in post-block corrections, only now you should be able to do it while you are stuttering. By now you should be able to recognize your errors almost instantly and know what corrections have to be made. Make the corrections, smooth out the sound, and complete the word. Practice this on any word you say. Stutter on purpose, get it under your control, and say the word.

You've gone through the Post-block and Block Processes of Correction. Now let's work on the stuttering even earlier. Let's work on it before it ever happens. This is the *Pre-Block Process of Correction*. When you come to a word you're going to stutter on—don't! Stop just before you start that word. Analyze how you would have stuttered on it had you said that word. Figure out the needed corrections and use them, saying the word just as you would a post-block correction. Feel the movements and fluency here too. With very little practice, you can eliminate the pause period and prepare for any feared word as you approach it. Take advantage here of your anticipation, expectancy, and fear of stuttering. An excellent way to work on this process is to select any word, feared or not, figure out how you would normally stutter on it, then figure out corrections, and apply the corrections when you get to the word.

You're now using *Predetermined Speech*. You are determining beforehand what movements you have to make, and how you have to make them, in order to say sounds and words fluently. You should be speaking fluently now, but don't fall into the trap of thinking you are a normal speaker. Normal speech for you is stuttering speech. Be proud of your abnormal predetermined fluent speech. Use it. Keep up your skills of controlling your muscle movements that produce speech. You have to eliminate your errors before, or while, they are happening. Once your speech is out beyond your lips, you can't pull it back and correct it. You must monitor your speech as you are producing it. Monitor your air flow, your muscle movements as you form sounds, and your movements through and out of sounds. Feel your fluency, and don't worry about the sound. That will take care of itself if you take care of the mechanism that is producing it.

Now you know why the kit was empty!

Putting It Together

CHARLES VAN RIPER

Now that you have read all of these suggestions you probably have some mixed feelings of confusion, helplessness and even disappointment. Perhaps you were hoping that at least one of these stuttering experts would have found a quick, easy, magical cure for your distressing disorder. Instead, it is quite evident that no such panacea exists and that, if you want relief from your miseries, you've got to earn that relief by making some real changes in the way you react to your stuttering and to your listeners and to yourself. As Dr. Emerick says, "The first thing to do is to admit to yourself that you need to change, that you really want to do something about your stuttering." Perhaps you are willing to make that admission but have some reservations about having to do what Dr. Boehmler calls the "dirty work of therapy." Some of the suggested procedures may at the moment seem far beyond your courage or capacities. Is the pay-off worth the cost?

All these authors answer that question with a resounding yes. I know these writers. They talk well and live well. All of them were severe stutterers. All of them know from personal experience your self doubts and the difficulties of self therapy but universally they insist that you need not continue to suffer, that you can change yourself as they have changed themselves and can become fluent enough to make the rest of your life a very useful and rewarding one. Perhaps you have already had some speech therapy and have failed and so feel that nothing can be done. If so, reread what Dr. Freund has told you about the success of his own self therapy after the best authorities in Europe had treated him unsuccessfully. Or you may be feeling that you are too old to begin now. If so, read what Dr. Sheehan had to say about the 78 year old retired bandmaster. Or you may be saying that you cannot do it alone without help, yet many of the authors agree with Dr. Starbuck's statement that essentially "The correction of stuttering is a do-it-yourself project. Stuttering is *your* problem. The expert can tell you what to do and how to do it, but you are the one who has to do it. You are the only person on earth who can correct your stuttering." While most of these writers would prefer to have you get competent professional guidance, they do not at all feel that it is impossible for you to get real relief without it. "Get help if you can," advises Professor Czuchna, "but if not, help yourself. You can!" They would not write so earnestly if they were not sure that you can do much to solve your difficulties. Moreover, you must remember that this is not the kind of false assurance or hope that you have received from others who never stuttered. This comes straight from persons who have known your despair and lack of confidence, from stutterers who have coped successfully with the same problems that trouble you.

At the same time, and as a measure of their honesty, they are realistic. They hold out little hope for what you have long dreamed of—the complete cure. Universally, they insist or imply that you can learn to live with your stuttering and to be pretty fluent anyway. This may be hard for you to accept—as it was hard for them too. The present writer has worked with a great many stutterers and has helped most of them to overcome their handicaps but only a few of the adult ones ever become completely free from the slightest trace of stuttering in all situations always. As Dr. Sheehan, the psychologist, advises, "Don't waste your time and frustrate yourself by trying to speak with perfect fluency. If you've come into adult life as a stutterer, the chances are that you'll always be a stutterer, in a sense. But you don't have to be the kind of stutterer that you are now—you can be a mild one without much handicap." We find this thought expressed by many of the authors. Dr. Neely says, "My own experience has been that nothing 'cures' an adult stutterer but one can effectively manage stuttering so that it ceases to be a significant problem throughout life". Dr. Murray writes, that he has known many adult stutterers who achieved a good recovery but not one who claimed to be completely free from disfluency. Dr. Barbara, the psychiatrist, insists that one of the major reasons for the persistence of stuttering is that the stutterer tries to speak too perfectly too often, that he has a "Demosthenes complex." Throughout this book, you have read many suggestions for the modification of your stuttering, for learning to stutter in ways that permit you to be reasonably fluent and free from emotional upheaval or social penalty. If these authors have one common message to you, it is this—you can change your abnormal reactions to the threat or the experience of stuttering and when you do so, most of your troubles in communicating will vanish. Is this bad? Is this not enough? As Dr. Emerick says, we cannot promise you a rose garden, but we can offer you a much better communicative life than the fearful, frustrating one you now endure.

But you may protest that you don't know where or how to begin. If you will read this book again, you will find author after author saying that the first thing to do is to study your stuttering and its associated feeling. In this, there is remarkable agreement. As Miss Rainey, the public school speech therapist, suggested to the young man she interviewed, you should get a mirror, and a tape recorder if possible, and start observing how you stutter, perhaps as you make a telephone call while alone, so that you can know how much of your avoidances and struggle is unnecessary and only complicates your difficulty. Dr. Johnson, Dr. Dean Williams and Dr. Dave Williams offer important sets of very challenging questions that you can ask yourself as you do this observing. Dr. Trotter advises you to count and time your blocks as you listen to yourself on the tape recorder and insists that "you will probably find that your blocks were not as long as you thought they were and that you actually stuttered about half as much as you expected you would." Other authors provide other ways that you can use to study your stuttering and feelings but all of them feel that this is how you should begin.

All of us know that this process of confronting yourself will not be pleasant but we also know you will find, as you observe and analyze what you do and feel when stuttering or expecting to stutter, that you will then know what you have to change. And will want to! Besides, isn't it about time you stopped pretending that you are a fluent speaker? Isn't it time, as Dr. Starbuck phrases it, for you "to become an honest stutterer," to come to grips with your problem, at least to look at it objectively?

To do so, you will have to accept another suggestion that these authors make almost unanimously. You've got to talk more and avoid less. You've got to start giving up what Miss Rainey called your "camouflage," the sort of tricks that Professor LaPorte lists for you in his article. We know that this too will be hard to do but over and over again you will find these writers insisting that they had to overcome their panicky need to hide their stuttering before they began to improve. They tell you, as Dr. Moses advises, to bring your stuttering into the open, to let it be seen and heard rather than concealed as though it were a dirty shameful thing rather than a problem that you are trying to solve. How can you possibly know what you have to change if you refuse to look at it? Aren't you tired to the bone of all this running away and hiding? Different authors outline different ways of decreasing this avoidance but you should be impressed by their basic agreement that you should admit, display and confront your stuttering openly and objectively.

There is another point on which almost all of them also agree. It is that you can learn to stutter much more easily than you now do and that when you master this, you will be able to speak very fluently even if you may continue to stutter occasionally. As Dr. Sheehan says, "You can stutter your way out of this problem." The idea—that it is unnecessary to struggle when you feel blocked and that there are better ways of coping with the experience—may seem very strange at first but if this book holds any secret for successful self therapy, it lies here. These writers say it in different ways. Dr. Aten advises you "to learn to substitute easy, slower, more relaxed movements for rushed, tight, forced movements," and to learn to decrease the tension. Dr. Trotter suggests that you "simplify" your stuttering. Dr. Emerick describes the process as getting rid of the excess baggage, the unnecessary gasps and contortions and recoils. In his account of his own self therapy, Dr. Gregory tells how he experimented with different ways of stuttering before he overcame his fear of it. Other authors tell you to learn to stutter slowly and easily. What they all seem to be saying is that it is possible to stutter in a fashion which will impair your fluency very little. Indeed, Dr. Murray suggests that if you study your stuttering, you will find that you already have some of these short, easy moments of stuttering in your speech and that if you will recognize them, they can serve as goals. If you read this article again, you will find him saying, "If you can learn to whittle the others down to similar proportions, most of your scoreable difficulty will have disappeared" and that "there are countless ways in which to stutter. You have a choice as to how you stutter even though you may not have a choice as to whether or not you'll stutter." Along with other authors, Dr. Agnello says that you should try different ways of stuttering, that you need not remain "bound" to your old patterns of stuttering. The present writer, now sixty-seven years old, agrees. For years he tried to keep from stuttering and only grew worse. Not until he found that it was possible to stutter easily and without struggling did he become fluent. He was born at the age of thirty years and has had a wonderful life ever since. How old are you?

So we suggest that you reread this book, this time to work out the design of your own self therapy. Your stuttering won't go away. There are no magical cures. You will not wake up some morning speaking fluently. You know in your heart that there is work to be done and that you must do it. This book contains many suggestions, and many guidelines. Your job is to sort out and organize those that seem appropriate to your own situation, to devise a plan of self therapy that fits your needs, and then begin the changing that must take place. Why spend the rest of your life in misery?

SPONSORED PUBLICATIONS

STUTTERING AND ITS TREATMENT *(Publication No. 1)*

Published in the interest of making available to speech therapists and other interested parties, the agreements reached by a group of leading authorities concerning the methods to be used in helping to relieve the adult stutterer or his problem—a 56-page booklet. 25c each.

STUTTERING WORDS *(Publication No. 2)*

An authoritative glossary of the meanings of the words and terms used or associated with the field of stuttering and in connection with its treatment. Definitions written with the cooperation of several speech pathologists—a 48-page booklet. 25c each.

STUTTERING: ITS PREVENTION *(Publication No. 3)*

Written by a group of eminent speech pathologists for parents who do not want their children to stutter and especially for those parents of very young children who think they have reason to be concerned about their child's speech—a 64-page booklet. 25c each.

TREATMENT OF THE YOUNG STUTTERER IN THE SCHOOL *(Publication No. 4)*

An outline of the problems encountered by the speech therapist working with stutterers in the elementary school. Answering questions asked by public school therapists as to how to work in therapy with the young stutterer—a 64-page booklet. 25c each.

STUTTERING: TRAINING THE THERAPIST *(Publication No. 5)*

An outline of a suggested course of study to be used in training speech therapy students how to cope with the baffling problems they encounter in working with the stutterer—a 96-page booklet. 25c each.

(Continued on next page)

SPONSORED PUBLICATIONS

(Continued from preceding page)

STUTTERING: SUCCESSES AND FAILURES IN THERAPY
(Publication No. 6)

Case histories of successes and failures in the treatment of stuttering by nine leading speech pathologists describing procedures and techniques used and the results attained—with comments of a conference reviewing these case histories—a 148-page book. $1.00 each.

CONDITIONING IN STUTTERING THERAPY
(Publication No. 7)

Exploring the conditioning approach to stuttering treatment with articles advocating its use and criticism of its desirability together with a summary of conference discussions and a glossary of conditioning terms a 160 page book. $1.00 each.

STUTTERING: AN ACCOUNT OF INTENSIVE DEMONSTRATION THERAPY *(Publication No. 8)*

A detailed report of a therapy project in which three master clinicians work with three stutterers intensively for a period of five weeks under the critical observation of fifteen experienced speech pathologists—a 124-page book. $1.00 each.

TO THE STUTTERER *(Publication No. 9)*

Practical therapy advice written by twenty-four men and women speech pathologists who have been stutterers themselves advising the adult stutterer what has helped them and what they believe will help the stutterer master or control his difficulty—a 116-page book. $1.00 each.

SPEECH FOUNDATION OF AMERICA
152 Lombardy Road
Memphis, Tennessee 38111

JOURNEY
TO HELL

Inside The World's Most Violent Prison System

DONALD MACNEIL

MILO BOOKS

First published in September 2006 by Milo Books Ltd

Copyright © 2006 Donald MacNeil

ISBN 1 903854 57 1

Typeset by Avon DataSet Ltd,
Bidford on Avon, Warwickshire, B50 4JH.

Printed and bound in Great Britain by CPD

MILO BOOKS LTD
The Old Weighbridge
Station Road
Wrea Green
Preston
PR4 2PH
www.milobooks.com

Contents

"Although known for their overcrowding, physical decay, and corruption, Venezuela's prisons are most notorious for their extreme violence. Over the past decade, thousands of prisoners have died violent deaths at the hands of their fellows. Some prisoners have been killed in headline-grabbing spasms of violence . . . but many others have died practically unnoticed, losers in the daily fight for survival in Venezuelan prisons . . . According to official statistics, 207 prisoners were killed and 1,133 prisoners were injured in Venezuelan prisons in 1996, most by their fellow prisoners. In other words, an average of four prisoners were killed each week and over twenty injured."

Punishment Before Trial: Prison Conditions in Venezuela,
Human Rights Watch

Nothing To Declare

"ABRIR ESTE MALETÍN, por favor."

Open this suitcase, please. My stomach knotted and I felt sweat running down my sides as the young sergeant, dressed in the camouflage combat fatigues of the Venezuelan National Guard anti-drugs squad, complete with pistol in a leather holster at his belt, began to demonstrate more than a passing interest in the luggage that I had deposited on the table in front of him. I had arrived at San Antonio airport some minutes before, ready to depart from Venezuela and travel across the Atlantic to Glasgow, via Paris and Amsterdam. The last thing that I needed at this stage was the intervention of an overenthusiastic military official to interfere with my plans.

There was nothing that I could do about it though, as my suitcase, carry-on bag and briefcase were first opened and then presented to a bored-looking sniffer dog. Despite the dog's obvious lack of interest, the official was not satisfied and proceeded to empty the carefully packed contents of each bag onto the counter and sift through them. I was aware of the glances of other travellers as they presented their luggage on either side of me and were rapidly cleared to proceed, after undergoing nothing more than the usual cursory check. Clearly, the "gringo" was in trouble. The search had also attracted the attention of other National Guards, and a couple of them were now hovering behind the sergeant who had first taken such an interest in me.

Only the dog remained aloof, appearing on the point of dropping off to sleep in the already increasing heat of the early tropical morning.

San Antonio is a small, provincial airport in the foothills of the Andes, right next to the Colombian border, its single runway occupying one of the few flat stretches in that mountainous region. It provides a quick link to the Venezuelan capital, Caracas, as an alternative to the gruelling, fourteen-hour road journey for the citizens of the city of San Cristobal, as well as the town of San Antonio itself and other towns and villages in the border area. It boasts a small, single-storey, concrete and glass terminal building, utilitarian and with few facilities, through which passengers must pass before exiting to the apron, where boarding is carried out using mobile steps. Due to its location, on the border with the country that is, by far, the greatest producer and exporter of cocaine in the world, Venezuelan officialdom is understandably alert to attempts to pass drugs through the airport.

The border between Venezuela and Colombia extends for more than 1,300 miles, much of which is difficult to control, consisting as it does of coastal deserts, mountain ranges and remote plains. Of the four hundred tonnes of cocaine produced in Colombia each year, it is estimated that more than half passes through Venezuela, before being exported by sea or air to North America and Europe. The fact that in the year 2005, fifty eight and a half tonnes of cocaine were seized by Venezuelan authorities would suggest that if anything, this is a conservative estimate.

Having found nothing to get excited about among the contents of my bags, the sergeant now began, bizarrely, to sniff at each bag, clearly convinced that his olfactory powers were superior to those of the trained dog. Had I been less stressed, I would have found it all mildly amusing, but my chances of boarding the flight were decreasing with each passing minute and it was very important not to show any emotion that might antagonise this official, who held such power over my immediate future. The last bag subjected to the "sniff test" was my briefcase, and the sergeant became even more animated and suspicious as he tested it time and again.

"How long have you had this bag, sir?" he asked, while passing the bag to another official for a second opinion.

"More than a year," I replied.

The other official shook his head and handed the briefcase back to his colleague. He had detected nothing unusual.

Even the late arrivals for the flight had by now passed through to the check-in area, and I thus had the undivided attention of the entire National Guard contingent at the baggage-check desk, some of whom began to sift through my belongings in a somewhat desultory fashion. Producing a flick-knife from his pocket, the sergeant again addressed me.

"Would you mind if I made a cut or two in the lining of this briefcase, so that I can examine the structure?"

Although politely phrased, I knew that it was a rhetorical question, as to refuse would probably result in still further delay, and I was in any case completely unsure of my rights in this situation.

"Okay, but please do as little damage as possible. In the meantime, can I please go to the airline counter and pick up my flight ticket?"

He shook his head emphatically, and said "No, just wait there – this will not take long."

Clearly enjoying himself now, he made several cuts in different parts of the lining of the briefcase and began to examine what lay behind, while I looked on, helplessly. Pouncing on one particular spot, he began to gouge out some of the fibre stiffening. This was subject to enthusiastic sniffing, and passed to colleagues for their opinion, following which the dog was startled into wakefulness, when the "sample" was rudely shoved under its nose. It turned away in disdain, and yawned, but the sergeant appeared to remain convinced that he knew better. He called for one of his colleagues to fetch him a test kit, as I watched the time remaining before the departure of my flight ticking inexorably away.

When the test kit was produced, the sergeant placed the sample inside and activated the test chemicals, as several officials gathered round to watch the outcome. Although I knew what the result had to be, it was still with a feeling of huge relief that I saw, from the reaction of the assembled National Guard officials, that the test had proved negative. With extremely poor grace, the sergeant invited me to re-pack my bags, which I hurried to do, acutely aware of the limited time available to me before my flight was due to leave. The sergeant had not quite finished with me yet, however, and as I rushed to throw my belongings into my luggage any old how, he came round to my side of the table and ordered me to remove my shoes, which he carefully examined before returning them to me.

The sergeant now turned to me, and said, "If you've swallowed any drugs, I would advise you not to travel today, as when you reach the international airport in the Capital, the National Guard there will almost certainly subject you to an X-ray body-scan."

For the first time, I allowed my irritation to show.

"As far as I'm concerned, they can subject me to investigative surgery. I'm not carrying any drugs!"

Once I had completed the repacking of my bags, the sergeant handed over to me my passport, together with the letter given to me by the court the previous week, which reported the decision that, as I had now served five years, four months, twenty one days and twelve hours, of a six-year, eight-month sentence, I was deemed to have completed the sentence imposed by the court on 21 June 2000, for drug smuggling, and was free to leave Venezuela. It was of course this letter, together with the absence of an entry visa in the British passport that had been issued to me only months before, that had attracted his attention in the first place.

As a parting shot, he said to me, "I'm sorry to have held you up, but from now on forward, you are going to have to get used to the nuisance factor, the frustration and the humiliation that are your just deserts as a recognised drug smuggler."

I mumbled something that I felt to be suitably conciliatory, then hurried away to complete the check-in process for the flight to Caracas. Since the other passengers had already been cleared through, I was able quickly to complete the formalities and entered the departure lounge just as the ground-staff announced that the aircraft was now boarding. As the other passengers queued at the boarding gate, I took a moment to compose myself before joining the line, boarding pass in hand. I detected more than a few glances of sympathy from among my fellow passengers. In Venezuela, as in many South American countries, there is little love lost between even the most law-abiding citizens and the National Guard troops and other forces charged with maintaining law and order; an attitude that is a legacy of a long history of oppression, brutality and corruption inflicted on the populace by these forces.

The air above the runway was already shimmering in the heat as we made our way across the apron and up the steps, and it was a relief to pass into the coolness and ordered calm of the aircraft's interior. Boarding the aircraft, which had almost all seats taken for the one-hour flight to Simon Bolivar International Airport in Caracas, I quickly found my seat, stowed my bag in the overhead locker, sat down and fastened my seat-belt. At last, I was on the way home.

Several hours later, and without having meantime endured the promised full-body X-ray scan, I felt a huge sense of relief as the fully laden Air France Boeing 747 Jumbo left Venezuelan soil and climbed into the night sky above Caracas, before shaping its course out over the Caribbean Sea, and then across the Atlantic on the nine-hour flight to Paris. As we left the Venezuelan coastline behind, I could see, twinkling in the distance the lights of the holiday island of Margarita, and I momentarily shuddered as I thought of what that place had come to mean to me in the past few years. I placed my seat in the reclined position, made myself as comfortable as possible, and let my mind freewheel over the events of the past few years as the aircraft sped me towards Europe, the beginnings of a new life, and what was sure to be my best Christmas for a very long time.

CHAPTER ONE

The *Pulse*

IN THE GATHERING twilight of the first Tuesday in November 1999, I walked round the outskirts of the marina and across the lock gates, making my way from my flat to the club that had become my second home. Catering particularly to the maritime fraternity, and situated in the centre of the docks of Hartlepool area, the Smallcrafts Club is a welcoming haven for those who sail on the north-east coast of Britain. With a character all of its own, it is filled with the gruff, no-nonsense friendliness that is characteristic of the people of that area. Housed in an old, two-storey Victorian building, it stands as a bastion of unchanging values, in contrast to the brash, ultra-modern buildings of the post-Thatcherite world which surround it and increasingly encroach upon its territory.

By the winter of 1999, I had been living in Hartlepool and working as a freelance yacht skipper and sailing instructor for three years. Hartlepool had formerly been a bustling North Sea port, a conduit for the export of coal from the Durham coalfields. In recent years, such activity had dwindled to zero following the closure of the coalmines, and by the Nineties Hartlepool was in depression, with little movement in the port other than the importation of Japanese cars and a few fishing boats chasing the dwindling stocks of North Sea fish. Light engineering companies, as well as the usual range of service industries, offered the only other employment in the town. In the mid-Nineties, the Teesside Development Corporation funded a large marina, as well as major housing and infrastructure around the unused parts of the docks, and those involved became infused with a new sense of hope and purpose.

There were only a few people in the club when I entered, the usual late-afternoon contingent playing dominoes and pool and arguing over such topics as the pros and cons of North Sea fishing quotas, as ever. I greeted a couple of people that I knew as I made my way to the bar, to be met by the usual warm welcome from the club steward. I ordered a pint of orange and lemonade, and sat at a vacant table near the bar to go over my notes for that evening's navigation class, which was to be on the subject of weather, a topic that I particularly enjoyed teaching, as it had always been a particular interest of mine.

I paid little attention when the phone rang, assuming that it was probably one of the usual calls from an irate wife attempting to track down the errant husband who'd left the house some hours before to "just have a quick walk round the docks, love". It was with some surprise that I heard the steward call my name, and he handed me the receiver as I approached the bar, saying, "It's somebody looking for you."

I vaguely recognised the voice but could not immediately place it. Only when I heard him say, "This is Mick Jowett; Denis and I are in the Mediterranean," did it register that this was someone I had briefly met a couple of times, and shared a few beers with, in the club earlier that summer.

"Are you working at the moment?" he asked.

"Nothing steady," I replied. "I'm just doing a bit of evening class work. Why?"

"Well, what's happened is, Denis and I have bought a yacht in Rhodes, in the Greek islands, a Bruce Roberts thirty-eight-footer, and we're bringing it back to Britain. However, we've discovered during a sail from Rhodes to Crete that managing a sailing boat is very different to the motorboat that we're used to, so we were wondering if you would be available to come out to Greece, and teach us how to sail it. Just for a month, while we sail across the Mediterranean to Gibraltar. By the time we get to Gibraltar, we should have learned enough to be able to manage it on our own.

"We'll pay you a thousand pounds for the month, plus all expenses," he added.

Denis and Mick had visited the club several times during the summer, as members of a diving club from the north-west of England who used to visit the harbour to dive on local wrecks. They seemed to fit in well, enjoying the company of several of the locals. Denis was a heavyset guy, of medium height, with fair hair and a ready smile. Mick was a small, stocky character, with dark hair and a neatly trimmed beard, who seemed to brim with self confidence and dynamism. Being ever ready to make allowances, I had dismissed his cocky attitude as the arrogance often displayed by people of short stature as some form of compensation for their lack of height. Little did I realise that just beneath the surface lay an explosive temper and a personality bordering on the psychotic.

I quickly ran through the options in my head. It was the quietest time of the sailing calendar, and I had nothing much on during the next month. The money offered was par for the course for that kind of work, and would come in useful with Christmas just round the corner; not to mention that it would also be nice to get away from the dreary British weather to enjoy a spot of winter sunshine in the Mediterranean.

With little hesitation, therefore, I said, "Yes, I'm available to do that. When would you like me to join you?"

"As soon as possible," he replied. "If you could be here by Friday, that would be great."

That would give me Wednesday to tie up a couple of loose ends, then I could travel on Thursday.

"OK, I should be able to manage it by then, so I'll hopefully see you in Crete on Friday."

He gave me a mobile phone number so that I could contact him once my travel arrangements had been made, said goodbye, and hung up. I slid the telephone across the bar, gleefully announced to the steward that I was off to the Med for a month, then hurried to collect my things and make my way to the local college, where I was due to give a two-hour lesson.

I have lost count of the number of times since that I have bitterly regretted that phone call. Why did I have to be in the Club at that particular moment? Had I not been, it is unlikely that Mick would have carried out extended efforts to track me down over long-distance telephone lines. If only I'd had other commitments and been obliged to regretfully decline the invitation. If only something in the nature of the call had triggered off alarm bells. Why, for instance, were two people, who had, as far as I was aware, shown no previous interest in sailing, now sailing a yacht that they had just bought across the Mediterranean and back to Britain in the winter time?

Nevertheless, one of the most endearing qualities of the yachting community has always been the number of eccentrics that it contains and the degree of eccentric behaviour that it tolerates, and so I gave such doubts not a second thought. Little did I realise that fate, time, place and circumstance had conspired to send me off on an endeavour that was to bring me years of hardship, pain and misery, and alter the course of my life forever.

Having celebrated my forty-fourth birthday that April, I had been working as a full-time professional skipper for fifteen years, and had logged over 100,000 miles at sea in command of sail training vessels, sailing school yachts and boats belonging to private owners. Most of my experience had been built up on the west coast of Scotland, where I had for nine years commanded a 41' sail training yacht for a local authority, mainly involved in taking youngsters from deprived inner-city areas to sea and showing them a different way of life, sailing around the beautiful west coast and the islands of the Hebrides, where I had been born and brought up.

A childhood spent on a small, remote island had been an ideal preparation for a career at sea, with the ocean and boats forming an integral part of everyday life. Having passed my eleven-plus exam, I was given the option of attending a secondary school on the Scottish mainland, and chose to go to Dunoon, on the Clyde coast, where I lived with an aunt and uncle during term time, only returning to my home island of Barra during the holidays.

Soon after moving to Dunoon, I joined the local sailing club, and learned for the first time the joy of harnessing the wind to make a vessel move across the waters as we sailed in small dinghies around the Holy Loch, always being careful to maintain a respectful distance from the American depot ship and floating dock moored in the centre of the loch at that time, which formed the core of the US Holy Loch Submarine Base. The penalty for straying too close in those relaxed times would be to have a jet of water from a high powered fire house directed at one's dinghy from the upper deck of the depot ship, harmless enough in itself, but a chastisement generally to be avoided except in the warmest of weather.

During those years in secondary school, I also began to explore the nearby Argyll hills, learning to use map and compass to navigate unfamiliar terrain, and developing the resilience and skills to ensure survival when conditions turned hostile, as they so often do, with little warning, in the Scottish mountains. I was also introduced to flying through the local Air Training Corps, with whom I attained the rank of Flight Sergeant, and eventually became a glider pilot, a sport I enjoyed for some years as an adult in civilian clubs.

While gliding is essentially a very safe sport, it does have its element of risk, and I came close to death at the age of twenty four while flying as second in command of an aircraft, being shown advanced soaring techniques above the Scottish mountains. A change in the wind speed resulted in the clouds suddenly closing in beneath us, and we became stuck above a blanket of cloud in an open-cockpit aircraft which carried no cloud-flying instruments. We both knew that, once we entered the cloud, which we would inevitably have to in order to descend and land, we would quickly become disorientated, and basically lose any idea of "which way is up", but I was horrified when my fellow pilot announced that the solution to the problem was to "spin" through the cloud.

While spinning like this places relatively low loads on the aircraft, and is a recognised technique for pilots faced with our problem whilst flying over the flat lands of southern England, the rate of descent is extremely high and carries an accordingly high risk of you simply drilling a hole in the ground if attempted through clouds stuffed with mountains.

An argument ensued, during which I tried to persuade him that it would be better to head the aircraft into wind, lock the controls between us, and depend on the inherent stability of the aircraft to get us down through the cloud in one piece, while hopefully making enough forward progress to keep us over the valley where the landing strip was. Nothing would persuade him, however, and in the end I had to acknowledge that he was pilot in command of the aircraft, and to sit back while he prepared the manoeuvre which would almost certainly kill us both.

In the end, we were in fact saved by the stability of the aircraft, as the old T21 glider is not fond of spinning, and unwound itself from the spin just as we entered the cloud. Our troubles were far from over however, and we ran the severe and terrifying risk that the wings would simply fail while, during the course of the following fifteen minutes, we "descended through cloud in various attitudes," as I would later enter in my flying log.

A sudden darkening in the cloud signalled our approach to ground. We were fortunately flying upright, level, and reasonably slowly when we hit a ridge between two mountain tops. It was nevertheless a heavy landing, breaking one wing in two and hurling the landing wheel upwards between our seats, which also collapsed on impact. We were both unscathed, and hill walking ability was now required as we faced into wind and walked over the top of the ridge before descending the other side and eventually breaking out of the cloud above the valley where our landing strip was. Club officials were just on the point of declaring us officially missing when we walked in, to a rapturous welcome, still shaking from our narrow escape.

A couple of years before the gliding accident, I had faced another brush with death while sea-kayaking with a group of friends off the west coast. Foolishly, we had not practised such skills as the Eskimo roll or rescue techniques, and when my kayak overturned when I encountered rough water as I approached a headland, I was obliged to bail out of it and we had no idea how I could climb back in.

One of my companions attempted to tow me, but the weight made his boat unstable and so I let go, instructing them to paddle ashore by the shortest route and pointing out on the waterproof map that I carried where I was likely to come ashore, on the edge of the huge bay we were in, given the direction that the incoming tide and my own feeble efforts would take me. I kept hold of my paddle, as an aid to push me along, and one of my companions took my boat in tow.

It was the loneliest moment of my life as I watched them quickly disappear over the edge of my limited horizon and contemplated the mess I was in, although I was thankful for their sakes to see them paddling off into the quieter waters behind the sheltering arm of the headland. I was semi-conscious and deeply hypothermic when I eventually came ashore four and a half hours later, to be met by my companions and a doctor. Shortly afterwards, a helicopter arrived and whisked me off to a prepared bed in the nearest hospital, where I spent the night being slowly rewarmed before being released the following day.

I immediately made it a priority to learn self rescue and team rescue for kayaking, and I have since paddled many happy miles on sea and river without incident. The techniques are easy to learn and apply, and absolutely essential for anyone thinking of embarking on such adventures. Nature is singularly unforgiving to those who venture out ill-prepared, and I was extremely lucky to survive to absorb that lesson.

I little realised then that the mental strength gained from experiences such as this would help maintain my sanity many years later, when faced with survival in a very different environment.

My ability to work with the kind of groups who benefited most from sail training had been enhanced by my previous job as a care officer in residential schools and ultimately as a senior assessment officer in a regional assessment centre, where I had worked with some of the most difficult and damaged children from the inner cities for a total of ten exhausting but rewarding years.

For a couple of years, before sailing commitments interfered, I had also been a member of a mountain rescue team, made up of volunteers who were willing to go to the aid of any climber or walker who got into trouble in the team's area. It was a quiet area, with few actual rescues each year, but the training was invaluable and gave me huge confidence during my own excursions in the mountains, enabling me to move safely in almost any weather conditions, by day or night. I completed the Scottish Mountain Leader training course, and the

Mountain First Aid course before later qualifying as an emergency medical technician.

By late autumn, sailing for the year was dwindling off as owners settled into the winter routine of storage and maintenance of their boats, while they themselves pored over charts and pilot books to plan their adventures for the following year. My only regular commitment at this time was to teach an occasional navigation evening class at a local college, in order to help out another sailing instructor.

As I described to my students the cycle of Atlantic depressions, with their bands of strong winds and driving rain, that are the predominant feature of British weather, it was with a perverse sense of pleasure that I envisaged the balmier conditions that I would be enjoying in a few days' time. I knew full well that the Mediterranean can be vicious at times, particularly in the winter, with its relatively shallow waters kicking up some nasty, steep seas, but I was confident I could cope, given my many years of experience sailing around the treacherous British and northern European coasts. A sturdy craft like the Bruce Roberts, crewed by three fit adults, should be able to manage most conditions, even if two of those on board had little experience. Above all, the temperatures would be considerably higher than in Britain and the rainfall a great deal less. At the end of the lesson, I announced to the class, with some delight, that they would not be seeing me for the next month, as I was off to the Med. Then I hurried home to sort out and pack the gear that I would need for the trip.

Searching through the Internet later that evening, I discovered that I could travel to London by train on Thursday, and then catch a flight to Athens in the late evening, which would connect with a flight to Crete. This would take me to Heraklion airport, on the northern coast of Crete, at around 6.30 on Friday morning. On Wednesday morning, I telephoned the number that Mick had given me and spoke to

Denis, who advised me that he would meet me at the airport, Mick had apparently left the boat for a few days, giving Denis and me the weekend to check the boat before Mick rejoined us for the next leg of the voyage. I also made sure that my rent and utility bills were paid in advance, in order to avoid any nasty surprises on my return.

Early on the Thursday morning, I locked the door on my Hartlepool flat, slung my kit bags on my shoulder, and walked the short distance to the train station, where I could get a massive all-day breakfast and a commuter train to Newcastle to join the mainline east-coast service to London. I was on my way.

IN NEWCASTLE'S BUSTLING central station, something happened as I boarded the busy express to King's Cross that I would later regard as an ill omen of what was to come. I noticed some activity among the train and station officials at the end of my carriage, and became aware that they were trying to resuscitate a young woman who had apparently collapsed in the toilet compartment. As they finally lifted her off the train and onto a waiting stretcher trolley, a needle could be seen sticking out of her left arm. It appeared that she had taken an overdose, presumably of heroin, which had led to her collapse. Attempts to resuscitate her had not been successful by the time she had been wheeled away and out of sight.

The train staff apologised for the twenty-minute delay and then we pulled smoothly out of the station on what was to prove an otherwise uneventful five-hour journey to London. But I could not help but think back to that young woman and her plight.

At King's Cross, I bought a ticket for the Gatwick Express, which disgorged its passengers into the heart of the sprawling, organised confusion of Gatwick's European terminal, where I would have some three hours to wait for the Olympic Air flight to Athens. I ate a light meal in the departure lounge while waiting for the call to board, little thinking that this would be my last meal on British soil for over six years. The aircraft was less that half full on that late-evening, mid-week flight, and I was able to snooze for part of the journey.

Athens airport was relatively quiet when we landed, at 2 a.m. local time, and I quickly found the check-in desk for the onward connection to Crete, then faced a further, two-hour wait. There were few fellow passengers for the commuter flight to Heraklion and dawn was beginning to break as, an hour and a half after take-off, we began our descent towards the island of Crete, where we landed in miserable weather, with lashing rain and a strong wind. I hurried to baggage reclaim to collect my kit bags, and then moved forward into the arrivals area, where I quickly spotted Denis's stocky figure among a handful of people standing around awaiting inbound passengers. He was casually dressed, and looking tanned and fit, although, as ever, a bit overweight. We briefly shook hands and exchanged greetings, and then he led me to a hire car.

The Cretan north-coast highway appeared like an elongated building site, with poorly signposted roadworks everywhere, and was extremely hazardous as the early morning traffic gradually built up in intensity. We talked little as Denis negotiated the various diversions and avoided the suicidally inclined local drivers, while peering through the rain and spray to spot the turn-off for the mountain road that would take us across to the south coast of the island, where the yacht was moored.

If the coast highway had been dangerous, the mountain road was terrifying, with visibility deteriorating as we ascended into the low-lying cloud and driving rain while negotiating a seemingly endless series of hair-raising hairpin bends, perched on the edges of precipitous ravines, all without the benefit of roadside railings that would have given at least an illusion of security. In better conditions, it must be a breathtakingly beautiful journey, as the road passes over successively higher mountain ridges to reveal verdant, dramatically steep hillsides, but at that moment it was simply breathtaking as, heart in mouth, I contemplated the imminent prospect of ourselves and the car becoming a permanent part of the scenery. I was far too nervous to be able to enjoy what little could be seen through the cloud and rain. Furthermore, heavy rain had dislodged the soft earth in many places, releasing landslides of hundreds of tons of red earth and stone onto the road below, leaving only a narrow, bulldozed track through the debris.

Eventually, we began the equally scary descent of the mountain road and, at long last, emerged from the cloud, to see the south coast of the island through the now diminishing rain. At last, I felt able to speak.

"So what is this boat like, then?"

"Oh, it's a real solid thing, built of steel, but we've had some really horrible weather, and we don't have a clue how to handle it," replied Denis. "It's a bit basic inside, but we can always improve that later on. There were a couple of times on the way across here from Rhodes when Mick and I were dressed in our dry-suits and life jackets, ready to jump off it and into the sea, thinking that it was about to be overwhelmed by the waves."

I reserved comment, but contemplated the number of times that I had come across this, to me at least, strange response of the landlubber to perceived danger at sea. Quite why anyone, no matter how frightening the situation, should feel that they could improve their lot by abandoning a still-floating, reasonably sizeable vessel to commit themselves to the mercy of the waves in a life jacket, or even in one of those little rubber boats known as "life rafts", was beyond me. That even relatively experienced sailors were not immune to this had been tragically demonstrated during what became known as the Fastnet Tragedy, when a fleet of racing yachts was overtaken by a storm in the seas to the south of Ireland in 1979. In the aftermath of the storm, rescue teams found several yachts still floating and intact, having suffered relatively minor damage, but whose crews had abandoned them during the night, at the height of the storm, and were now lost for ever. It has always been my maxim that, with the single exception of an out-of-control fire, one should only abandon to a life raft when obliged to step *up* into it.

With such thoughts running through my mind, we arrived at the "marina". It turned out to be under construction. What would one day be car parking and hard-standing for boats was currently a sea of ankle-deep, glutinous mud, and only a couple of pontoons for mooring boats to had been placed in the water. Not even the foundations of any marina buildings had yet been laid. No more than five small yachts and fishing boats were moored there. It looked desolate on that grey November morning. The one positive note was that the rain had now stopped and a watery sun was trying to break through the cloud cover.

Denis pointed out the yacht *Pulse* lying on the far side of the inlet, moored outside a larger vessel and looking sturdy and seaworthy, if quite angular, as a result of her steel construction. She was a single-masted yacht with a cutter rig, meaning that she could fly three sails at any one time: a foresail or headsail, right at the bows, with a smaller sail known as a staysail behind it, then finally the mainsail. The steering position was in the middle of the boat, in what is known as a centre-cockpit design, with the accommodation below decks arranged forward of and behind the cockpit. This arrangement would ensure that the person steering would be in a relatively stable, sheltered position, protected from sea spray as well as waves washing along the decks in all but the worst conditions.

I collected my kit bags from the rear of the car and we trudged round the little harbour while Denis regaled me with more tales of their adventures in getting the yacht there. As we stepped aboard, I cast an eye around the deck, then something caught my eye that made me cry out in horror. The mast was, as is usual, held upright and supported by wire stays, which were attached at their base on the deck by screw-in adjusters known as bottlescrews. Once adjusted to the required tension, these would normally be locked off with seizing-wire to prevent them accidentally working free. I noticed that the necessary seizing-wire was absent from each of the bottle screws. Denis was dismayed to learn that they had been in even more danger than they had imagined during their trip from Rhodes, as the simple lack of a few bits of wire had created the risk that the mast, having lost its support due to one or more of the bottlescrews coming loose, could have come crashing down at any time.

It was a very chastened young man who led me below and showed me my bunk, and we agreed to get straight down to drawing up a list of checks to be done and jobs to be carried out to ensure that the yacht was fit to put to sea again in a few days' time. The "to do" list was quickly drawn up, and ranged from a non-functioning toilet to a clearly faulty steering system. One item I quickly sorted was the cooker. Denis had mentioned to me, almost in passing, that it was, of course, impossible to cook while the vessel was at sea, and that their intention was therefore to stock up on Mars bars and vitamin tablets to sustain them through passages of more than a day. I was extremely surprised at this assertion, having happily cooked aboard yachts at sea, in all kinds of conditions, for years. Denis assured me that even trying to boil a kettle to make a hot drink had proved impossible, as the kettle would simply come flying off the top of the cooker.

I examined the offending article, and found it to be a bog-standard, two-ringed yacht cooker with oven, mounted on a swing known as a "gimbals", which ensured that the cooker stayed level even when the yacht was leaning over, or "heeled". Undoing the catch that held the cooker in a fixed position while in harbour, I established that the gimbals mechanism worked perfectly, and then, catching the look of surprise on Denis's face, the truth dawned on me. The concept of the gimballed stove was clearly a new one to them, and they had been trying to use the cooker at sea while it was fixed in its locked, harbour position. I was beginning to realise the enormity of the task that lay ahead of me over the next few weeks! A glance at the self-help book on sailing that they had brought with them as their guide through the learning process only served to confirm that feeling.

Over the next couple of days, Denis and I got stuck into the various tasks that we had identified to prepare the yacht for sea. These included fitting the mainsail. This had, until now, been stored in its bag, in the accommodation, as they had been unsure how to attach it, had not wished to appear ignorant in front of the critical eyes of the sailing community of Rhodes, and had been unable to contemplate fitting the thing once at sea. Jobs such as this allowed me the opportunity to show Denis how various parts of the boat and its rig functioned, and thus to begin the process of converting him into a competent deckhand. Several hilarious hours were spent in encounters with Greek hardware shop assistants, as we tried to explain to them, with the help of a distinctly non-technical phrase book, that we were looking for seizing wire. Eventually, however, we found what we were looking for, and set ourselves to adjusting the rigging and securely locking it with the wire.

As I prowled around in the depths of the yacht's bilges, I came to the conclusion that Mick and Denis had, perhaps more by luck than good judgement, secured themselves a strong, well built yacht, with no obvious signs of corrosion around the multitude of joints that made up hull and frame. The steering was dismantled, greased, and reassembled, but I suspected that it would need closer attention before long, as there appeared to be a fundamental design or construction fault in its mechanism.

As Denis had previously described to me, the accommodation was indeed badly designed, particularly for sea-going. It consisted of two single bunks in the forward cabin, aft of which there was a passageway, which had a toilet, or "heads", compartment on one side and an oilskin hanging area, or wet-locker, on the other. Behind that, there was the saloon, or main living area, with the much-maligned cooker on one side and a single bunk on the other. On one side of the cockpit was the navigation area, and on the other a passage containing a single bunk. This passage led through to the aft cabin, which was equipped with an enormous double bunk that would be very comfortable in harbour but totally impractical for use at sea. The three-cylinder diesel engine was mounted in a compartment directly beneath the cockpit.

The weather stayed dry but the wind remained very strong over the weekend, becoming so strong on the Saturday evening that I decided that it would be prudent to mount a harbour-watch that night, taking it in turns to stay awake and look after the safety of the yacht, ensuring that lines remained secure and that the fenders, whose function was to prevent the vessel from being damaged against the hull of the boat alongside us, remained in their proper places. This decision was met with disbelieving horror on the part of my companion, who was clearly still clinging to the landsman's notion of time management, it being considered sensible and normal that one should be awake and active during the daylight hours and asleep at night. The seaman's concept of eternal vigilance, even when in harbour, as being the price paid for safety, and sleep deprivation being an integral and necessary part of any voyage, was obviously an alien one. "Look after the ship and the ship will look after you" is an idea ingrained in the soul of any competent sailor, but it was clearly going to take a lot of hard sell to get this across to Denis.

On the Monday morning, Michael Jowett returned to the yacht. He had apparently been to Germany, visiting a woman whom he had met in Rhodes and subsequently fallen in lust with. A bit of a diminutive George Michael lookalike, he looked extremely dapper in his designer clothes, and I did hope that he had something more suitable for life at sea somewhere in his luggage. He was now impatient to be off, and his lack of acknowledgement of the effort that Denis and I had put in, while he had been off satisfying his carnal desires, was the first of many unpleasant aspects of his character that were to emerge over the next few weeks.

The following morning dawned bright and clear, with a fresh wind coming from the north east. As soon as breakfast was over, we prepared the yacht for sea, then started the engine, cast away the lines and manoeuvred into the clear area of water in the middle of the marina, where I turned the yacht head to wind and ordered Denis to hoist the mainsail, which he did in the manner in which he had been instructed. As soon as it was fully hoisted and tied off, I allowed the bows of the yacht to fall away from the wind and headed for the marina entrance channel, adjusting the sail to catch the wind as we altered course. The engine was now ticking over in neutral and there were cries of delight and amazement from my two companions as they realised that we were proceeding under sail in this confined space, a feat that they had previously thought well beyond the powers of mortal man.

Once established in the channel, I ordered the headsail unfurled and set and we were soon proceeding towards the open sea at a respectable pace. Mick and Denis were stunned to see the demon yacht, which had previously defied all of their efforts to control it, now behaving with perfect docility. We hurried to tidy away the mooring lines and fenders as we cleared the outer end of the marina entrance channel, at which point I switched off the engine, giving the customary sigh of contentment as its sounds died away, to be replaced by the sough of the wind over the sails and the occasional splash of water against the hull. It was nice to be at sea again, under sail, beneath a clear blue sky, with the winter sun easing the early morning chill. As we left the shallow, coastal waters behind, I placed the yacht on the pre-calculated course towards the island of Malta, switched on and set the self-steering, or autopilot, and then we hoisted and set the staysail and were soon clipping along at a good speed, under full sail. The only fly in the ointment was the fact that the autopilot appeared to be struggling a bit to keep the yacht on course, and I was reminded that it was likely that we would need to dismantle the steering before too long in order to diagnose and fix the reason for its inherent stiffness.

Soon, we moved away from the shelter of the land and we reduced, or "reefed", the mainsail a little, to make the motion more comfortable as the breeze freshened. Now that we were settled down and on course, we began working the watch-keeping routine that we had agreed and which followed the time-honoured tradition of the sea. This involved each of us taking it in turns to work for four hours on deck, keeping a lookout, checking on the steering and adjusting the sails as necessary. Each of us would have time for ample rest during our eight hours off, in addition to cooking and washing up and keeping things tidy down below. As skipper I would, of course, be on call at any time, to go on deck and sort out any difficulty, and I urged my companions to call me in the event of the slightest concern, exhorting them on each occasion that I left the deck, "If in doubt, shout!"

The upbeat mood of our first day at sea was considerably dampened by Mick in the late evening. After dinner, he had retired to the aft cabin to spend the remaining six hours of his off-watch time there. He had claimed that spacious area, with its double bunk, as his own immediately on his return on Monday, encountering no opposition from me. It was not long before he exploded on deck, complaining bitterly.

"How can anyone sleep on this fucking boat with all this going on?" he roared, glaring balefully towards the stern.

"All what, Mick?" I asked, in what I hoped to be a calming tone, being unsure what the hell he was on about.

"That fucking racket. And all this fucking throwing about." He was incoherent with rage. "I'm fucking knackered, I've only got a couple of hours to get some sleep, and now this poxy boat won't let me. You'd better sort it out, pal."

There appeared to be two problems: firstly, the area of the bunk allowed him to be mercilessly rolled about as the yacht rode over the waves, and secondly, the sound made by the yacht's wind generator, which was mounted above his cabin, was making sleep impossible.

The wind generator was one of several features about the yacht which suited her for long-distance cruising. Its propeller, turned by the force of the wind, provided electrical energy to the yacht's batteries, where it was stored until needed to provide power for navigation lights, instrumentation, radios and other equipment, as well as the cabin lights. It, together with the solar panels that provided electrical power during daylight, greatly extended the independent cruising range of the vessel. The only alternative to those systems was to run the diesel engine for an hour or more each day in order to generate electricity and charge the batteries, thereby using up valuable fuel and causing wear and tear on the engine.

On this occasion, however, it was clear that Mick was, under no circumstances, prepared to live with the low, thrumming sound given off by the wind generator at work, and so I reluctantly put it out of action by locking its blades in a fixed position, with the hope that, as the voyage progressed, Mick would become more tolerant of such background on-board noises, and that we would then be able to set it to work again. As far as getting thrown around his bunk was concerned, I suggested that he try to wedge himself in place using spare sails and life jackets. With extremely poor grace, he retired below in order to try this, leaving a very thoughtful skipper on deck. What, I wondered, is this guy doing buying a sailing yacht when he appears to have so little sympathy for the cruising way of life? It was a question that was to haunt me for a few days to come, as it became increasingly clear that Mick was simply not suited to life at sea on board a small sailing vessel. The answer, when it came, would be chilling.

CHAPTER TWO

Damned If You Do

AS WE SAILED across the Mediterranean towards Malta, Mick began to make, initially oblique, references to a sizable sum of money, asking what I would do if I were to come into possession of a lump sum of cash. At first, I dismissed it as simply chat to help pass the hours, along the lines of "What would you do if you were to win the Lottery?" However, as his questions persisted, I began to sense that there was a deeper purpose behind them. My answers were, given my background, fairly predictable: I would buy a yacht and go off to do some long-distance sailing.

The weather was very kind to us on the four-day voyage to Malta, until, on the final day at sea and with the eastern extremity of the island in sight, the wind began to increase significantly and the barometer to drop dramatically, which indicated the approach of bad weather. We reduced sail to suit the more windy conditions and enjoyed some hours of delightful sailing, running before the fresh breeze, which was still in a very favourable direction, and almost surfing down the building waves in the sparkling sunlight. The scene ahead looked ominous, though, with banks of huge, towering cumulus developing off the northern coast of Malta, and the plunging barometric pressure indicating that we were sailing into a localised storm zone. I decided that it would be prudent to reduce sail further, to prepare the yacht for what was going to be some nasty weather.

Shortly after sunset, Mick was taking his turn on deck, steering by hand as the autopilot had proved unable to cope with the boisterous conditions, and Denis and I had just begun to eat our evening meal, when the full force of the electrical storm-cell broke loose over our heads. Torrential rain lashed the steel deck and deafening thunderclaps exploded around us, as the yacht's angle of heel increased dramatically in response to blasts of cold, accelerated wind pouring out of the storm system and hitting the sails. It is never comfortable to be on board a yacht at sea in the middle of an electrical storm, and one is always conscious of the height of the mast, sticking up into the air, almost inviting lightning to strike. In reality, following the line of least resistance, lightning generally prefers to earth directly into the surrounding ocean, but strikes have been recorded, and I hurried to switch off the radios and unplug their antennas as a precautionary measure.

Just then, Mick knocked on the hatch, shouting to be heard above the sound of wind and wave.

"You'd better come up and sort this out; I don't know what the fuck's going on here. This thing's just doing whatever the fuck it likes."

"Okay, Mick, I'm on my way," I shouted, pulling on a waterproof jacket. I leaned out of the hatch, remaining below the shelter of the canopy, and took stock. Mick had clearly become disorientated and the yacht was twenty degrees off course. I eased out the mainsail a little to take the weight off the wheel, and then took over the steering, without moving from the shelter of the hatch. Returning the yacht to the required course, I checked for a few minutes that it was easy to maintain the course in the current conditions, and then said to Mick, "Okay, you should have no problems like that, take the wheel."

After waiting for a few minutes to ensure that he was managing, I said, "Right Mick, that seems to be fine, call me again if you need me." I then retreated below, closing the hatch behind me. To have brought the situation under control again without leaving the hatchway was, I suppose, a petty piece of point scoring, a way of demonstrating to him that I was in my element and that he was far out of his, but his general attitude was by this time beginning to irritate me, and I thought to myself, well, you've bought the damn thing, so now you can bloody well learn to take the rough with the smooth. In any case, there was no point in two of us getting wet.

The sight on deck had, indeed, been awesome. The yacht was enveloped in stygian darkness, broken frequently by the blinding flashes of forked and sheet lightning cracking through the air, each one quickly followed by a thunderclap that seemed to shake the very air. The surface of the sea appeared to be boiling; strangely calm, as if the waves were being held down by the sheer weight of rainwater pouring down from above, which churned the surface into a mass of white foam. The wind was gusty and fluky, as air masses of different temperatures and densities rolled and collided inside the roiling clouds, which now had their base almost at sea-level. At irregular intervals, gusts of near-freezing wind would scream towards us, howling through the rigging and laying the yacht on her ear, until the newly arrived energy was converted into forward speed and the yacht rose into a more upright position as she surged forward. This was nature in the raw, red of tooth and claw.

I had laid the yacht on a "safety course", which would take us obliquely away from the northern coastline of the island of Malta. I had earlier seen the lights of a long line of coastal fishing boats, operating two or three miles off the coast, and without radar I had no desire to either try to pick my way through them or attempt an approach to the harbour of Valetta until conditions had improved. After about an hour, the rain suddenly stopped, the cloud cleared as if a curtain had been swept aside, revealing a mass of twinkling stars in a clear sky, and the wind dropped to an eerie calm. The coastal lights of Malta, and of the fishing vessels, seemed magnified in the crystal clear air, and were reflected in the glassy sheen of the sea, which had quickly assumed the stillness of a mill-pond.

It was clear that we would need to motor to enter Valetta before midnight, and so I started the engine and put it into forward gear. Nothing happened. It appeared that drive from the engine was not being transmitted to the propeller, and an investigation in the engine compartment quickly revealed the reason why. A pin linking the drive shaft from the engine to the propeller shaft had simply dropped out of its position and was now lost in the depths of the engine room bilge. A replacement was quickly found, in a box containing an ominous number of spare pins, but proved to be the wrong size. I returned to the deck, to make whatever progress I could under sail in the direction of Valetta, leaving Mick, a self-confessed mechanical genius, to come up with a solution to the drive problem.

A long, frustrating night followed, with insufficient wind for most of the time to even keep the vessel on course, punctuated by minutes at a time of elation as Mick's latest "fix" was tried, before inevitably failing. Dawn had broken by the time we were off the harbour entrance, and we were able to limp into harbour under engine, at slow speed, powered by a drive-coupling which Mick had jury rigged and which failed like all its predecessors just as we came alongside a pontoon in the yacht marina. We hastily moored the yacht securely to the pontoon, and retired for a few hours of much-needed sleep.

Around mid-morning, we got up and spent a bit of time tidying up the yacht after the four-day sail, as well as the dramas of the previous night. Just before midday, Mick said, "Let's all go ashore and find a café to have lunch."

Entering the first café that we came to, which was almost deserted, we ordered three beers, and then Mick turned to me.

"I've got something that you and I need to have a chat about," he said conspiratorially. "I need to speak to you on your own, let's grab that table over there."

He and I made our way to a quiet table, out of earshot of the few customers, while Denis remained at the bar.

"You must have wondered what is going on, with us and this yacht," he said, by way of preamble.

"Well, I must admit that I have rather begun to wonder what it's all about. You guys don't seem all that keen on sailing, so what are you doing buying a sailing yacht; especially at this time of year?"

I had already learned to be careful in my conversations with Mick. He took himself extremely seriously and was quick to take offence at anything that he took to be a slight or a challenge. He had a great deal of pent-up aggression and a low fuse point, and generally gave the impression of being like an unexploded powder-keg. Now he sat, hunched forward across the table, almost seeming to vibrate with internal energy or stress as he looked directly into my eyes, his face deadly serious.

"The way it works is this. Big does and little does," he said, lapsing into one of his favourite expressions. "And without beating about the bush, we are going across to the Caribbean to pick up a large cargo of cocaine and bring it back across the Atlantic. I want you to come with us. You'll be well paid for the job and you'll have no contact with the cargo, we'll look after all that part of things. What do you say?"

Well, I thought to myself, what do you say? I struggled to maintain an outward calm, drawing on years of command experience to keep my face impassive while my mind was a whirlwind of emotions as I tried to come to grips with this new turn of events. I immediately knew that the manner in which I handled the next few minutes was going to be crucial. Through my mind raced everything that I had heard and read about the trade in cocaine and the people who managed that trade.

Given that he had mentioned a "large cargo", that people involved in this trade were often extremely dangerous people, and that now I knew about it I was in a very precarious position, I was faced with a horrible quandary. How likely was it, should I say, "No, I'm not interested, forget it," that they would simply shrug their shoulders and let me walk away, knowing that I knew their identities, their plans and their modus operandi? From their point of view, it would be safer and more logical to simply give me the "deep six" – knock me on the head and sling me overboard – and so ensure that their plans remained confidential. Mick, I felt sure, was perfectly capable of such an action, and Denis appeared to be under his spell to the extent that he would probably be prepared to go along with whatever Mick decided to do.

On the other hand, going along with the plan for now might give me the chance, later on, to walk away from the situation with impunity. Perhaps if I took them across the Atlantic, I would have earned sufficient trust to, at that stage, be able to announce that I was not prepared to do anything more and that I now wanted to return home, but assure them that their knowledge was safe with me. Whatever I decided, the answer must come in the next few seconds, or there would always be an element of doubt in Mick's mind as to my loyalty and commitment. Given his headstrong, impulsive, aggressive nature, such doubt could easily prove fatal for me at some point in the future. I could feel his eyes boring into me as he awaited my response.

I played for time a little, asking, "So how much are you paying, then?"

"Forty thousand pounds," was his immediate reply. "Once we get to the other side, you will be put up in a top-class hotel and have a holiday, while we load the yacht. You can then come on board, once it has all been put away, and sail us back across the Atlantic."

The sum was derisory, given what I was being asked to do, and only served to increase my sense that the real prize for accepting this proposition was to be allowed to continue living. What the hell have I got myself into here, I thought. Just how exactly has this crazy situation come about?

It was now or never, though, so I took a deep breath, and said "Okay, count me in." It was a decision that will haunt me for the rest of my days, and I can never be one hundred percent sure that I did not, at that time, exaggerate in my own mind the danger that I was facing should I refuse to take part. It continues to be my feeling, though, that I was a disposable asset in a game being played for very high stakes, and that my disposal would not have caused Mick a single sleepless night.

A look of relief crossed Mick's face when I uttered the fateful words. "Okay," he said. "What I want you to do is give me a list of everything you need to take us and the boat across the Atlantic, and then we'll go about putting it all together."

I nodded assent.

"Now, you've got to know that, should you cross us, or talk, there is nowhere in the world that you can hide." Thus he confirmed my sense that I was now involved in something that was way too deep for me to handle. "Let's join Denis," he concluded.

As we rejoined Denis at the bar, Mick gave him a brief nod and I detected a strange look of relief, coupled with anxiety and sorrow, cross Denis's face. As we left the café a minute or so later, with Mick striding on ahead, Denis whispered to me, "Welcome to the cheap seats." It was not a remark designed to improve my frame of mind, but one that was to ring more true with each successive event over the following few months.

Mick was in buoyant mood when we returned on board *Pulse*, confidently asserting that money was to be no object in the equipping of the vessel for the Atlantic crossing. When I announced that I would like to buy a plastic sextant, and the associated books of tables, to back up the GPS satellite navigation systems on board, his response was derisive.

"Plastic! You'll have a proper brass one, lad. There will be no expense spared."

In the event, we were to set sail from the Canary Islands a month and a half later without even a plastic sextant on board, but I had by that time become more or less inured to the yawning chasm that existed between Mick's promises and what he was able to deliver.

He declared himself keen to buy a radar set, and was not a little miffed that my response was less than enthusiastic. I saw radar as being an unnecessary expense, unnecessarily draining power from the limited supply in the ship's batteries when we would be crossing an almost empty stretch of ocean, where fog was almost unheard of and one of us would always be on deck to keep a lookout. I suggested that radar, as well as a weather-fax machine, would be well worth considering for the return voyage across the North Atlantic, where storms were to be avoided and fogs were a not infrequent occurrence. With poor grace, he acceded.

As we made our way along the narrow, bustling streets of Valetta, looking for a chandlery shop in which to buy some minor items that we needed, Mick announced that he wanted to buy an outboard motor for the yacht's inflatable dinghy. When I asked him if he was sure that the dinghy was fitted with a mounting board for an outboard, and if so, what was the maximum horsepower that it was designed to take, he fell into a moody silence. Clearly this was another area where Mick's desire for glittery gadgets was out of synchronisation with reality. Later examination proved that the dinghy had never been designed to accept an outboard motor.

It was decided that our next port of call would be Agrigento, on the Italian island of Sicily, and our departure for that port, following a three-day stay in Malta, provided another episode in the developing personality clash between Mick and me. Having carried out a more permanent repair to the propeller shaft coupling, we motored out of our berth and moored alongside the fuel tender, which was moored mid-channel in the outer harbour. There we topped off the fuel tanks, following which, having judged the wind direction, I decided to continue the instruction of my companions in sailing techniques. I therefore set about arranging the mooring lines so that we could easily slip them from aboard the yacht, and then asked for the mainsail to be raised. Mick's reaction to this straightforward request astounded me.

"We'll fucking well not be doing that, for starters. We'll just motor out into the middle of the outer harbour like normal folk and put up the sails there."

"But there's nothing unusual or difficult about what I want to do," I reasoned. "It's a standard technique in a sailing boat, and the conditions are just right for it."

"We're not doing it, and that's it and all about it," he heatedly replied. "So you can just get the fucking engine started and there'll be no more about it."

"What do we need the engine for, it's a bloody sailing boat," I angrily responded. "That's what it does best, sail. Do you want to learn how to handle the boat or not?"

"I can handle a boat! Don't you tell me I can't! And I don't want to learn anything about poxy sailing boats, I just want to get this heap of shit across the Atlantic, get the job done, and that's that. Now get the fucking engine started and let's get the fuck out of here," he roared, by now incandescent with rage.

In the end, Mick was the "owner" of the vessel, as well as

being in charge of the enterprise, and I therefore had to concede defeat. Clearly I was to be required to act as skipper of the yacht whenever this was necessary to save their skins, but must otherwise adopt a back-seat role. I supposed that there was a dual reason for this dispute: Mick was still smarting from what he would perceive as his humiliation in the thunder storm, wanting to get his own back while on familiar territory, and I was now on his "team" and needed to be shown who was the boss. The more I got to know this character, the less I liked him.

It was therefore with a feeling of considerable relief that I heard Mick announce, as we were approaching Sicily, that he intended to get off the yacht there to fly to Germany to see his girlfriend. He asked Denis and me to sail the yacht to Gibraltar, where he would meet us. Despite them apparently being life-long friends, I believe that Denis was also pleased to see Mick climb into a taxi and speed off for the airport, secure in the knowledge that his brooding, malevolent personality would be absent for at least the next two weeks.

After a stay of only twenty-four hours in Sicily, Denis and I headed to sea again for the two-day crossing to Sardinia, where we would berth in Cagliari for two days before setting off for Gibraltar, at the entrance to the Mediterranean. Although we had to work additional hours in the absence of Mick, Denis and I settled into a comfortable routine, and life on board was considerably more pleasant.

There was little opportunity for conversation, as we each worked four-hour shifts, or watches, followed by four hours off, throughout the twenty-four hour period. The person going off watch would always be anxious to get some sleep, and would quickly make his way below after some quick words about the weather or anything of interest seen during the watch.

The voyage from Sardinia to Gibraltar would be our longest of the trip so far, taking about five days. By the end of the second day, Denis had became so exhausted by the routine of watch-keeping, coupled with an inability to sleep properly when off watch, that I offered to work his next watch for him while he caught up with sleep and got his body adjusted to life at sea. Working for twelve hours in succession was tiring but well worth it, as Denis awoke from a long, deep sleep greatly refreshed, ate a good meal, and was able to undertake his share of the work on board for the remainder of the voyage.

The wind remained favourable throughout our sail to Gibraltar, and we were able to maintain good daily average speeds. During the last twenty-four hours of the voyage though, the wind steadily increased and we were obliged to reduce sail regularly until we had eventually reduced to our minimum sail area as we arrived off the port in the wee small hours of our fifth day at sea. Tuning to the frequency of the port radio, we learned that the port was closed to all commercial traffic due to the severity of the conditions, and we could see the lights of many large vessels anchored in the bay, awaiting an improvement in the weather and permission to enter port.

As a small, private vessel, the closure order did not affect us, as we were not so vulnerable to the effects of wind when manoeuvring at slow speed during the process of coming alongside as were the large, high-sided tankers and other commercial vessels. We continued to make our way further into the bay, now working against the wind, as we left the Straits of Gibraltar behind and headed for the port. Starting up the engine, we folded away our sails and motored the last few hundred yards towards the marina, which is very close to Gibraltar Airport, with its runway jutting out into the bay. Dawn was now breaking, and the Rock looked spectacular, capped with cloud and with a trail of cloud continuously being torn away in the gale and streaming off downwind, looking for all the world like the plume of smoke from an active volcano.

Berthing alongside a vacant pontoon, we snugged the yacht

down, laying out additional lines to cope with the ferocious downdraughts which were accelerating down off the face of the Rock above us, and then put the kettle on while we waited for the Customs and Immigration officials to come on duty so that we could check in with them.

We spent a pleasant four days in Gibraltar, resting and recuperating from our voyage and enjoying the tourist attractions of this, one of the last bastions of British Imperial might, although for me the experience was overshadowed by the new reality in my life and the nature of the enterprise upon which we were engaged. I racked my brain in an attempt to think of a way out of this mess that would not put me or my family in danger, but to no avail.

A telephone call to Mick elicited the information that he would not now be joining us in Gibraltar, but would instead be awaiting us when we arrived in Lanzarote, in the Canary Islands. This news certainly helped to brighten up at least my stay in the town, and I don't believe that Denis was too disappointed either to learn that it would be another week or so before we were once more in Mick's company.

LATE IN THE evening of December 3, we slipped from our berth in Gibraltar's yacht marina to take advantage of a favourable wind that would push us out through the Straits at the start of an estimated seven-day sail to Lanzarote. This would be our longest sail of the trip so far, a prospect considerably sweetened by the knowledge that we would be sailing south, to the land of eternal summer, and that the weather should get ever more pleasant, and certainly warmer, as we progressed along the route.

Leaving Gibraltar Bay, we remained close to the coast to avoid the steady stream of commercial traffic entering and leaving the Mediterranean through the Straits. After several hours we were clear of the western end of the Straits and were able to shape a course south so as to cross the shipping lanes at right angles and then finally to set the yacht on the final course for Lanzarote. Helped along by a steady breeze, we made good progress southwards, and by the morning of the second day at sea the temperature had increased markedly and the cloud all but disappeared as we encountered the warm winds blowing off the North African coast.

Denis and I had by now established a routine for our periods at sea and the days passed in a pleasant fashion as we enjoyed the increasingly benign conditions, in sharp contrast to the cold and wind of our final couple of weeks in the Mediterranean. After a few days under way, I baked bread, and Denis was impressed that we could be so self-sufficient at sea that we even had our own on-board bakery! It was a far cry from the Mars bars and vitamin tablets on which he and Mick had envisaged surviving during longer periods at sea. During these periods when we were sailing, I was able to put the purpose of our voyage to the back of my mind and to concentrate on the job in hand, which was to get the yacht and ourselves safely and efficiently to the next port.

All too soon, at least for my liking, the peaks of Lanzarote could be seen pushing up over the horizon, and by late morning on the seventh day we were coasting down the eastern side of the island, enjoying good views of the dramatic, volcanic landscape, as we made for the port of Arecife, about mid-way down the length of the island. We found a berth in the busy marina, completed the necessary paperwork with the port authorities, and then went ashore to phone Mick's mobile telephone number and see whether he had yet arrived on the island.

Mick answered immediately, and declared that he was with his family at a resort complex very close to Arecife. Apparently he had returned to England following his sojourn in Germany with his girlfriend, and decided to take his wife and two children on a two-week, pre-Christmas break to Lanzarote. Perhaps to assuage any feelings of guilt that he harboured about swanning around Europe like some jetset playboy while Denis and I got on with his project, he announced that we could have two nights in a hotel to relax after our trip before we got stuck into the extensive preparations necessary to ensure that the yacht was ready to cross the Atlantic.

Denis and I were more than happy to take advantage of his "generosity", and we enjoyed two nights in a four-class hotel, running up considerable bar and dining room bills, after which we returned on board the yacht to nurse our hangovers and begin to figure out how we could best schedule the work that needed to be done on her. An early priority was to lift the boat out of the water, as I had decided that both the propeller shaft and the steering system needed close attention. Both of these were jobs that required the yacht to be out of the water and propped up ashore.

I contacted a firm of engineers at the marina who were prepared, at reasonable cost, to convert the propeller shaft coupling into a secure keyway link and to reduce the diameter of the rudder shaft slightly, to allow it to revolve freely in its housing. Mick reluctantly agreed to meet the cost of these crucial modifications, before informing us that he had been looking at resorts on the Caribbean island of Antigua, our next destination, and that he intended to fly his German girlfriend out there for a two-week vacation to coincide with our arrival on that side of the Atlantic.

It was becoming increasingly clear that Mick was intent on channelling the maximum amount possible of whatever funds he had been allocated to bring this project to fruition into his own pocket, and using them to fund a hugely extravagant lifestyle. Mick never did tell us how much his budget was for the trip, and made only very occasional reference to those behind the enterprise, calling them the "lads", or the "big boys".

Most of the time he preferred to avoid giving any suggestion that anyone other than himself was the mastermind and driving force behind the whole affair.

Pulse spent just over a week propped up on the boat park, with Denis and me living aboard while the modifications were carried out, before being relaunched in the week before Christmas. Now the autohelm could easily cope with the loads produced by the steering, and we knew that the propeller was not going to suddenly disassociate itself from its attachment to the engine. We set about gathering the stores that we would need for the voyage, while Mick exhorted us to ever greater efforts, announcing that he was flying back to England with his family and would spend Christmas there, but would be returning on New Year's eve and would expect the yacht to be ready to leave as soon as he returned. He gave us enough cash to pay the engineering firm, and a little spending money, before bidding us farewell and heading off.

With Mick gone, we settled into a routine of spending a few hours each morning carrying out a few odd jobs on board the yacht, then walking or sunbathing in the afternoons, before buying an evening meal out of our steadily diminishing funds. Now that *Pulse* was virtually ready to go, time began to weigh heavily and we were keen to be off, if only to break the monotony of being stuck on a holiday island with little money to spend. Christmas came and went, a period when I spent a great deal of time thinking back to previous Christmases spent happily in the company of my daughter and other family members in the Outer Hebrides, and longed for my life to return to its previous simplicity and moral certainties. However much I desired to get out of this situation, though, I could think of no way that I could do so without the prospect of spending the rest of my life looking over one shoulder.

Eventually, we awaited Mick's arrival on December 31. When he hadn't appeared by early evening, we telephoned his home, to discover that he had misread the flight ticket, which was in fact valid for travel on the 30th, and that he would not now be able to get a flight until January 2.

Denis and I turned out our pockets and discovered that we had enough money left to buy one beer each. We agreed to have this around midnight, and meantime, retired aboard the yacht to spend the evening reading. The irony of the situation was not lost on either of us. Here we were, on the brink of the new Millennium, well established on Mick's "money no object" project, without enough cash between us to even celebrate the New Year. Denis's previous comment, "Welcome to the cheap seats," kept running through my mind as celebratory fireworks began to soar skywards from all over the island. With midnight approaching, we sauntered disconsolately up to the marina bar, where we bought a beer each with the last of our cash and half-heartedly toasted each other. Church bells began to chime in the distance, and the sky was lit up by a veritable barrage of fireworks as the locals celebrated in style.

"Happy New Year, Happy New Millennium," we both said, with heavy irony.

ON THE AFTERNOON of January 2, Mick finally appeared and to our amazement began to harangue us about our level of spending during his absence, accusing us of living the high life and squandering all the money.

"I know you two have been lording it up while I've been away, and have pissed away all the money," he said. "Don't think I'm stupid, I know what's been going on."

"That's not fair," we rejoined, angrily. "We've spent the money on the yacht, and had almost nothing to spend on ourselves. Look, here are the receipts for what we've bought and had done on the boat."

"I don't want to see any fucking receipts, I know what the score is. You two had better watch your step, because I'm well pissed off with this. You can't pull the wool over my eyes," he shouted. There was no point in continuing the argument in the face of such irrational behaviour.

Mick had returned with very little in the way of cash and had obviously managed to blow almost all of whatever budget had been allocated to him by his bosses, and now wished to try and shift the blame, at least in his own mind, onto Denis and me. He had ensured that his vacation in Antigua was bought and paid for, however, and he was eager to be off, as his girlfriend would be flying in to Antigua on January 28, a date arranged on the basis of my prediction that our crossing of the ocean should take about twenty-three days. I explained, yet again, that this prediction was very much a guess and that on such a long crossing it was impossible to predict one's arrival with real accuracy, given the number of factors that could influence the time taken on passage. This was brushed aside, however, with some bullshit about his having "every confidence" that I could get us there on time. So now I had additional, unwanted pressure. I not only had to get this circus act across the Atlantic, I was expected to do so to a timetable.

Early on the afternoon of January 4, we slipped our berth in the marina and headed out to sea. By sunset, we had left behind the coastline of the island of Gran Canaria, which lies to the south of Lanzarote, and were making our way out into the open ocean, travelling at fine speed in the accelerated wind coming off the islands. As the islands began to sink below the horizon, in the last rays of the setting sun, my companions expressed surprise that I didn't appear excited about our undertaking. I could not explain to them that I was too preoccupied by the nature of our undertaking, and too filled with presentiments of trouble ahead, to take any pleasure in the prospect of the Atlantic crossing that lay before us.

We quickly established our watch-keeping routine and enjoyed some pleasant sailing in quite flat water for the first twenty-four hours. By the evening of the second day at sea, however, as we moved deeper into the ocean, we encountered the full force of the ocean swell that is a feature of the Trade Wind crossing. It came at us from an awkward angle, causing the yacht to move in a very uncomfortable, corkscrewing motion. This was not at all to Mick's liking, and shortly after sunset, as I was settling down in the cockpit for the eight to midnight watch, he hurtled on deck, beside himself with rage, and instructed me to "do something about this motion, now!" I pointed out to him the corrugated nature of the water all around us, and explained that as long as the yacht was floating on the surface, she was obliged to conform to the undulations. His response took me completely by surprise.

"I'm telling you to put a stop to this rocking about *now* or you'll be going over the side! I mean it. You're doing this deliberately."

I had no doubt that he did indeed mean it, and that in his present state of mind he would be capable of any act of madness, and so I tried to placate him, pointing out that, while I was greatly impressed by his threat, there was nothing I could do to ease the yacht's motion, given the sea conditions. During my seagoing career, I had faced many difficulties and dangers, but never had felt such fear as I did now, being confronted with a completely irrational human being.

An extremely tense twenty minutes followed, before Mick eventually calmed down a bit and accepted my argument that we would just have to get used to the motion, as there was no way of easing it. He stormed off down below to wedge himself in as best he could, and grab whatever sleep he could, before being called for his next watch period, leaving me on deck with the night and my thoughts for company. In my mind, the width of the Atlantic Ocean had just increased enormously. I wondered what further human dramas lay ahead over the next three weeks or so and wished, not for the first time and certainly not for the last, that my companions had accepted my oft-repeated suggestion that I would sail the yacht across the Atlantic alone and meet them on the other side.

Following his outburst on the second evening at sea, Mick seemed to settle down, resigning himself to his situation and getting on with the job, and an uneasy peace was established on board as we sailed south in order to get established in the Trade Wind belt, before altering course to the west en route to Antigua. As for me, I kept a wary eye on Mick and his moods, ever watchful for another descent into madness.

The weather remained very kind to us, with warm sunshine and blue skies each day and the wind blowing steadily day and night, from a fixed direction, as wind and current pushed us towards our destination at a respectable pace. We ran the engine for two hours each evening to provide power for the yacht's lights and instruments through the night. It was possible for each of us to have a warm-water shower each day, as I had pierced the bottom of a bucket with several holes and hoisted it into the rigging. Filled with sea-water that had been collected in used drinking water containers and warmed up in the sun all day on deck, it made a very effective, if rudimentary, shower. Every third day we had freshly baked bread, whenever it was my turn to work the four to eight morning watch and prepare breakfast. I would make the bread down below, taking regular trips up on deck to ensure that the horizon was clear and that no ships were bearing down on us on a collision course.

In fact, we only saw two ships in the course of the entire crossing, one of which passed astern of us during the night, and the other, a large oil tanker, which overtook us one day around lunchtime. Each morning there would be a few flying fish to be cleared off the deck that had flown aboard during the night, as they desperately took to the air in their attempts to avoid the gaping jaws of larger predatory fish. Once a week, we would have a hair-cutting session, using battery operated hair clippers to give each other a trim almost "to the bone", a strategy designed to help us keep cool in the tropical heat and make it easier to keep clean. Clothes were washed by the simple but effective strategy of tying them to a line and trailing them behind the yacht for an hour or so, before hanging them in the rigging to dry.

Each evening, after dinner, I would calculate and plot the current position on the chart, and it became reassuring to see, as the days went on, that we were maintaining at least our target distance run of one hundred and twenty miles each twenty-four hours, and it began to look increasingly possible that we were going to get Mick to Antigua in time for his "date". In this manner, we passed the crossing in almost a cocoon of timelessness, until, on the evening of the twentieth day at sea, we were able to pick up the signals from a commercial radio station in Antigua, and so confirm what navigation was telling us, that we were fast approaching the end of our voyage, further proof being the number of sea birds that we now saw around us.

Early in the morning of the twenty-third day at sea, we could just make out the highest point of the island of Antigua, jutting up over the horizon dead ahead. It was, for me, a moment of quiet satisfaction at a voyage successfully undertaken, but I was not able to share the jubilation of the others at the approach of land. I went below to re-check the harbour information for our approach, leaving Mick and Denis to their mutual backslapping on deck.

As we negotiated the entrance to English Harbour, with its distinctive, crenellated, harbour walls, around two thirty in the afternoon, a large aircraft was descending towards the airport in the north of the island, and Mick declared that, due to the hour, it had to be the Lufthansa 747 bringing his girlfriend in for the beginning of her two-week vacation. He was cock-a-hoop at this coincidence of timing, and went so far as to congratulate me on a job well done, saying, "I knew that you could do it." I smiled wryly at his compliments, taking comfort in the knowledge that I would shortly be free of the company of this odious little man for at least a couple of weeks.

As soon as we had moored the yacht, we delivered our laundry bags into the care of an enormous, beaming black woman who had appeared as if by magic while we were tying up. We then retired to the local hostelry, converted from what had been the timber store in the days when Antigua had been an important base for the British Navy's Squadron of the Leeward Islands, to enjoy a couple of bottles of the local beer, Wadadli, named for the old native Carib Amerindian name for the island. Mick then rushed off to his holiday resort in the north of the island, leaving Denis and I to soak up the atmosphere of this quintessentially Caribbean island.

As ever, there were jobs to be done on board the yacht following her 3,000-mile sail, and we once more established what had become, for Denis and me, our regular harbour routine: working on board in the mornings, sunbathing and relaxing in the afternoons. True to form, Mick had left us with almost no funds, but would grudgingly dole out a few Antiguan dollars during his occasional visits to the yacht. Towards the end of his two-week holiday, he announced that he would not be sailing with us on the next leg, but intended instead to fly back to Europe with his girlfriend and rejoin us in a few weeks' time in the next port of call, Saint Lucia.

Thus it was that, following a one-month stay in Antigua, Denis and I slipped our moorings and headed out of English Harbour for the forty-eight-hour sail southwards, past the islands of Guadeloupe and Martinique, to the port of Castries on Saint Lucia.

CHAPTER THREE

A Tale Told By An Idiot

OUR VOYAGE WAS uneventful until early in the morning of our second day at sea, when I was shocked awake by Denis repeatedly shouting from his station on deck.

"Pirates! Pirates!"

I hurried into the cockpit, heart pounding, pausing only to pick up the box of rocket flares that we carried for emergency use. Denis was pointing to an open motor launch rapidly approaching us across the swells, with two people to be seen on board. We frantically signalled to them not to come any closer as they began to manoeuvre as if to come alongside us.

A shouted conversation followed, during which the men explained, "We are lost. We went out fishing, lost sight of the island, and have been at sea for two days. Please help us, we do not know where we are."

They certainly looked to be in poor condition, suffering from hours of direct exposure to the tropical sun, hunger, dehydration, and fright. One of them had a nasty gash on his right shin. I quickly made up a bag of bits that would be useful to them – a couple of bottles of water, some biscuits and a small hand-compass – and threw it across to them. They immediately drank some of the water, but stared blankly at the compass. Eventually I suggested, "Just head directly towards the sun, and you should see the island within half an hour."

They quickly sped off in the direction indicated, leaving us to plod on at our usual five knots, and then, just before they disappeared over the horizon, we could see through the binoculars that they had begun to wave wildly at us. We took this to mean that they had caught site of their island home, and forty-five minutes later we ourselves could see the shape of the island's hills appearing through the misty atmosphere. Two hours afterwards, we were berthed alongside in Castries, where we stayed for four days, but never caught sight of our putative pirates again. However, during our visit to Saint Lucia, I became aware of one phenomenon that perhaps might help explain their navigational mishap. On several occasions, I saw fishermen of a clearly Rastafarian persuasion preparing to go to sea, whose final act before slipping their lines was to stand in their boat and, with great solemnity, smoke an enormous joint.

Mick told us by phone that he no longer intended to join us in Saint Lucia but would fly out to Grenada in a few days' time and meet us there. So Denis and I set sail from Castries, bound for Gouyave, on the east coast of Grenada, just over twenty-four hours' sailing time south of Saint Lucia. We passed Saint Vincent and the Grenadines during the night, then, in the early morning, as the bulk of the northern part of Grenada began to shelter us from the Trade Winds, we started the engine to motor for the last few miles. A loud, persistent vibration issued from the engine compartment. I discovered that one of the cast iron engine mountings had sheared, causing the engine to vibrate unduly on the rubber feet of its remaining three mountings. To prevent further damage, we shut down the engine, deciding to use it simply for the final berthing process on our arrival in Gouyave, meantime trickling along in the light breeze blowing off the island's steep hillsides. Evening was approaching as we made our way into the tiny but picturesque harbour and found a place to tie up.

The next day, Mick arrived, looking more like George Michael than ever with his tan and full of his own importance, as usual, and we moved berth a few miles further south, to Saint George's. There we removed the broken engine mount and took it to a local engineering shop for repair. We also got yellow fever vaccinations, as well as visas for Venezuela, where Mick had announced that Margarita was to be our final destination.

MARGARITA IS A small island lying off the north-eastern coast of Venezuela, which itself is at the northern end of South America. Like many of the Caribbean islands, it has long been a popular holiday destination, boasting as it does a glorious climate, with year-round sunshine and miles of idyllic beaches. Its popularity as an international resort island has dwindled in recent years, though, because of the lack of personal security, and most tourists nowadays are native Venezuelans.

We spent a further couple of days in Grenada before setting off for the twenty-four-hour sail to Margarita, during which we ripped out the yacht's water storage tanks to make room for the drugs that were to come aboard. These were simply thrown over the side, where they quickly sank to the bottom of the sea. Arriving in Margarita, we anchored among several small fishing vessels in Pampatar Bay, on the south east corner of the island. Rowing ashore in the dinghy, we discovered that a new marina had been built next to the Hilton Hotel, between the towns of Pampatar and Porlamar. We therefore returned to the yacht and motored the short distance to the marina, where we moored up in the late evening.

The next morning, as soon as the customs and immigration formalities had been concluded, Mick announced that we would move into a hotel during our stay on the island, and so we drove off in a taxi to find one nearby. The taxi driver recommended the Kamarata, which was basic and cheap but clean and with a good-sized swimming pool in the central court.

Mick then went off to rent a mobile phone that would be used to give us our final instructions as to how and where to collect our cargo. It appeared that the nightmare was finally coming to a head. It was now the end of March, and having been told that nothing would happen for a fortnight, Mick arranged for his German girlfriend to fly out to Margarita. The two of them moved into an exclusive resort on the northern coast of the island for ten days, while Denis and I sat by the pool, with little or no money, and waited.

Once Mick rejoined us, we continued waiting through the rest of April, in an agony of nervous frustration, with Mick promising on an almost daily basis, after returning from having made mysterious phone calls, that "in a couple of days' time" we would load our cargo and be away. As the month wore on, I hoped against hope that the whole plot had come apart at the seams and that we would simply be told to sail back to Britain, or even leave the yacht where it was and fly back.

Meanwhile, Mick was becoming increasingly concerned about his wife's health. Each time he called her, he returned with his face looking gloomier. Apparently she had been diagnosed with breast cancer and would need investigative surgery to find the extent of it.

"I'm really worried about her. It doesn't look good. It's so difficult being so far away from her at a time like this. I mean, big does and little does. I may play the field a bit, as you know, but that doesn't change the fact that I really love her."

Eventually, he said, "Look lads, I can't hack this any more. She was crying today when I spoke to her. I really need to be there for her, you know? What would you guys think about my going back to England to look after her?" It was a suggestion that, given the circumstances, met with complete support from Denis and me, despite our misgivings about being left with the job of lifting and loading the drugs and sailing with them for Spain.

Finally, after much procrastination, Mick decided that he would have to go back to England, although he was full of apparent concern for the situation that he was leaving Denis and me in.

"I really feel bad about leaving you guys in the lurch, but my mind's just not on the job while I've got the worry of my wife's health hanging over me."

We hastened to reassure him, pointing out how important it was for him to be back in England at this time, and that we could manage all that was to be done in connection with the cargo. We therefore drove him to the airport in the vehicle that we had hired for the drugs pick-up, and he boarded a holiday charter flight for Amsterdam, from where he could get a connecting flight to Manchester. For me at least, it was a great relief to say goodbye to him at the airport, knowing that I would now be free from his brooding, malevolent presence. It was to be several months later before we discovered that his wife had not suffered a day's concern over her health, and that the whole story had therefore been an utterly cynical tissue of lies, designed simply to avoid his own continued involvement in an operation that he presumably suspected was compromised, or that he himself had compromised.

In the meantime, Denis and I waited, expecting each day that the phone would ring with instructions for the pick-up. I still secretly harboured the hope that the whole thing had gone pear-shaped and that we would be sent home. It was increasingly clear to me that, should this not be the case, it was extremely likely that we would be caught, as the whole thing had been such a shambles, from start to finish, that no other outcome seemed feasible.

Finally, on May 5, Mick contacted Denis by telephone and said, "This afternoon, at four o'clock, leave the car in the car-park of the restaurant in Porlamar that we spoke about before and put the keys on top off the offside front wheel. It will be returned to the same spot, loaded with three hundred kilos of cocaine, at four p.m. tomorrow. Good luck."

The operation was then to be repeated over the following twenty-four hours, with a second cargo of three hundred kilos. Denis went off to leave the car at the pre-arranged place, and then a sleepless night followed, as the full implications of what we were embarked on, and what its likely consequences would be, not only for me but for those closest to me, rolled tumultuously around in my mind.

Though I didn't know it at the time, the street value for the total haul back in the UK would apparently be almost £50 million.

DENIS AND I tried to remain reasonably calm as we waited for the pick-up time to come round. We spoke little as the day wore on, each deep in his own thoughts. After what seemed several ages had passed, it was time for Denis to leave.

"I'll meet you at the top of the main shopping street at four thirty, and we can then both go on to the marina and load the drugs on board *Pulse*," he said.

"Okay then, I'll see you there."

At a little after four o'clock, I walked to the corner where Denis had arranged to pick me up. As he drove up and I opened the car door, I was met by a sight that took my breath away. The rear of the car was stacked with open-weave onion bags, the contents of which could clearly be seen through the weave. Each bag was loaded with blocks of white powder, each one of which was about the size of a video cassette and wrapped in transparent plastic, with a large ace of clubs card on the front. I shook my head in despair as I climbed into the car and fastened my seat belt.

"I don't believe this," I said. "This is just bloody madness. Why don't we just drive down Porlamar high street and hand blocks of it out to the public – we might as bloody well."

Now I had the final confirmation, if such had been needed, that the entire organisation was a disaster, and I knew beyond a shadow of a doubt that we were heading for prison, and soon.

Denis was unable to say anything to reassure me, as he had not yet recovered himself from the shock of opening the car door to reveal the shambles within. All we lacked was an orange flashing light, a musical horn, and a sign on the roof reading "Cocaine Couriers".

Reaching the marina entrance, I alighted from the car in order to pay the marina fees for another three days' stay. Before doing so, I shook hands with Denis, saying, "It's been nice knowing you, mate." He weakly replied, "It'll be right," but I don't think even he believed it.

The person on duty at the marina was all smiles as usual, and we had by now refined the negotiations necessary to apply and pay for a further extension of our stay in the marina to a very few words and gestures. I did notice an unusual radio on the desk in front of him, apparently VHF but distinct from the marine VHF sets that I was used to. Suddenly this unit erupted into rapid, excited Spanish, not a word of which I could understand, and the official quickly leant across to turn the volume right down before handing my change over to me. I left the office and walked round the marina in the gathering dusk, to where *Pulse* was berthed, to find that Denis had already begun to empty the car and transfer the bags on board the yacht. I hurried to help him, feeling sick to the stomach and sure that we were only minutes away from arrest.

Within a matter of minutes, we had emptied the car and

thrown all the bags into the cockpit of the yacht. We then transferred them down below into the accommodation. As soon as this was done, Denis went off with the car to deliver it back to the pick-up point, while I got on with the work of stowing our cargo into the spaces previously taken up by the water tanks. By the time all the blocks had been accounted for, the storage spaces were full – and we had another three hundred kilos being delivered the following day.

By this time, however, I was past caring, being convinced that we were simply going through the motions until such time as the authorities had time to get their act together and came to arrest us. Attractive as the thought of simply disappearing was, the fact that I was sure that we were about to be arrested made it more rather than less difficult to do so. I was sure that, should I run, the full blame and consequences for the failure of the operation would land on my head.

Around seven o'clock, Denis returned on board, having dropped off the car, to find me sitting in the cockpit, having a cigarette and enjoying what I felt sure were to be my last hours of freedom.

"What do you think we should do now?" he asked.

"Why don't we go and have a beer?"

"That seems to be a good idea."

So we locked up what had, at a stroke, become the most valuable yacht in the marina and began to make our way around the edge of the marina towards the exit, each deep in his own thoughts.

AS WE ROUNDED the top end of the marina, we noticed a convoy of vehicles making their way through the marina entrance. Ominously, each of the vehicles was travelling without lights, and I felt that a cold hand had gripped my heart. Despite my long expectation that this would be the final outcome of our misadventures, it was chilling to be faced with the stark reality. There was no point in trying to run, as there was nowhere to run to, with acres of flat land all around. One of us, I don't remember who, muttered needlessly, "I think this might be for us," as the leading car in the convoy of six assorted vehicles began to slow down as it approached, drawing to a halt as it came abreast of us. By this time, we could make out armed soldiers hanging outside the cabs of the trucks that followed this car.

The passenger window rolled down, and a heavily accented voice asked us, in English, "Are you from the British yacht *Pulse*?" I replied that we were, upon which he politely asked "Would you mind returning with us to the yacht?" We agreed to do so and turned around, walking alongside the car as the line of vehicles escorted us at walking pace back around the edge of the marina to the yacht we had left only minutes before. On the way, the official that had first spoken to us asked "Are you armed? Do you have any guns?" We hastened to assure him that we did not, and the rest of that seemingly interminable walk was conducted in silence.

Arriving at the yacht, the official, dressed in civilian clothes, alighted from the car and about twenty armed soldiers descended from the other vehicles, having first parked them in an arc facing the water so that their headlights, now switched on, illuminated the yacht. The official asked me for the keys to the yacht and requested permission to board it in order to carry out a search. I was hardly in a position to refuse, and the official and five troops went aboard and opened up the accommodation. Denis and I were then escorted aboard by a further two soldiers and were kept under surveillance in the saloon area while the search began in the front cabin.

After what seemed an age, but could have been no more than four or five minutes, we heard a shout go up from the front cabin, and knew that they had come across the packages stowed there underneath the bunk cushions. Denis and I were immediately removed to the cockpit, while the soldiers, who sported shoulder flashes reading "Guardia Nacional", proceeded to tear apart the yacht's internal furniture in their continued search for the rest of the drugs.

This search did not take long to bear fruit, and before long a chain gang of troops was set up between the interior of the yacht and the jetty to transfer three hundred kilos, block by block, onto the concrete and pile it up in front of the waiting vehicles. Denis and I were escorted ashore and told to sit down on the low parapet of the jetty, while our captors bustled about importantly. A test kit was produced from one of the vehicles and applied to a sample extracted from one of the white powder blocks, while I clutched onto the last vain, wild and desperate hope that Mick and his masters had been duped and that we were in fact carrying nothing more than a very large cargo of talcum powder. Once this test had quickly demonstrated that we were in fact carrying cocaine with a very high level of purity, Denis and I were again approached by the official who had first spoken to us.

This man now introduced himself as a Fiscal of the Ministry of Justice and, reading from a card, said, "I am placing you under arrest, charged with having been involved in the illegal transportation of cocaine. You have a right to remain silent, but anything that you do say, may be written down and used in evidence against you."

We were handcuffed by one of the Guardia Nacional troops, an action that starkly underlined the fact that we had crossed a frontier into new, frightening and, for us, uncharted territory. We were then left alone again while the soldiers got on with counting and recounting the packages of cocaine and then loading them onto a truck. I was in a state of shock, frightened and bewildered and experiencing a strange feeling of unreality, as if I was standing outside all that was happening around me, almost as if I were watching a movie.

51

This sense of unreality deepened in the next few minutes as the scene around us descended into farce. Having decided to send the drugs back to their headquarters, a couple of the Guardia Nacional troops jumped into the truck and attempted to start it. As the starter motor engaged, the headlights dimmed almost to nothing, and it was apparent that the battery had been flattened while the truck was being used to illuminate the scene. Shouted recriminations followed, after which frantic efforts began to push the heavy truck in order to jump-start it. Once it had been sent on its way, a quick check revealed that all their vehicles were in similar condition and each had to be jump-started. For me, it was the only moment of light relief in an otherwise utterly miserable evening.

With the remaining vehicles repositioned in an arc, now with their engines running, Denis and I were instructed to turn out our pockets and all our possessions were listed and taken away, including passports and what money in US dollars we had with us. We were allowed to keep the small amount of local currency that we each carried. Several items that they had removed from the yacht were displayed for our inspection and explanation as to their purpose, including our mobile phone, a handheld radio telephone and the yacht's satellite distress beacon. I particularly struggled to make them understand the nature of the satellite beacon and the importance of not setting it off by accident while playing about with it, as its activation was likely to initiate a full-scale international rescue effort.

Satisfied, they loaded Denis and me into the backs of separate trucks, each with an escort of five troops, before driving off towards the Guardia Nacional headquarters in Porlamar. As we drove round the marina, I was taken aback to realise that several of the soldiers with me were attired in various articles, sailing jackets and the like, that they had clearly rifled from the yacht and were delightedly showing them off to each other. Then one of them, who apparently spoke a little English, looked at me, shook his head, and said, "I very sorry you. You prison, twenty-four years." He then sat back, smiling proudly at his colleagues, apparently having exhausted his mastery of the English language.

While he had said little, it had been enough, and eloquently enough expressed, to take me from abject misery to total despair.

CHAPTER FOUR

Liberty Lost

A TEN-MINUTE drive took us from the marina to the headquarters of the Guardia Nacional, a collection of single-storey, brick-built edifices within a fenced compound. As I was led inside, I caught a brief glimpse of Denis, looking pale and shocked, before we were again separated. I was taken to a raised, balustraded area in the main entrance hall, sat down on a plastic chair and handcuffed to the balustrade next to a wall displaying framed photographs of former commanders of the Margarita Guardia Nacional detachment. There I was to remain for the rest of the night.

As I took stock of my surroundings, I became aware of a sound that I had not heard for at least ten years, and which was as chilling to me as anything that had happened so far. It was the rattle of manual typewriters, coming from offices in various parts of the building. I felt as if we had been taken back in time at least a generation, and wondered whether the treatment we might expect over the course of the days, months and years ahead might be equally backward. All I could do was hope that their attitudes to human rights issues and the general treatment of prisoners were more advanced than their office equipment.

With the passage of the hours during that seemingly interminable night, my restricted position became more and more uncomfortable, and my efforts to ease the discomfort only succeeded in further tightening the handcuff around my left wrist. My thoughts remained a confused jumble of misery, fear, shame and concern about the effects on my family. Various people came and went as the night wore on, but all seemed busy about their own affairs and paid me no attention.

Around six-thirty in the morning, just as dawn was breaking, an officer who appeared to hold considerable authority entered the building and immediately approached me, asking in broken English if I had had coffee, and if not, would I like some? Greatly impressed by this display of kindness, I nodded, upon which he immediately dispatched one of his subordinates to fetch some. The coffee, when it came, was black and sweet, served in a small disposable cup, and I tried to savour it for as long as possible, relishing the familiar flavour in the midst of this strange environment.

Perhaps an hour later, Denis was escorted out from a side room, looking tired and upset, and then I was unshackled from the balustrade and we were both taken outside for a brief walk in the fresh air on the parade ground before being returned inside, this time being allowed to take up adjacent seats in the entrance hall, handcuffed to each other. We said little to each other; we were each caught up in a tangle of emotions too complicated for words.

Shortly afterward, we were escorted through a maze of corridors by a civilian official and an armed soldier. While waiting outside a door marked "laboratory", the civilian asked if we needed to go to the toilet, and I took advantage of the offer, being escorted to a nearby toilet in order to empty my bladder. Minutes later, we entered the laboratory, where swabs were taken from our fingers for chemical analysis and we were asked to provide urine samples! After a considerable struggle, I was eventually able to produce enough to be tested.

After a further period of waiting, an English accent could be heard resounding through the building, and we were shortly afterwards taken one by one into an office for an interview with a tall, middle-aged, patrician gentleman who stated that he was "attached to the British Embassy".

"Please tell me how you became involved with all this," he asked.

His main function seemed to be to establish whether we were able to cast any light on the players further up the chain of the drug smuggling organisation, and he quickly became satisfied that we were unable to do so.

"I know that there was a third person on the boat," he said. "I have a picture of him here. Do you recognise this man?"

The photograph he showed me was of Mick. Once convinced that we could be of no further help, he left, after relatively brief interviews, and we returned to our seats in the entrance hallway.

Around lunchtime, we were taken to the Guardia mess hall, where we were served soup, although neither of us had much appetite. When we returned to the main office block, a large number of troops were assembling, before departing in a convoy of vehicles. A couple of hours later, they returned in jubilant mood, with five, clearly Venezuelan, people under arrest, and then began to carry blocks of cocaine into the building. We could see through a doorway that they were arranging a small mountain of these blocks in a large room, and TV cameras arrived soon afterwards to record the size of this haul. It was obvious that they must have followed our car the previous evening and now had detained those who had delivered the drugs to the island and captured the remaining three hundred kilos of cocaine.

In the early evening, we were taken outside, loaded into a cage in the back of a van, and then, with two armed troops mounted on a platform at the back of the van, and preceded and followed by two cars, each full of soldiers, we moved off at high speed with lights flashing and sirens blaring, bound we knew not where.

After twenty minutes or so, we halted at a side entrance to a modern, four-storey building, which was clearly a courthouse. Surrounded by armed troops, we were hurried up the stairs to the third floor, where we were made to sit at the back of a large room which seemed to be some kind of an office. Those present deferred to a large man in shirt sleeves, who began to examine papers and bark questions at those around him. We understood nothing of what was going on, and our confusion deepened when we were led out of the building again, without anyone having spoken directly to us. Much later, we were to learn that what we had just experienced was the first part of the Venezuelan judicial process, whereby the accused and all relevant paperwork must be presented before a judge within twenty-four hours of arrest for him to decide whether the continued detention of the accused is justified by the evidence so far available.

Clearly, in our case the judge had decided that we should remain in detention, as we were bundled on board the van and driven back to Guardia Nacional HQ. When we arrived, however, we were not invited to step down from the van but instead were left sitting there for half an hour, before the troops resumed their places and the convoy took off again, driving through the almost deserted streets of Porlamar before stopping in front of another official building.

Hustled inside, we were handed into the custody of some officials dressed in civilian clothes, each of whom wore a pistol stuffed into the waistband of his trousers. They took us to the back of the building, where we were offered the opportunity to go to the toilet before being placed in a seven foot by ten foot cell, one of a row of four, made up of three walls constructed from blocks, and the fourth, front wall, consisting of bars, with the door set into this front wall. Two foam mattresses were thrown in after us, and then the door was slammed shut and locked. It was the first time since arrest that I had experienced the terrible finality of a slamming cell door, and it was a defining moment, as I slumped disconsolately into the far corner, sitting atop my, still rolled up, mattress.

We were both terribly apprehensive, as the language barrier meant that we now had no idea in whose hands we were, or what form of treatment we might expect to receive from our current custodians. True, we had been treated with civility up to this point, but we had been unable to hold even the most basic conversation that we could use to measure their attitude and intentions towards us. We were the only occupants of this little cell block, a fact that did little to relieve our anxiety, and we tensed whenever we heard anyone approaching the bars leading to our block.

"I wonder what's going to happen to us now," said Denis. I could only reply, "I have no idea." As far as I was concerned, anything was possible.

After a sleepless previous night, very little sleep the night before that, and having expended masses of nervous energy in the last thirty hours, we were both exhausted and we soon rolled out our mattresses on the concrete floor, where I fell into a fitful sleep.

I had no idea how long I had slept when I was woken by the sound of loud voices, a great clattering of keys and the opening and slamming of cell doors. This lasted only a few minutes and I quickly fell back into a deep, dreamless sleep, until woken by the first glimmerings of dawn through the barred window set high in the back wall of the cell.

Soon we could hear movement and talking in the adjacent cells, and I realised that the sounds during the night had been those of other prisoners arriving. We found out they were four of the Venezuelans involved in our case, who had been arrested the previous day. They seemed a cheerful enough bunch, and one of them even spoke a very few words of English. They were to prove invaluable to us over the next few weeks, as we struggled to learn some Spanish and to gain some understanding of the legal process we were involved in.

Shortly after sunrise, an official equipped with the customary pistol in his waistband allowed us to visit the toilets, opening the cells one at a time and taking the occupants through to the toilet area. We caught a glimpse of our fellow prisoners for the first time. Two of them were aged around fifty, short and big-bellied. The other two appeared to be in their late twenties or early thirties, of medium height and slim. All had jet black hair, swarthy complexions, and were dressed simply in T-shirts and shorts.

Once all had completed their ablutions, the guard brought a bottle of drinking water to each cell. We were soon to learn that this toilet visit was a once a day privilege, and that for the remainder of each twenty-four-hour period we would be expected to urinate into empty drinks bottles, which were supplied to us for the purpose.

Around lunchtime, another official appeared, bringing us each an *arepa*, the traditional Venezuelan flat bread made from maize flour, together with a slice of a cold, greasy, processed meat, which we would soon know only too well, and hate deeply. It was reassuring to know that we were to be fed, although in our innocence Denis and I had not been too concerned that we would not be. It was only later that we learned that it was not at all the norm for prisoners to be fed whilst in police custody, family members being expected to visit daily to bring food, while foreign prisoners had to resort to giving money to visiting family members so they would buy food for them, or alternatively, persuade a policeman to shop for them, which they were normally prepared to do for an exorbitant backhander. Those without resources were reduced to begging food from their fellow prisoners or carrying out menial tasks in return for food.

As the day wore on, we began to talk with our companions, learning that they were José and Oliver in the cell to our left, and Alexis and his son Adrian in the cell to our right. They told us that they were from the mainland of Venezuela, and therefore had no relatives on the island that could visit them. It soon became clear that they knew as little of British life as we did of Venezuelan, being aware only of the Queen, Princess Diana and Margaret Thatcher. My reaction to the mention of that last name was soon to have amusing repercussions, when a heavily pregnant stray dog began to appear around our cells at meal times, and was promptly christened Margaret Thatcher by the Venezuelans in honour of that, from my point of view, most damaging political figure in recent British history.

My own name proved almost impossible for the Venezuelans to pronounce, and they chose instead to address me as "Capitan", a name that was to remain with me for the rest of my prison life.

As evening fell, we were invaded by clouds of tiny, biting mosquitoes, which the locals said were called *zancudo*. They showed us how to make long paper tapers, known as *maceras*, out of tightly rolled toilet paper; when lit, one of these would burn for up to an hour, with the smoke helping to keep the *zancudo* at bay. Nevertheless, we were to get bitten many times each evening, particularly around the feet and ankles.

Early on the morning of our second day, a Guardia Nacional trooper appeared, carrying the overnight bags that we had left in our hotel room. We were delighted, as at least we now had some changes of clothes as well as toiletries and towels. From that point forward, we were allowed out of our cell for half an hour each morning to have a shower and wash a change of clothes. Hung on the bars of our cell, clothes dried in a matter of hours in the tropical heat.

Later that same day, Denis and I were taken to meet a visitor. At the police rest-room, we were met by a tall, distinguished-looking man.

"I am Douglas Weller, Honorary British Consul on the island. Are you being treated all right here?"

Once we had told him that, at least so far, we were being well treated, he explained his function in regard to prisoners, advising us that he would be visiting us on a monthly basis both while we were in police custody and later, should we move on to San Antonio, the island's prison.

"You are in a very unusual situation," said Mr Weller, "in that you are being held by an organisation called DISIP, which is the Venezuelan State Security Police. Normally, newly arrested prisoners are held by the local police forces. You are quite fortunate in that regard, as conditions are pretty terrible in the police cells, very overcrowded and with a great deal of violence. Also, it seems that you are being fed here, which just doesn't happen when you are in the custody of the normal police force."

He explained the probable course of our trial and took contact details so that, with our permission, immediate family could be informed. Mr Weller also gave us some notepaper and details of an organisation called Prisoners Abroad, which provides help to Britons in all parts of the world who find themselves in a similar situation to ours. He gave us some Freepost envelopes which we could use to send letters back to Britain, as well as an application form for grant aid from them, and he finally wished us luck and left, saying that he would see us again in a month's time. We returned to our cell considerably buoyed up; at least now people back home would know that we were well, if in serious trouble, and we felt that the contact with British officialdom would help to ensure our continued good treatment.

I wondered about the effects of the news on my family and

close friends, and settled down with pen and notepaper to write the most difficult letters that I had ever had to write. Denis did the same on the other side of the cell, and so we sat in silence until an officer arrived with our evening meal, of *arepa* with sardines. Loathing all forms of seafood, I carefully scraped off the sardines, gave them to Denis and made do with *arepa* for dinner.

We had noticed that each time officials came into our cell block, our fellow prisoners would chat amicably to them for minutes on end. They now announced to us that this fraternisation had borne fruit, as one whom they had already christened "el corrupto" was prepared to collect items from a neighbourhood shop for us if we gave him the money. As we still had the local currency we'd been allowed to keep on our arrest, we drew up a shopping list, with the eager assistance of our companions, and passed the appropriate amount of money to the neighbouring cell so that they could negotiate the purchases, thereby avoiding "Gringo tax".

So it was that a couple of hours later we had a large bag of sweet bread and a couple of bottles of cola to share with our four new friends – and with our even newer friend, the said el corrupto. Even this pleasant interlude led to a harsh learning experience for Denis and me, however, as we woke up several hours later having been bitten on the lips by massive cockroaches that were crawling around our cell. We soon learned that all traces of food, particularly if sweet, must be carefully washed away using some of our precious store of drinking water if we were not to suffer attack from these revolting creatures.

Our life in the DISIP cells soon took on a routine as we waited for the next court appearance, which would give us an opportunity to plead guilty or not guilty to the charges against us. Mr Weller had explained that should we plead guilty to the charges against us at that appearance, we would be sentenced immediately, and this is what we had decided to do, given that the evidence against us was overwhelming.

One major problem for me during that time lay in the difference in personalities between Denis and myself. While difficulties, and emotional turmoil, lead to me becoming quiet and introverted, they have the opposite effect on Denis, who becomes extremely garrulous. Each morning when he awoke, he would begin to relate to me a rambling succession of tales from his past life, slipping from one story to the next, seemingly without pause for breath, throughout the length of the day, while I grunted monosyllabic replies at appropriate moments. After a very few weeks of this, I felt I knew every member of his family, down to the family pets, intimately, was acquainted with every friend he had had from infant school onwards, and could repeat every incident of note, and many of no note whatsoever, throughout his life.

"Did I ever tell you about my dog, Eric?" Denis would ask.

"Yes, I believe you did," I would reply, in an attempt to avoid the inevitable tale.

"He was a cracker; mad as a hatter," Denis would continue, oblivious. "Went with me everywhere, he did. Staffordshire bull terrier, he was. He used to sit in the passenger seat of the wagon, when I was working on deliveries in the plumbing trade. Never had to lock the van when he was with me, anyone who opened the door would get his arm taken off! He used to eat cigarette stubs. Mad, he was; brilliant dog. One day, my mate . . ."

Even the Venezuelans took note of what was going on, and used to joke that all they could hear from our cell was:

"Blah, blah, blah."

"Aha."

"Blah, blah, blah."

"Aha."

"Blah . . . etc."

I wished I had enough Spanish to be able to ask for solitary confinement! Denis and I have since become extremely good friends, but at that time I could cheerfully have strangled him. Eventually, I took refuge in the only book that we possessed, John Grisham's *A Time to Kill*, and I read it over and over again over the course of several weeks. Based like most of Grisham's books on his experiences as a trial lawyer in the US, it is a powerful depiction of events around a racial murder case in the Deep South. Grisham's strong characterisations and witty style held me in thrall, allowing a temporary escape from reality, even after many readings.

Another activity that helped to pass the time, and was to prove of great help later, was the effort to learn Spanish. One of the police officers was in the habit of bringing in a daily newspaper, and I managed to borrow a Spanish/English dictionary from another. Thus, I was able to sit down each day and work my way through the newspaper, looking up each new word in the dictionary and noting it on notepaper. Our Venezuelan fellow prisoners helped by annotating diagrams of body parts and suchlike, as well as by correcting pronunciation.

Another activity that I took up in an attempt to keep my brain active was writing, and when my very dilapidated bath towel finally gave up the ghost, I decided to write a poem in its honour.

Ode to a Dead Towel

Farewell my friend, I loved you well,
But now I have to say you smell;
You've stood by me through thick and thin,
But now, you're ready for the bin;

I've tried to treat you with great care,
But you clearly are the worse for wear;

On countless morns, you left me dry,
Your sad departure makes me cry;

You covered me when I was bare,
And I walked around without a care;
But now you're old, and are so tattered,
That my ego is at times quite shattered;

For your fabric, I had much to pay,
Now through it I see the light of day;
You dried the floor when I washed my cell,
All in all, you've done quite well;

I worked on you with needle and cotton,
Although your fabric was quite rotten;
I fixed you up, you looked OK,
But you only lasted one more day!
I'll think of you with great pleasure
Now you're going to your leisure
I wish you well in your new role
Blocking up that draughty hole!

Another set of verses written at that time aimed to show the extent to which the attitude taken towards us by the police officers in charge of us could affect our psychological state.

A Better Day

A smile as my bars were closed this morning;
Perhaps a better day is dawning;
That's all it takes to make our day,
A crumb of comfort along the way;

Each time we hear the clink of keys,
We stoop to peer and try to see;
Who will bring to us our food?
Will he be evil, will he be good?

A snarl can ruin all our rations;
Why do we rouse such evil passions?
It's not our fault his wife was surly,
Or that his kids created a hurly burly;

As our only link with the world outside,
It's hard when they make us feel despised;
But a smile as my bars were closed this morning;
Perhaps a better day is dawning?

One morning, when I went out as usual for my shower and moved my bag, a small snake came darting out from behind it. I didn't think a great deal of it, as it was only a couple of inches long, but my Venezuelan companions reacted with terror. They backed away and began jabbering so quickly amongst themselves that I was unable to understand a word. Then one of them grabbed a nearby sweeping brush and, being extremely careful to keep his bare feet well out of the snake's way, he began to attack it. The aggressive reaction of the snake to this attack confirmed that it had both the tools and the ability to defend itself, but a blow to its head finally put paid to it.

The same evening, another snake of similar size entered the area, and the police officer who came to attend to our frantic calling and whistling released our snake "expert" from his cell for long enough to dispatch it. He explained that, although these were young snakes, they still carried a considerable dose of venom and were extremely dangerous. We sincerely hoped that Mum or Dad didn't choose to pay us a visit, and blocked up the space between the bottom of the cell door and the floor with newspaper in a weak attempt to prevent the entry of more snakes. Although we did not get any more such visitors, we did hear that one of the police officers had found and killed a snake just outside the building, and there was little sleep to be had that night.

The heat had been making it difficult to sleep in any case, and so we were extremely pleased when it began to rain the following evening, and we looked forward to a good night's sleep in the cooler conditions. No sooner had the rain begun to hit the ground however, than what appeared to be the entire frog population of the island assembled outside our window and began to rejoice in the change of weather, setting up a chorus that lasted all night.

ONE INCIDENT THAT broke the monotony was when the Commander of the DISIP unit appeared and led Denis and me to a side office, equipped with comfortable couches, where we were introduced to two people, who declared themselves to be defence lawyers. They were very well dressed and wore lots of expensive jewellery, and the DISIP Commander seemed to behave with some deference as he introduced them before retiring to another room.

One of the visitors spoke a little English and spent some minutes confirming that he had a thorough grasp of our current situation before assuring us that, on payment to them of $70,000, we would be at home within ten days. I jokingly replied, "Do you take cheques?" Denis's response was to mutter that this was a waste of time and we should end the conversation immediately, to which I replied, "Hey, we're sitting on nice comfortable chairs instead of on the floor of our cell – keep them talking." It quickly became clear to our visitors that it was their time that was being wasted, so they shook hands with us and left, upon which we were ushered back to our cell.

Another break in our routine came a few days before our trial, with a visit from a veteran British journalist called Tom Mangold and a television crew. They were filming a documentary about the drug trade for the BBC's *Panorama* programme. Denis and I agreed to be interviewed only after we had been repeatedly assured that the documentary was purely designed to show our true story, in order to act as a warning to others to avoid our predicament. It was a decision that we were later to regret bitterly once the documentary had been screened and its true nature, as a shop window for the might of the British Security Service, became clear to us through the reaction of family members and friends who saw it. Perhaps the less said about that particular episode, the better, although it certainly left us with the feeling that we had been abused, exploited and demonised at a time when we were at our most vulnerable, and led us to question the moral compasses consulted by certain TV journalists in the course of carrying out their work.

On June 22, Denis and I, together with the four Venezuelans, were taken under tight security to the courthouse for our pleading diet and were placed in a large, ground-floor holding cell. A couple of extremely tense hours of waiting followed, after which we were escorted up to the third floor, making ludicrous progress on the stairway as a result of being linked together by handcuffs in a chain of six persons. Once in the corridor outside the courtroom, two men approached us. One introduced himself, in barely passable English, as the court-appointed interpreter, and said that his companion was our attorney from the Public Defender's Office.

They checked that we intended to plead guilty and then coached us on the form of words to be used to submit that plea to the charges against us, as well as agreeing a signal that the interpreter would use to prompt us at the appropriate point in the proceedings. We then filed into the courtroom, which was already occupied by some ten people seated in what appeared to be the public benches. We sat down in the front row of seats before a raised bench equipped with three chairs, one of which had a word processor set up in front of it.

After a few minutes, three casually dressed women entered the raised platform through a side door and took their seats behind the bench. The proceedings were brought to order, and the young lady behind the word processor began to read out what appeared to be a long summary of the circumstances of our arrest and the charges against us. After an interminable, rambling discourse, none of which we could understand, our names were called, and first Denis and then myself stood up and gave the reply in the way we had earlier been coached, saying, "Yo acepto los hechos, soy culpable." I sat down, feeling that I had just passed through another portal on this unstoppable, nightmare journey. The four Venezuelan prisoners entered a plea of not guilty, having decided to try their luck before a full trial, notwithstanding the much higher sentences that they would face should they be found guilty.

Shortly after we entered our pleas, we were removed from the courtroom and returned to the holding cell, where we waited in an agony of doubt and anticipation for several hours before Denis and I were again called upstairs to the courtroom, where our sentences were read out.

"You have each been sentenced to a prison term of six years and eight months," said our interpreter. "The sentence is based on a sentence of ten years, with a third taken off for your guilty plea."

Shocking as it was to hear, we knew that we had been very fortunate, in view of the amount of cocaine involved. In a daze, we were removed once more from the courtroom and escorted downstairs before being bundled aboard the waiting transport to be returned to our cells in DISIP to begin our sentence.

✶

THE FOLLOWING WEEKS followed the pattern of those that had gone before, our time spent almost exclusively locked up in our cell, with the exception of the half-hour allowed each morning for washing ourselves and our clothing. Denis was anxious for us to be moved on, becoming frustrated at our confinement, but I held that, despite the limitations and frustrations of our current situation, we would look back on the period in DISIP as being the "best" of our prison term – and so it was to prove.

Finally, on July 27, the day came when we were told that we were to be moved to the prison of San Antonio, and we collected our few bits and pieces together in preparation. The Venezuelans prisoners were to remain, as they were still awaiting trial, and it was a very emotional parting from those who had been our only companions for so long.

When we were taken out to the waiting car, all the police officers on duty that morning came out to wish us goodbye, and particularly good luck, in our new setting. When the commander came out and repeated the "good luck" message, we began to feel extremely nervous, wondering why such luck would be needed. The only transport available that morning was a hatchback, and so we and our bags and mattresses were squeezed into the rear luggage compartment, while our Guardia Nacional escort got into the front. In this cramped fashion, we undertook the twenty-minute journey to the place where we expected to spend the next three or four years. We already understood that it was possible to reduce the time physically spent in prison, by working and/or studying, activities which, according to a formula laid down by the Ministry of Justice, qualified for a reduction in the original sentence.

Our first view of our new home, as the car jolted over the rough approach road, was not encouraging. All we could see was a concrete perimeter wall, topped with razor wire and with guard towers spaced at intervals outside its length. The car drew up outside what appeared to be the only entrance through the wall, a concrete gatehouse.

We were escorted into the gatehouse, where a bored-looking sergeant of the Guardia Nacional sat behind a bare desk. On the wall was painted a sign, in large letters, which I translated as "Prison is for reform, not for punishment". Soon I would realise that it would have been more appropriate for the words "Abandon every hope, ye who enter here" to have been inscribed above the doorway. The official produced a ledger from a drawer and began to take down our names, nationality and dates of birth. The sergeant indicated to me that my beard, which I had sported for the previous twenty years, would need to go within twenty-four hours. Our escort then emptied our bags out on the floor, and any items of black or dark clothing were removed before the remainder was stuffed back in the bags, which were then handed over to us. We were ordered to pass through a metal detector into another room, where we were quickly strip-searched, then invited to dress again, before being escorted into the prison.

Nothing in my life had prepared me for the sight that met my eyes when we passed out of the gate house and entered the inner compound.

CHAPTER FIVE

Welcome To Hell

MY STOMACH LURCHED in dismay as I left the prison gatehouse and began to make my way across the inner compound towards the offices. The compound was an area of about an acre, bounded on two sides by high concrete walls and on the other two sides by single-storey buildings, whose bare facades were broken only by concrete louvers near the tops of the walls. Within the compound were about ten of the most miserable souls that it had ever been my misfortune to clap eyes on, dressed in little more than scraps of clothing and looking ill-fed and miserable. An air of menace and gloom hung over the place, and I wondered how I was ever going to survive several years interned within, and if I did survive, what my mental state would be like at the end of it all.

As we waited in a corridor of the administration block, a prison officer passed, dressed in the blue, short-sleeved shirt worn by functionaries of the Ministry of Justice. He was clutching an armful of evil-looking, obviously homemade, knives, some of which were more than a foot long. His attitude towards his haul appeared similar to that of a school janitor who has confiscated a bunch of catapults, exuding a sense of "the lads have been a bit naughty again" as he walked along, wryly shaking his head.

Any remaining optimism about the nature of the place that we had just entered vanished a few minutes later when a tall, blond, skeletal European, dressed in little more than rags, his face drawn from the effects of hunger and stress, approached us and exclaimed, in a distinctively Danish accent, "Welcome to Hell!"

"We have got a bit of a war on, at the moment," he added "between the two sides of the prison. Try and get yourselves into Pavilion Four. That's where the more peaceable people live."

Already, I could feel myself longing for the unrelenting boredom of my cell in DISIP. This was "first day at school" multiplied by a factor of several hundred, and we had not the remotest idea how one went about trying to get into Pavilion 4, in this strange and hostile environment and with our rudimentary knowledge of the language.

The next person to pass by was someone we recognised: Mr Weller, the Honorary British Consul, who was on a routine visit to the British subjects detained in the prison. "I'll see you two once you have completed all the admission formalities," he said, "and then I'll introduce you to the rest of the British prisoners."

The procedures did not take long, as they simply entailed being photographed, fingerprinted, and a rudimentary file being created for each of us, containing basic information about our nationality, dates of birth, nature of offence and length of sentence. We were then taken to the room where the Consul had gathered the remaining British prisoners, following which we were to have an interview with the prison social worker before joining the rest of the inmates in what we had now learnt, with some relief, would indeed be Pavilion Four.

There were four men and three women in the room with Mr Weller, and the atmosphere, as well as the appearance of those people, acted to further confirm the growing impression of being in a dreadful place. Although the group seemed superficially to be in high spirits, happy to be receiving mail as well as money sent by relatives or by Prisoners Abroad, and further buoyed up by meeting new people, there was an almost tangible tension and the evidence of strain and deprivation was clear on the faces of those who had been in the prison for some time. The hopelessness and lack of purpose visible in their eyes was chilling. Was I, I wondered, gazing into my own future?

There was mail for both Denis and me, which we hurried to open. This was the second time since our arrest that mail had got through to us, and it was a huge boost to morale to know that there were people out there who cared for us and were willing to maintain the contact in spite of all that had happened. Particularly cheering for me was a letter from my friend Robin, in Scotland, a colleague when I was based in an outdoor centre who now worked in a maintenance squad for Scottish Hydro Electric.

Robin reported that he was organising a "support group" of former workmates and acquaintances, who would each contribute to a fund so that they could send money to me each month to allow me to buy food and other basic essentials. This support was to continue throughout the following years, and helped me to survive the Venezuelan prison regime. Equally important was the psychological boost from this support. Perhaps it was inevitable that I should regard it in maritime terms, and thus, in the terrible times that lay ahead, I was to think of it as a lighthouse beacon beaming at me through the darkness of the storm from the other side of the Atlantic, showing me the way home, to safe harbour.

After our meeting with the Consul, Denis and I were taken to see the prison social worker, while the other British prisoners returned to their respective areas. The social worker was a small, heavyset woman who didn't even look up from her desk as she barked a number of questions at us about family relationships and health, while filling in her part of our files. She showed little patience with our inability to understand some of her questions or to convey the replies in a manner that she could readily understand. We left her office feeling even more depressed.

We were now escorted by a prison official, who carried a pump-action shotgun casually resting in the crook of his elbow, across the inner compound to a large gate in one of the perimeter walls, leading to a further compound beyond. At least twenty prisoners were gathered inside this gate, and we had to wait while the wires locking it shut were released from inside before we could enter. As we entered, the prison official turned tail and headed for the offices again, leaving us to our own devices. Passing through the gate, which was quickly shut and secured behind us, we were accosted on all sides by shouts of "Hello, my friend!" and "Cigarette!" Being a smoker, I had some with me, but maintained enough presence of mind to reply, "Yes, please!" leaving the erstwhile beggars bewildered. Point one in the psychological battle for survival had just been scored and at a crucial juncture.

With some difficulty we pushed our way through the crowd, many of whom were anxious to "assist" with our bags, and headed in the direction of the building we could see in front of us. At this point, George, a tall, skinny, dark-haired young Cockney whom we had earlier met with the other British prisoners, approached and, shouting at the locals to give us peace, escorted us through the open steel door near the right-hand end of the single storey building, along a narrow corridor, and into a cell fitted with three bunk beds. He bolted the door of the cell from the inside, inviting us to sit down on one of the bunks and take a breather, which we were more than glad to do, feeling frightened and traumatised by our first contact with the locals in large numbers.

As I took deep breaths, I tried to bring my feelings of "I just can't do this" under control. It was such a blessed relief to be behind a locked door, but I could hear the voices of the locals congregated outside and knew that sooner or later I would have to face them again. When I did, I also knew that I would need to put on a façade of confidence and step out with my head held high, but it seemed so difficult to contemplate when confronted with a mass of the scariest-looking people that it had ever been my misfortune to meet.

Cockney George began to tell us something about the way in which the place operated. "The guards have fuck-all to do with what goes on in the compounds," he told us. "Everything that goes on here is sorted out by the prisoners themselves. You don't want to be seen to have any money on you or the locals will just want to take it off you."

He pointed out that having small amounts of money would lead to constant pestering, and anything over 10,000 bolivars (less than £10) was more than one's life was worth.

"I'll take you to meet a guy who can be trusted to look after your money for you. What you need to do is get credit for things like coffee and ciggies, which are all you can buy here anyway, apart from drugs. Then you can pay a lump sum when no-one is about. Don't go alone to any of the quieter parts of the prison 'cos all the locals carry knives, and there's guns all over the place, some homemade and others factory made."

He then told us, with particular emphasis, that we should at all times of the day and night have shorts, T-shirt and a pair of trainers to hand, and put them on and be ready to run should we hear the call "Agua Verde" (literally "Green Water") being shouted around the compound. This was the signal that the Guardia Nacional troops, normally responsible for external security, were entering the prison on a raid. Their practice was to come in shooting live rounds, and it was wise to run to the assembly point before they deployed around the compound, as latecomers had to run the gauntlet and risked being beaten with ceremonial swords or shot with plastic pellets fired from shotguns. The call "Agua" simply meant that prison officials, known as *vigilantes*, were entering the compound, and could safely be ignored.

None of this was helping in the slightest with my efforts to regain my composure, but he did go on to say that, generally speaking, if one acted discreetly and sensibly, one was safe from physical harm. Food was served three times a day: at 7 a.m., noon, and again at around 4 p.m. It was up to each prisoner to somehow obtain a bowl or plate and eating implements, and then queue at the hole in the kitchen wall through which food was passed out. We were little surprised to learn that the food was generally revolting, and that hygiene standards were deplorable. The ever resourceful George undertook to obtain for us a loan of food bowls and cutlery for the early evening meal, which was due shortly. I asked him not to bother on my account, as I really wasn't feeling hungry.

The next problem was to find us a place to sleep, as it appeared that the prison was full and all available beds taken. We decided to ask around as to what might be available and so we all went out, leaving our bags behind and carefully locking the cell door behind us. The initial excitement of our arrival had dwindled, and only a few people approached us when we went out into the compound, where it was now raining heavily. George took us into the area where he slept, which was through another door in the same building but separated by a dividing wall from the area that we had just left.

He told us that about twenty people slept in this area, which was simply a large, rectangular room with two cells at the top end. Immediately to the left of the doorway was a bricked-in compartment containing a single toilet bowl without lid, seat or cistern, flushed by a constant flow of water from a pipe jutting out of the wall. A valve on this pipe could be turned to force the water further up the pipe, where it emerged above head height to form a rudimentary shower. With an open doorway and no shower curtain, no privacy was afforded to anyone using it.

Built along each wall of the room were tent-like constructions, consisting of bed sheets stretched over a frame made from fencing wire. George explained that these were known as "bugaloos" and showed us the one where he was currently living, shared with another British guy and a German. While those inside obviously slept on their foam mattresses placed on the floor, it did at least provide some privacy and personal space, as well as offering a barrier to the general mass of people who slept on the floor outside.

No space was currently available in a bugaloo but permission was obtained, we knew not from whom, for us to move into this accommodation, where the majority of European prisoners currently lived and where a space would be found for us to sleep on the floor. We arranged to store our bags and, during the day, our mattresses in George's bugaloo.

At this point, the cry of "Rancho!" could be heard resounding around the compound, and Denis went off with George to join the food queue, while I went outside in order to view the proceedings. A solitary official, bearing the ubiquitous shotgun and waving a blunt-edged sword, was trying to organise around one hundred prisoners into some semblance of an orderly line. The majority had their food bowls on their heads, wearing them as hats, and more than a few had simply stripped a banana or palm leaf from one of the many tropical trees scattered around the compound to use as a receptacle for their meal. Some others could be seen rummaging desperately through the hedges bordering the pathways around the compound, clearly searching for food bowls that they had thrown in there after the previous meal. Some shouting and hauling matches broke out in the queue as someone thought he had spotted another person bearing his bowl and that person defended the receptacle as his own.

Suddenly, a group of four prisoners on the roof above the kitchens caught my attention. They were standing behind a bulwark of large stones, concentrating their attention on the far side of the prison. Two guns were in evidence, one clearly homemade and the other a revolver. One of those on the roof now descended to ground level bearing four bowls and shouting, "Garita! Garita!'" He made his way directly to the head of the queue, where he passed the bowls through the hole in the wall into the kitchen. They were quickly returned full and he headed back to below the guard post, balancing his load, and then passed the bowls up to his companions before climbing to join them. I later learned that this post on the roof was one of two *garitas*, or guard posts, in our compound that were manned with an armed guard throughout the daylight hours, when the pavilions were unlocked and the prisoners had access to the compound. They formed part of the measures to prevent attack by the other main compound of the prison, with whom our compound was in a state of permanent war.

The poor souls that we had earlier seen in the inner compound were the refugees from this conflict; the dispossessed who, for one reason or another, had made themselves unacceptable to either side. They slept where they could, ate what no-one else wanted, and were living on borrowed time, aware that either side could take pot shots at them without fear of retaliation from the other side. This group was deeply distrusted by those in both camps, who were aware that, with so little to lose, they were always vulnerable to being utilised by the other side to carry out some desperate deed for the chance of acceptance in one of the compounds.

When the last person had been served at the kitchen hatch, the *vigilante* began to shout and everyone made their way into their respective accommodation. Denis and I hurried to retrieve our bags and mattresses from the cell where we had left them and transfer them to our new abode. The steel door was now closed and locked from the outside by the *vigilante*.

The overcrowding was only too apparent. With twenty-two people milling about the restricted area, there seemed to be scarcely room to breathe and the floor was quickly converted into a sea of mud from the many wet feet following the afternoon's rainfall. We talked for a while to George and his two companions, Fred, another Englishman, and Johann, a German, as we continued our attempts to build up a picture of life in the prison and look for clues that would aid in our survival. Like all foreign prisoners in Venezuela, they were in prison for drug offences. One of the most striking features about our new companions was the air of depression, almost despair, that they gave off. One would hardly expect someone embarking on a long-term prison sentence, particularly in a foreign country, to be happy, but this went much deeper, and I found their level of depression quite alarming. Within a few minutes, our conversation was interrupted by a cry of "Numero", and we all queued inside the door, ready to exit for the evening headcount.

As soon as the door opened, we streamed out and round to the rear of the building, where we lined up around the perimeter of a basketball court. Denis and I had been pre-warned about this procedure and advised to stay near the start of the line, in order to be among the lower, easier to remember, numerals. A Guardia Nacional trooper passed along the line, pointing at each prisoner in sequence, as the prisoners shouted out the successive numbers. Another trooper passed along the line behind the prisoners, waving a *penilla*, or blunt-edged ceremonial sword, ready to strike any prisoner who made a mistake in calling out their number. On this occasion, the count passed without incident and we were quickly dismissed to return to our pavilions, where we would be locked in for the night.

Once locked in again, the prisoners began to relax, some queuing to use the shower whilst others began to reheat their food in a desperate attempt to make it more palatable. At this point, I became aware of the incredible condition of the electrics in the building. Venezuela uses the 110-volt system, and there was one double cable running through the building. From this, dozens of spurs had been led off in all directions, so that each bugaloo, as well as the two cells at the back, had their own power supply. A further lead came down a wall in the main part of the building, for communal use. Each of these leads ended in a length of bare wire, and connecting a light or cooking appliance was done by the simple expedient of hooking its supply cables onto these hooks. As might be imagined, spectacular bangs and flashes were often the result of anything being clipped into this "network", and the whole appeared a fearful fire risk.

Cookers were homemade contrivances, each one consisting of an electric ring mounted on an old paint tin. Spacers, which were again made from old cans with wire handles were used to give a degree of heat control to the cooking process. With these fearsome devices, the locals happily prepared their beloved maize flour bread, or *arepa*, without which they felt that no meal was complete.

I went over to talk to the two remaining Europeans in the block: Frank, an Englishman who looked to be about fifty years old, and Hans, another tall, skeletal Dane and friend of the Danish person who had spoken to us some hours earlier. In addition to his emaciated state, Hans's legs were covered with pockmarks, the result of having been hit by plastic "crowd control" pellets fired from a shotgun. These wounds had festered in the tropical heat and it appeared to me that he would be permanently scarred.

Having been in prison for some time, Frank and Hans were well organised, enjoying the relative comfort of a bunk bed, as well as a TV, and having a cupboard filled with an assortment of cooking pots, plates and bowls, and a two-burner electric stove.

Frank, who came from Crewe, had by this time spent four years in the prison, and seemed happily immersed in self-pity. One of his first questions to me was, "Can you fight?" To which he added, "I hope you can, because you're going to need it here!" Whilst I mumbled some non-committal reply, it was a question that I found oddly reassuring. In my experience, it was not something one was ever asked by anyone versed in the pugilistic arts, but rather stemmed from the false bravado that is so often used in an attempt to cover deeply felt fears. If such a person was able to survive in this environment, it increased my confidence that perhaps I could, too.

Frank always claimed to have psychic powers and a close connection with the spirit world. I for one always wondered why the spirits of people he had known in England only ever came to visit him *after* he had received a letter informing him of their death. It was not unusual for prisoners to claim that they were possessed of psychic powers but it was always a puzzle to me why such people had not managed to avoid arrest in the first place!

A disturbance among the Venezuelans attracted our attention, and we looked outside the bugaloo to see what was going on. A young black Venezuelan, known as Chico, was spread-eagled naked on the floor, being held down by four of his companions while a fifth proceeded to shave his pubic hair. Chico had been complaining of a heat rash that had developed in his crotch and his "friends" had decided that an essential part of his treatment was to remove all body hair from the affected area – using a clearly blunt safety razor. They ignored his howls of protest and chuckled at his discomfort. The remainder of his "treatment" would be to remain unclothed for all but the morning and evening head-count and mealtimes. I was in a world where even the most basic medical facilities and medicines were unavailable.

The steel door to our accommodation was badly deformed, bellying outwards in the centre. This was as a result of having been repeatedly hammered on many occasions with a piece of scaffolding pole kept nearby for the purpose. Apparently this was the only method of summoning aid from the *vigilantes* should someone fall ill during the night, as the duty staff remained in their office on the other side of the prison throughout the night.

Shortly after nine, a half-hearted attempt was made to clean up the mud-spattered floor, and people began to lay their mattresses down for the night. The door was unlocked and opened, and a short, overweight man was ushered inside, preceded by a rank smell of sweat and grease that overcame the already ripe atmosphere of the overcrowded accommodation. He turned out to be Kurt, a German prisoner, who worked in the kitchen. Kurt's entry was met with a barrage of catcalls, which he cheerfully ignored, beaming around in greeting to all and sundry. He was dressed in what had once been a white T-shirt, but which had clearly not met water or soap for some time. Once inside, he began to rummage around inside his equally filthy shorts, from the depths of which he proudly produced two pieces of beefsteak of a distinctly greenish hue, which he then offered up for auction to the highest bidder. Given the doubtful provenance of the goods on sale, and the undoubted horror of their most recent storage, it was hardly surprising that the very few offers he received were derisory, the hunger of his audience notwithstanding.

Having eventually sold the meat to a clearly unscrupulous

buyer, Kurt retrieved his mattress from its storage place above
the toilet wall, rolled it out on the floor, wrapped himself in a
grubby sheet, and was soon fast asleep. I was told that in the
morning, he would be woken half an hour before the morning
head-count, at which time he would simply roll up his mattress
and stow it, then proceed directly to the kitchen in order to
begin his day's work, starting with the preparation of our
breakfast. My stomach turned at the thought of this loathsome
creature handling my food, but I suspected that, by morning,
hunger would force me to overcome my scruples. So it was to
prove, and when I received my food through the hole in the
wall in the future, I simply tried to put out of my mind the
horrors that lay beyond the serving hatch. This process of self
delusion was aided when, two days after my arrival, the
Venezuelan prisoners threw Kurt's mattress outside the door
and refused to allow him to return to our block. Thereafter he
was forced to sleep in the kitchen, along with the other kitchen
workers, and I only caught the occasional glimpse of him in
the distance, invariably dressed in the same filthy garb that he
had worn when I had first clapped eyes upon him.

Most people were by this time settled down for the night,
and so I retrieved my mattress and, finding a clear space on the
floor as far as possible from the odorous Kurt, laid my mattress
down and, using some rolled up clothing as a pillow, lay down.
Before falling asleep, I chatted briefly to my immediate
neighbour, a large, very friendly Venezuelan, who told me that
he was known as Mancho, and had been a fisherman before
being arrested eight months earlier on a charge of murder. I
tried to react to this latest revelation in the same deadpan
manner as it was imparted, and perhaps I succeeded, for over
the following months Mancho was to become my guide,
mentor and protector in the prison, before his own life was
brought to a tragic, dramatic and violent end.

He was an uncomplicated person, with a great zest for life

and a fine sense of mischief, and I appreciated his ability to look one straight in the eye during conversation, which was a trait noticeably lacking in many of my prison companions. In many ways, Mancho was like a child who had never grown up, and it was only the uncontrolled behaviour induced by his addiction to crack cocaine that had led to his incarceration. In many ways, it was his straightforward approach to life, seeing the world in black and white without making allowances for moral uncertainties, that would lead to his demise.

— CHAPTER SIX —

Agua Verde!

BY 5.30 a.m., a few people were starting to rouse themselves, and at 6.00 the door was unlocked and kicked open to the call of "Numero!" We all scrambled for the door and made our way round to the basketball court to parade for the morning roll-call. This passed without incident and we all trooped back to our pavilion, where we were locked in for another hour until we were let out for breakfast at seven.

Breakfast consisted of a cold chocolate drink and two finger rolls of bread, which most people ate outside, in the growing warmth of the tropical morning. I used the time to acquaint myself with more of the European prisoners. As soon as the *vigilante* who had supervised breakfast left the compound, most people from our neighbouring pavilion, number five, were ushered round to join the rest of us in front of Pavilion Four. I learned that this was an unfailing ritual in the daily routine, when only a small number of trusted prisoners were left behind the buildings in order to unearth the bulk of the weapons stores, which were buried each evening before roll-call, then dug up again in the morning for distribution to the guard posts. Only one pistol was routinely kept in each pavilion overnight.

Once access was once more allowed to the rear of the buildings, Fred and I went for a walk to explore the compound. Crossing the basketball court where we paraded for roll-call, we came to a small, fenced-off area of cultivated land, containing banana, coconut palm and mango trees. The ground then rose, and a line of concrete steps took us up to a large building, known as the workshop. Entering, we found about twenty Venezuelans busily working, some carving wood to make cup-holders with cartoon character faces, others constructing folding chairs from strips of wood, and still others hammering away at old catering cans to produce spacers for cookers. The only tools visible were the ubiquitous knives, with stones being used for hammers. In the centre of the room stood an ancient circular saw, without benefit of safety guards. Watching someone attempt to cut a curve into a piece of wood with this fearsome implement was to suffer the anticipation of imminent calamity, and several thumbs were lost or partially severed by that terrible blade each year. Passing out through the main door again, we walked further along the outside of the building and entered a smaller room, where one of the Venezuelans from our block, a young man known as Witchle, was cutting hair. He was just finishing with a customer when we walked in, and finding that the price for a haircut was 500 bolívares, I decided to have a trim. Witchle, another former fisherman, could turn his hand to virtually anything, and was adept at repairing items such as shoes and sandals using the most basic of materials. Addicted to crack cocaine, he would negotiate the highest possible price for his services and was not averse to helping himself to any items left unattended, but I never saw him become violent, relying instead on an inherent charm and wit to extract himself from problems with his peers, as well as to extract cash from anyone whom he thought might be generously disposed towards him.

There were several bugaloos in the workshop, and I learned that these were for use on visit days by those who did not have space in the accommodation to build one. Visits took place on three days each week: Wednesday, Saturday and Sunday, between 9 a.m. and 3 p.m. Saturday and Sunday were family visit days and Wednesday was set aside for conjugal visits. Visits took place within the compounds and visitors, once admitted to the prison, were allowed to wander freely around the grounds and into the accommodation blocks. Visit days were a hugely important part of the prison routine and the pavilions were carefully cleaned in preparation. All prisoners were required to have showered and to wear long trousers, long-sleeved shirts and shoes and socks throughout the visit period, and to behave with due decorum towards each other, and particularly towards visitors. Children could play and run around the grounds in complete safety, as no secret was made of the fact that anyone behaving in an inappropriate manner towards a child would be summarily executed by the other prisoners the moment the last visitor had left.

Leaving the workshop behind, Fred and I continued, walking behind the workshop to a large area of flat waste ground bordered on two sides by a high perimeter fence, with a guard tower in the top corner occupied by a bored Guardia Nacional trooper. No divide existed between the two compounds in this area, and it was across it that any attack from the other side would most likely come. We remained close to the perimeter fence, where we were well out of pistol range of the guard posts on the other side, retracing our steps when we came to the corner. We had now explored the limits of the area which was destined to be my home for the next few years, which extended to about the size of four football pitches, and we returned to the pavilion, buying a coffee from the little café outside our access gate on the way. Of course, this was a cue for half-a-dozen locals to crowd round, asking us to get them a coffee as well, but we managed to fob them off eventually. The area in front of the pavilion was now very busy, as those not involved on the guard posts or working up in the workshop were washing clothes out in the sunshine and draping them to dry on the hedges bordering the paths. There was a single pipe near the bottom of the compound, constantly streaming water, and one person was showering under it while others waited their turn. Those not otherwise engaged were busy sharpening their knives on the kerbstones; the sound of sharpening knives was a constant background noise during my time in the prison.

In the glorious sunshine, it appeared on the surface to be a scene of calm relaxation, but an underlying tension permeated the atmosphere. Those involved in guard duties never for a moment relaxed their vigilance, keeping their guns pointing in the direction of the other compound, with T-shirts tied round their heads to protect from the burning rays of the sun. I was pleased to hear that foreign prisoners were not expected by the small group of prisoners who ran things to take part in guard duties, although we were expected to pay additional money to the fighting fund each month in compensation for this lack of active participation. Money for the fund, known as *apoyo* or "support", was collected from the locals by the gangsters in charge at the end of visit on a Sunday, to the tune of 2,000 bolívares per week, and was apparently used to purchase bullets and occasionally, guns and grenades. Foreign prisoners were "taxed" at a rate of 15,000 bolívares, about £15, per month. Anyone not paying without reasonable excuse would be dispatched to the other side of the prison.

As we entered our pavilion, we were approached by Julio, the young Venezuelan prisoner in charge of our accommodation block. He produced a gun from behind his back, pointed it at my head, cocked it, and carefully pronounced the words in English, "Give me money." I took the fact that he had spoken in English as a clue that he was probably not being serious and struggled to keep my face impassive, although it was extremely difficult with the business end of a loaded revolver inches from my face.

"I no have money," I managed to say.

His face broke into a smile, as he slowly released the hammer and returned the gun to his waistband. He then walked off, chuckling and saying, "You no have fucking money, that too fucking bad, man." As I slowly recovered from the shock, I hoped that, if it had been some kind of test, then I had passed. I later became aware that it was a game that Julio liked to play from time to time, with foreigners and Venezuelans alike, and it was not made any more reassuring when, a few months later, he one day managed to shoot himself in the leg whilst playing with the gun in his room.

On the morning of my second day in the prison, I was sitting in the morning sun shortly after breakfast when I heard the call "agua verde" being shouted from the roof, and all the prisoners in the compound exploded into action. The guards on the roof scrambled down and rushed to hide their weapons, while everyone else made a dash for their accommodation in order to don trainers before returning outside to join the stream of people making their way round to the back of the building to assemble on the basketball court. Within minutes, shots could be heard as the Guardia Nacional entered the prison, firing as they came. By the time we had all assembled on the basketball court, the soldiers were in the compound, close behind us, and they began shouting, indicating that we were to run to another sports pitch at the rear of the prison, behind the "enemy" compound.

Everyone began to run in that direction, only to find that the soldiers had cut between the buildings and were waiting in ambush on the path. Some swiped with their swords at passing prisoners, while others randomly fired pump-action shotguns to encourage prisoners to run faster. The effect was terrifying, and as I ran I was only able to gather fleeting impressions of what was going on. Prisoners desperately swerved and dodged to avoid being hit by swords or peppered with crowd control pellets fired from the shotguns. The Guardia Nacional troops seemed to be everywhere and it was difficult to pick a clear route through them. They were very clearly enjoying their sport.

Reaching the sports field, I saw that those who had already arrived were sitting in rows on the concrete surface. I spotted a few faces that I knew on one side of the pitch and hurried to join them. As the last prisoners arrived, the soldiers began to shout at us to keep our heads down and to bunch up closer to the person in front, until our legs overlapped their bodies. Anyone raising their head was beaten with a sword, and thumps and yelps could he heard from various points around us. The next command was to remove our clothing and lay it beside us, all without changing position or raising our heads. The soldiers now moved around the prisoners, organising the rows in order to facilitate a head-count, using their boots and rifle butts indiscriminately to encourage the naked prisoners to shuffle into the required positions.

Once the count was completed to their satisfaction, troops began to make their way among the prisoners, randomly selecting piles of clothes that they submitted to detailed searches. The whole process took about an hour, while the tropical sun beamed down unmercifully on our naked bodies. One of the most frightening things for me was not knowing what would happen next. The arbitrary nature of the brutality was horrendous.

Eventually it came to an end and one row of prisoners at a time was ordered to stand up, get dressed, and run back to their quarters. We entered our pavilion to find a scene of destruction. Clearly, one group of troops had been busy in our accommodation while the other was occupied with us. Bugaloos were in ruins, their sheets having been torn down, and the contents of lockers and bags had been emptied over the floor. Several holes had been dug into the walls, presumably in search of arms caches. With all prisoners now inside, the door was slammed shut and locked, and with a few half-hearted grumbles, people set to, to restore order from amongst the chaos. Obviously my companions were well used to this treatment, and regarded it as routine.

I, on the other hand, was incensed, both by the treatment meted out to us personally and the unnecessary havoc wreaked upon our living quarters. It was difficult for me to accept that this kind of thing could go on, at the beginning of the twenty-first century. People had so little, and it was therefore utterly galling to see such things as flour, sugar and coffee scattered on the floor and thereby ruined.

Once I had my own bits and pieces packed away, I joined Frank and Hans, who offered to share a joint of marijuana with me. I accepted, feeling that something to help calm me down after the morning's excitement would be most welcome, and began to question them as to whether what we had just gone through was the norm whenever a *raqueta*, as these searches were known, took place.

"Oh," said Frank, "that was quite a mild one compared with the usual. They behaved themselves quite well today."

Hans nodded his agreement.

Outraged by this notion, I asked if no-one ever took action to put a stop to this behaviour, as it was unacceptable in modern times for people in prison to suffer this abuse.

"You couldn't risk anything like that," asserted Frank, while Hans again nodded in accord. "It would be suicide. If the Guardia realise that someone has been complaining about them, they'll just come in at night, with balaclavas on, and do away with those responsible. You don't know what it's like here; I do, 'cos I've been here four years, you know."

Recognising that their fear was genuine, I decided to do nothing for the moment and keep my own counsel. I felt, however, that sooner or later we would have to take a stand, as improvements in human rights situations had never been brought about by people quietly accepting the barbarous treatment meted out to them by those in authority.

That nothing had been achieved by the destruction was evident, as all around the pavilion people were unearthing their hoards of drugs and lighting up, while Julio was busy cleaning his gun, whose hiding place in the pavilion had already survived countless searches. It was apparently very rare for drugs to be found during *raquetas*, and almost unheard of for weapons or ammunition to be discovered.

A little over an hour later, the door was unlocked and opened, and we were allowed out for lunch. The pavilions remained open for the rest of the day and "normal" life was resumed within the compound.

Within a short period, the behaviour of the Guardia towards us became so outrageous that I was to decide to take action, regardless of the risks.

OVER THE DAYS following the *raqueta*, I continued to familiarise myself with the prison. The more I did so, the more I realised that it resembled what I had read about prisoner of war camps much more than it did anything that I knew about prisons. The inmates were left to their own devices day after day, with the only interest the authorities showed in them being the prevention of escape, confirmed by the head-counts at the beginning and end of each day. Prisoners pottered away all day on make-work exercises of their own invention, and the main activity which gave a focus and a *raison d'etre* to many was, ironically enough, the state of hostilities existing between the two sides of the prison.

Many prisoners were serving extremely long sentences, some as long as thirty years, and even those on shorter sentences had no real idea when they would be released, due to the chaotic nature of the administration of sentences. A large number of prisoners were awaiting sentence, and many of those had been in the prison for up to two years. At least two that I knew of had been held in the prison for three years without ever having appeared in court.

The fact that suicide was extremely rare was probably due to an irrepressible optimism that is a character trait in South American people in general and Venezuelans in particular. Almost all believed that better things were just round the corner, that the President would declare an amnesty on the next Prisoners' Day/Christmas/Easter/Independence Day, that the National Assembly would bring out new laws declaring much shorter sentences and that these would be applied retrospectively. This last hope was held against all logic, at a time when the number one concern of citizens throughout Venezuela was the high level of insecurity, violence and crime in all parts of the country. There was no realistic chance that any government hopeful of re-election would bring in legislation whose principal effect would be the release of a large number of offenders to roam the streets once more.

Unfortunately these misplaced hopes, together with a well-founded fear of the Guardia Nacional, based on several well publicised massacres carried out in Venezuelan prisons combined with an equally misplaced macho pride in putting up with atrocious conditions and beatings without complaint, predisposed the native prisoners not to challenge the conditions in which they were held, nor the treatment meted out to them by those in authority. Prison was hell, always had been and always would be; the only salvation lay in getting back outside as quickly as possible, to which end, God willing, El Presidente would soon be signing an amnesty.

It was an attitude that I found deeply frustrating, being already convinced that the brutality of the guards needed to be challenged and that the most successful way of doing it would be with the full support of all sectors of the prison population.

After three days in the prison, I experienced my first visit day. The atmosphere of the prison was completely transformed as women and children streamed in to the compound, laden with bags of groceries, and the whole place took on a gala atmosphere for a few hours. About one third to one half of prisoners received visits, while the remainder maintained constant guard on the rooftops or hung around the peripheries. The lunch was generally better than usual on visit days, typically chicken drumsticks with rice, but foreign prisoners had little chance to obtain a meal on these days as visitors were given priority at the serving hatch, followed by the prison hard men, with the result that there was usually little left by the time foreign prisoners were allowed to pass forward in the queue. To protest was useless, if not downright dangerous, as raised voices were regarded as "showing a lack of respect for visitors", which was considered a major infringement of the code of behaviour within the prison.

As soon as the last visitor had left the compound, the drug addicts among the Venezuelans began to make their way round the compound, offering for sale at bargain basement prices items brought to them by their visitors, such as toothpaste, toilet rolls, soap, coffee, food on occasion and, from time to time, articles of clothing. While the prices were undoubtedly very low, there was always a hidden cost to buying such items. If one bought a tube of toothpaste, for instance, the result was that the seller now knew that one had toothpaste, while he had none, and so he would appear each morning armed with toothbrush, requesting a gift of "just a little toothpaste". To refuse such a reasonable request was to be loudly denounced as an egotistical, uncaring swine, totally unconcerned for the wellbeing of fellow prisoners, and having no regard for the concept of *convivencia*, which translates literally as "living together" and was used to describe the idea of sharing and mutual support deemed to be necessary within the prison. While it is a laudable concept, it seemed from my experience to be very much a one-way street in the relationship between Venezuelans and foreign prisoners. While it is true that, generally speaking, we Europeans were better off than the great majority of local prisoners, there were a number of Venezuelans who were considerably better off than we were due to the degree of family support that they enjoyed, and these were not noted for their generosity towards their fellow inmates.

Purchases had to be carried out with great care, with goods on offer being examined minutely, as a bottle of shampoo for instance might be watered down and sold as three bottles to the unsuspecting. The Sale of Goods Act most certainly did not apply. Each day was an endless, gruelling round of negotiation and counter-negotiation as one struggled to acquire and maintain a small supply of the basic necessities of life in the midst of what seemed to be a global conspiracy to deprive one of such items.

At the end of visit on a Sunday, an unnatural quiet would settle over the prison as the ledger was produced and each Venezuelan prisoner was required to produce his 2000 bolivar payment for *apoyo*, or a very good explanation as to why it could not be paid that week. At the same time, the drug dealers and coffee sellers were busy collecting their debts, and it was always a time of great tension as prisoners tried to juggle their limited resources in such a way as to keep everyone reasonably happy. Heaven help the unfortunate creature who did not pay his *apoyo* and was then spotted a few hours later buying drugs for cash.

Almost invariably on Sunday afternoons, several volleys of shots would be fired from the roof in the general direction of the other side of the prison, to convey the message that stocks of ammunition had once more been replenished and that we were well equipped with the means to defend ourselves against any attack. We would then wait, with bated breath, expecting a reaction from the Guardia Nacional in the form of a *raqueta*. These very rarely materialised, however, the Guardia seeming to accept the Sunday shooting as a routine part of prison life. I grew to particularly dread Sunday afternoons due to the terrible air of menace that hung over the compound and the tortured expectation of a raid by the Guardia.

During my second week in the prison, the water supply was suddenly cut off without warning. In the unbearable heat this was an incredible deprivation, and no indication was given as to when we might receive a water supply again. No alternative arrangements were made and we simply had to do without, when it was normally necessary to drink at least two to three litres daily to counteract dehydration. On the second day, some locals began to take water from a stagnant pool below the workshop, boiling the water on their improvised stoves before letting it cool and then drinking it. I avoided this desperate measure, although I knew that if the stoppage lasted one more day, I too would have to resort to it in order to get some fluid into my body. On the evening of the second day, the water was turned on again, but had a vivid green colour for a further two days. I used a clean T-shirt folded several times to strain the water and then boiled it thoroughly before drinking it, not knowing what the effects of drinking this vile-tasting liquid would be but desperately needing to re-hydrate. Fortunately I suffered no ill effects, but Fred and Johann both became extremely ill with dysentery and took many weeks to recover.

One evening, Mancho began smoking crack cocaine, spending whatever money he had accumulated and, in the nature of that terrible drug, feeling he needed more. He sidled over to me, and said, "Capitan, I need two thousand bolivars." I replied that I had no money, at which point he produced his extremely large knife and began to wave it menacingly in my direction.

"I need two thousand bolivars," he repeated.

"I don't have it," I replied, attempting to remain calm and not show fear of the knife. He continued to menace me for about ten minutes, before giving up and heading to the other end of the accommodation.

Next morning, when I confronted Mancho about his behaviour of the night before, he broke down in tears as he apologised, saying, "I'm sorry Capitan, you have always been right with me. I should never have behaved like that. It will never happen again."

I replied, "Hey, it happened, and it's over, let's forget it."

Mancho never again threatened me in any way, even when he was extremely high on crack cocaine, and he became more than ever my devoted shadow.

Not long after I entered the prison, Frank and Hans had a falling out, and Hans decided to move next door to live with his compatriot. Naturally, he took all his belongings with him. I was amazed to see that when he had done so, Frank was reduced to possessing only the mattress upon which he slept. I had assumed that the possessions in their bugaloo had been accumulated jointly over the years, and could not believe that Frank had spent four years in prison and made no attempt to gather together even the basic necessities to make life tolerable.

Several days later, I experienced a *raqueta* much more along the lines of brutality that Frank had described. Following the fatal stabbing of a prisoner in our compound, the Guardia entered. This time, our assembly point was the basketball court within our own compound, and we all quickly sat down in the far corner. As usual, the troops came in shooting, but when they appeared round the corner of the building, it was clear that they had assembled and entered in a hurry. They were dressed in an assortment of military uniform, and one was actually dressed in T-shirt, shorts and flip-flops. The sight of that particular figure, running full tilt towards us firing his FAL automatic rifle as he came, was terrifying. If he was to trip over his totally unsuitable footwear, he would be spraying 7.62 rounds directly into the assembled prisoners.

Fortunately, he maintained his footing and the rest of the *raqueta* followed the now familiar routine: being ordered to strip off, then kicked and beaten into ranks in a sitting position for a head-count. Once they were satisfied with the numbers, we were left to be guarded by four troops, while the remainder headed into the accommodation in order to wreak their usual destruction.

One feature of every *raqueta* was the behaviour of the two dogs that the prisoners had in the compound, a bitch called Nina and a dog called Tom. At the first hint of a *raqueta*, Tom would scurry off with his tail between his legs, emerging from his hiding place behind the workshop only when it was all over. Nina, on the other hand, who seemed to have a lot of Border collie characteristics, would remain among the ranks of prisoners, barking and snarling her defiance at the troops, and frequently had to be restrained from rushing out and attacking them.

That same night, we were woken shortly after midnight for yet another *raqueta*, which was a frightening affair. We were herded out of our block into a darkness only relieved by the beams of torches and the muzzle flashes of rifles and shotguns. The soldiers had lined along the path before opening the door and were thus able to beat almost everyone passing with their swords as we ran round the building to the assembly point.

Following this latest incident, I again approached Frank, as the British prisoner with most experience.

"Listen Frank, I think we've got to do something about this. We can't just sit back and take this kind of abuse. I'm going to write a report to Prisoners Abroad, with a copy to the embassy. Someone needs to know what these guys are up to."

Frank was adamant that what I proposed was the wrong approach.

"All you'd be doing is sticking your head in a noose. The Guardia will not put up with anyone making complaints against them. I know what it's like. You're just new here. Anyway, nobody out there cares about us. We could all be killed tomorrow and nobody would give a damn. At the end of the day, you can do what you like, but don't ask me to sign anything. I'm having nothing to do with it."

I decided to leave Frank to wallow in his misery and proceed on my own, so I wrote a letter to the London-based charity, Prisoners Abroad, which had been set up to assist British citizens imprisoned overseas, copied to the consul in Caracas and detailing some of the abuses we had suffered since my arrival at the end of July. Having explained what I was trying to do to the boss among the prisoners, a guy known as Miguel, who had recently returned to the prison following a period "in exile" in the prison colony of El Dorado, I managed to collect thirty signatures for this report, most of them from Venezuelans. This letter was sent off with the rest of the mail during the consular visit towards the end of August.

Some form of action seemed to have been taken, as shortly afterwards, the British prisoners from our compound were taken to the director's office, where present was the lieutenant in command of the Guardia Nacional detachment at the prison. The director promised us that things would improve, and that they were very conscious of human rights issues. The lieutenant, who chain smoked throughout the meeting and had a noticeable nervous twitch below his right eye, assured us that he was totally against violence. We were all too astonished at this outrageous falsehood to be able to formulate any kind of suitable reply in Spanish, and so confined ourselves to nodding sagely.

It was noticeable however that over the following few weeks we endured four *raquetas*, during which no prisoners were beaten, and we began to feel that perhaps we were making some progress.

Around this time, Johann, the German prisoner who shared a bugaloo with Fred and George, came up with what seemed to me a reasonable plan. He suggested that we make a bid for European prisoners to be housed apart, immediately outside the exterior wall of the prison but within the perimeter fencing. There was a disused military barracks there which would be suitable for accommodation, and we could convert the surrounding land into a communal farm, producing a reasonable percentage of our food requirements. It would be a vast improvement in our situation, at one stroke removing us from the violence and bloodshed within the prison, placing us in living quarters that we could maintain to our own standards, relieving us of some of our dependence on the dreadful food prepared in the prison kitchens, and give us healthy and productive work to do. It seemed to us that all this could be achieved with very little disruption to the prison organisation or routine.

Having thrashed the scheme around at length and ironed out the details in so far as that was possible, it was decided that I should produce a proposal for presentation to the prison director. I wrote out the details in English and then proceeded to painstakingly translate them into Spanish. Several of us asked for a meeting with the director and handed him the plan for a prison farm in which to house Europeans. He seemed enthusiastic about the idea and promised that he would take it to his superiors and let us know the result.

Unfortunately, a few days later he called us into his office again to let us know that the proposal had been turned down by the authorities in charge of the prison, largely as a result of security concerns expressed by the Guardia Nacional. Our friend, the non-violent lieutenant, had clearly been at work. We were greatly disappointed, as the idea that we might be able to resolve the dangers and difficulties that we faced on a daily basis had buoyed us all up for a couple of weeks.

For some unknown reason, George at this time had a difference of opinion with his companions, resulting in his creating an individual bugaloo in his portion of the previously large bugaloo. A week later, he decided to move to the kitchen to live and work, and offered his bugaloo to me for the grand sum of 3,500 bolivars, about £3.50. I was more than pleased to buy it at that price, and delighted in the increased degree of privacy offered, although it contained only enough room for me to stretch out my mattress, and no more.

My pal Mancho obtained some whitewash from somewhere, painted the walls, and for a small sum made me a folding wooden seat. I then gave a visitor some money to bring me in a ventilator fan to somewhat reduce the stifling heat. Mancho took to sleeping in the doorway of my newly acquired bugaloo, thus earning himself the rather unkind sobriquet "Rover" from the other British prisoners.

On September 22, following an exchange of fire between the two compounds, a particularly vicious and frightening *raqueta* took place. Over the years, people from rival gangs on the island of Margarita had been imprisoned in San Antonio and had naturally drifted to opposite sides of the prison, where they maintained an armed standoff against each other. From time to time, this erupted into full-scale confrontation. What follows is a letter that I wrote the following day and sent to the Consul in Caracas, describing the events, and pleading for action to be taken to end the abuses by the Guardia Nacional.

Reten Judicial de San Antonio
23.9.00
Jackie de Laraburre
HM. Cónsul
Caracas

Dear Jackie,

Treatment of Prisoners in San Antonio

Further to previous correspondence and discussions on this subject, I wish to draw to you attention the horrifying events of yesterday, which once more highlight the perilous situation in which British subjects held prisoner here find themselves.

Mid-morning, with the situation otherwise quiet, a brief exchange of fire took place between prisoners in the 'guard post' on the roof of our building, and those on the other side of the establishment.

Immediately, the siren was sounded to summon the Guardia Nacional personnel into the prison, and to alert all that a raqueta was about to take place.

On hearing the siren, all prisoners in our compound assembled in the corner of the sports pitch which is our assembly point, and sat quietly there for some minutes, presumably while the Guardia detail gathered, prior to entering the prison. A number of shots were then heard, coming from the approaches to our compound. There were a mixture of weapons being fired; semi-automatic rifles, pistols and shotguns. Further rounds appeared to originate from the perimeter guard towers. All the prisoners were seated, huddled together, when Guardia Nacional personnel appeared around the corner of our accommodation block, continuing to fire as they approached. Shotguns were aimed into the group, firing 'crowd control' plastic pellets. By this time, all had thrown themselves flat on the ground and were trying to protect their faces from those hazardous projectiles, but the firing continued.

Orders were shouted to move into the centre of the area in a running crouch, and to sit down, immediately followed by instructions to strip off, and then lay down again.

Once all were naked, instructions were shouted to move some metres away from our clothes, at a running crouch, then lay face down again on the scorching surface. Throughout this period, shots continued to be fired, to punctuate the instructions and encourage alacrity in carrying them out. A number of prisoners were hit by pellets, fortunately none seriously injured.

Most prisoners suffered burns from the hot surface during the half-hour or so we were kept in this position, with threats that anyone raising their head would be shot.

Towards the end of this period, small groups of prisoners were picked out and ordered to return to their clothes and dress, and then sit down. Once all were dressed, we were kept for a further hour or so while the buildings and grounds were searched, before being told to return to our quarters, where we were locked in for the remainder of the day, except to collect our lunch and dinner, and attend roll-call, or 'numero'.

On both occasions that we left our quarters for meals, we were supervised as normal by two vigilantes with their shotguns. All prisoners quietly collected their food, and returned to the pavilions.

Come evening numero however, a sizeable group of the Guardia Nacional were waiting in ambush at the corner of the building, some pointing rifles directly at the passing prisoners, while others struck at them with their swords. A large number of people, including one European, were beaten as they ran past. Further intimidation of this nature took place as prisoners were instructed to run back to their quarters.

This morning, normal routine was established, and Saturday visiting, with families, including babes in arms, roaming freely around the grounds. That in itself lends a surreal quality to the whole experience, which in my view is as psychologically damaging as any other part of it.

It is very frightening to be in the situation where your life is in the hands of excitable, undisciplined, trigger-happy apologies for military personnel, whose weapons training leaves a great deal to be desired.

If there was a really serious incident within the prison, I have little doubt, following yesterday's events, that the reaction of the Guardia Nacional would lead to a blood bath. In any event, an incident such as yesterday's can easily end with someone being accidentally shot, as was demonstrated when a stray bullet entered the kitchens and ricocheted around the room, narrowly missing at least one person.

A report of yesterday's incident has been passed to Prisoners Abroad and to Amnesty International.

I personally feel so threatened following these dreadful events, that I have prepared letters to be dispatched to friends and loved ones in the event of my death here. You should receive these under separate cover. I have encouraged other foreign prisoners to do the same, and I believe that a considerable number are so concerned that they intend to do this.

It has often been claimed, following the kind of tragedy that is a constant threat here, that 'we had no idea that the situation was so serious'. It is my intention to ensure that no-one in any position to influence our situation here can make that claim following the event.

I urge you to take whatever action is possible, and to seek assistance from whatever bodies, national or international, as required, to ameliorate the dangerous situation that we face here.

Thank you in anticipation of your attention to this matter.

Yours sincerely
Donald MacNeil

Two weeks after this incident, the British prisoners were again called to the director's office for a meeting, together with the

Guardia Nacional lieutenant. We had barely begun to talk when we were interrupted by the arrival of a number of officials. They turned out to be the colonel in command of the Guardia Nacional in Margarita, a public prosecutor, a police chief, a forensic doctor and a police photographer. They had entered the prison to investigate the treatment of prisoners by the Guardia troops. "We will prosecute, if we find evidence of human rights abuses," they announced. We never did learn the outcome of their inquiries, but that same evening, half a dozen of the Guardia troops who usually dealt with us had been replaced and we did not see them again. It appeared that history was being made.

These events were to have an effect on the attitude of the other inmates towards foreign prisoners. The leaders among the Venezuelans, who were essentially gang leaders within their own communities on the island who had brought their methods of operating into the prison with them, began to regard the Europeans with greater respect, and it was made clear to all that any abuse of European prisoners would be severely sanctioned by the "management" and the perpetrator banished to live on the other side of the prison. It seemed that on several fronts, things were beginning to improve.

CHAPTER SEVEN

We'll Be Home
By Christmas

THE SITUATION REMAINED stable in the prison over the following few weeks. The lieutenant tried a new tactic during the next *raqueta* that took place after the official investigation of abuses. Once we were all sitting naked on the basketball court, he ordered all foreign prisoners to stand up and move forward, before sitting us down again with our backs to the other prisoners. We did as we were ordered, wondering what new devilment was in store. Once we were sat down, with two soldiers to guard us and to ensure that we remained facing forwards, we could hear the remaining troops moving among the Venezuelan prisoners, the thuds of blows being struck and shouts of pain from among the prisoners.

Incensed by this outrage, I afterwards spread the word that, during any future *raquetas*, foreign prisoners would refuse to move, responding that, "If you are going to beat my companions, you will have to beat me as well." Clearly, word of this must have got back to the lieutenant, as it was designed to, because he never tried to repeat that particular exercise, and the routine beating of prisoners, as well as the random firing of live rounds by the Guardia during *raquetas*, was, to all intents and purposes, brought to an end.

Meantime, though, tensions between the two sides of the prison began to escalate. Exchanges of fire between the opposing guard posts increased, and, in the first week in November a shot from the other side reached its mark and hit one of the prisoners on our guard post. As they were operating at the maximum range of their weapons, however, the bullet hit him in the chest with only sufficient force to break the skin. Within the hour, a bullet from our side hit one of the sentries on the other side in the hip, with such force that he had to be hospitalised. The tension within the prison became unbearable, as we simply had no idea what would happen next. At any given moment, we expected one side or the other to launch a full-scale attack or for the Guardia Nacional to enter the prison and run amok.

On the Wednesday of that week, the consul visited, and while he was chatting to two or three British prisoners in the inner compound prior to moving to the offices, a shot rang out above our heads. Mr Weller scuttled off to the offices as fast as his legs could carry him, and was clearly extremely anxious to do what he had to do and then get out of the prison as quickly as possible.

When we returned from the consular visit, we were told that one of the prisoners in our compound had suffered a heart attack during our absence. I was amazed to learn that no attempt had been made to resuscitate this man, who had simply been loaded onto a stretcher trolley and wheeled out of the compound by the *vigilantes* before being taken to hospital, where he was declared dead on arrival.

On the Friday evening, it was noticeable that the Guardia troops who entered, led by the lieutenant, for *numero* were dressed in old, worn battle fatigues. As soon as we were locked into our pavilions after the head-count we discovered the reason, when they all climbed onto the roof and began to dismantle the guard post, hurling what seemed to be tons of rocks onto the ground below. This concerned us greatly, as it further increased the likelihood of an attack by the prisoners from the other side.

As soon as the pavilions were opened in the morning, work began at feverish pace on the rebuilding of the guard post; dozens of prisoners scurrying around and passing up rocks to the roof and bearing a startling resemblance to ants repairing a disturbed nest. Within half an hour, the work was half finished, at which point the lieutenant, together with three of his troops, entered the compound. Two of the troops climbed onto the roof and began to demolish the structure once more, while the lieutenant and the remaining trooper kept the prisoners at bay at rifle point.

Having completed their demolition, the military personnel left the compound, upon which work began with renewed vigour to replace what they had removed. This time, though, before the work was complete, a shot from the other side hit one of the young prisoners involved in the construction process on the roof. He was fortunate in that the bullet entered his belly on the right side and exited on the left without penetrating too deeply or making contact with any vital organs, as he was able to walk, with a little aid, to the offices, where arrangements were made to take him to hospital. He returned to the prison later the same day, patched up and apparently none the worse for his injury. Meanwhile, angry representations to the prison director over the provocative and dangerous actions of the lieutenant and his men led to the director granting permission for the guard post to remain. By lunchtime it was completed, and an uneasy peace settled over the prison once more.

AROUND THIS TIME, a small hunger strike took place, when twenty-two of the Venezuelan prisoners decided that they had had enough of waiting for liberty that they felt was overdue. It lasted for eight days, at the end of which four of them were released and the remainder were promised that their cases would be quickly processed.

During the strike, they were held in separate accommodation, taking only water, sweetened tea or coffee, and boiled sweets. They made the most of their status, announcing after the second day that they were too weak to emerge for the twice daily head-count, thus obliging the Guardia troops to enter and count them within the building. On the first visit day after the strike began, dramatic swooning was the order of the day, and the stretcher trolley was in constant demand to wheel comatose patients across to the doctor's office.

The building in which they were housed was the church, a small accommodation block between our pavilion and the kitchen. It was normally home to its congregation, who slept there as well as using it for their twice daily evangelistic services. Members of the church lived under a set of particular rules. Participation in the various services was compulsory and they were not allowed to use foul language, smoke or consume drugs. No weapons were allowed into the building, to the extent that even the prisoners' leaders would temporarily deposit their pistols or knives with someone if obliged for some reason to enter the church.

Whenever outside the building, church members were obliged to at all times carry with them a Bible. This served as a symbol of their status and protected them from any form of abuse by the other prisoners. The penalties for attacking a member of the church were grave. During *raquetas*, church members would wave their Bibles at the Guardia Nacional troops, but these were not above beating them just the same. I was oddly reminded of the stories of sailors in times gone by ordering crucifixion scenes to be tattooed across their backs in a vain attempt to avoid the scourge of the lash.

During November, the already overcrowded prison began

to fill up still more, apparently as an exercise to clear out Margarita Island's police stations in the run-up to Christmas. Quite a number of foreign nationals entered San Antonio that month. They were largely of Dutch origin, and mainly black, but all spoke English, which helped a great deal to relieve our sense of isolation. Introducing them to the prison was a useful distraction from the monotony of daily life.

With the new arrivals, there came a strange phenomenon; the propagation of silly rumours. The principal, and most persistent, was that all foreign prisoners were to be thrown out of the country on December 15 and returned to their countries of origin. This rumour originated from a Dutch prisoner who spoke some Spanish and claimed to have heard the measure being announced by the President on the television. Much as I wished to believe such news, I found it hard to accept, particularly as nothing was ever said about it by the locals, some of whom had access to television sets. I pointed out to all who would listen that I found it very strange that locals were still happy to extend credit for such items as coffee and cigarettes, which would hardly be the case if they felt that we were all about to be spirited away within a few weeks. Nothing I could say, however, would alter the conviction of the majority of foreign prisoners that salvation was just round the corner.

As a means of exploring this new phenomenon, I decided to seed a rumour of my own, to the effect that the Venezuelan Government had been considering the cost of the exercise and had concluded that it would prove too expensive to fly us all back to Europe. They had therefore decided to charter a large yacht, and I was to be asked to skipper it and deliver the foreign prisoners back to Europe. Sure enough, not four hours had gone by before someone came charging into my bugaloo, in a state of high excitement, to announce this "news". It was definitely true, because "everyone knew about it"!

Over the following days, I was consulted by various people on such aspects of the voyage as the expected length of the trip, the weather to be encountered *en route*, and the most effective cures for seasickness.

"Cappy. Will I be able to take my suitcase with me?"

"What happens if it rains?"

"I've never been on a boat before, I might get seasick!"

I expect that my reply that the single most effective remedy for seasickness is to sit quietly beneath a tree did little to relieve the confusion.

As December 15 approached, and it became clear to even the most hopeful or deluded that no deportation was imminent, there was yet no sign of the deep disappointment that I expected among the foreign prisoners. Instead, word went round that there had been unexpected delays in implementing the deportation order, and the entire exercise had been put back until January 15. It is possibly a measure of the horror of our situation that people found reality too bleak to contemplate and were instead content to put faith in hopes and dreams, no matter how unlikely, much as a drowning man might clutch in desperation at a straw in order to try to save himself.

A deep sense of disappointment was felt by the group of British prisoners at the beginning of December, when we were visited by the consul from the embassy in Caracas. Her first announcement on meeting the assembled group of anxious and expectant prisoners was, "I'm afraid I've got bad news for you. I had Christmas parcels from home for several of you, but I'm sorry to say that they were stolen from my car shortly after I arrived on the island." She did not have a list of the packages that had been lost, so that no-one knew what, if anything, they had missed out on.

I do not think that consular officials ever had a true appreciation of what their visits meant to us. While it might be argued, with justification, that we were a group of convicted criminals serving time for a crime that society abhors, it is also true to say that we were a group of human beings in a desperate situation, maltreated, malnourished, fearful for our future and even for our lives. We relied completely on consular visits for our contact with friends and loved ones back in Britain, as well as to bring the nature of our plight to the attention of human rights organisations and bring us news of what was being done to facilitate our repatriation to the United Kingdom. The money that we were sent from friends and families, which was essential to our survival, as well as the money and vitamins sent to us from the charity Prisoners Abroad, was all channelled through the Consular Service.

Yet monthly visits would be cancelled without explanation, money would be left in Caracas and not forwarded to the island to coincide with visits, and the local consul would arrive uninformed and, apparently, uninterested in what was being done either to improve our situation or to effect our return to UK prisons to serve out our time. The announcement of a consular visit would engender a stomach churning feeling of anxiety mixed with hope, but the visit would almost invariably end in anger or frustration for some, if not all, of the group, usually engendered by some administrative error or omission.

Certainly there were times when some prisoners spoke to the consular officials in an entirely inappropriate manner, but this was almost invariably an explosion of frustration by men living in desperate straits, with every hour bringing a new challenge to survival, in response to a relatively simple task left undone which would now have to wait for at least another month. A week may be a long time in politics, and a blink of the eye in terms of Civil Service administration, but a month is an enormous length of time in a Venezuelan prison, and always carries the potential of being a lifetime.

I think it is fair to say that, as British prisoners, we always felt like the poor cousins of our European companions in terms of the care and concern meted out to us by consular staff. When the Dutch prisoners were, within the year, returned *en masse* to their home country to serve out their sentences in a "civilised" situation, that feeling increased a hundredfold.

Another example of the cavalier attitude taken towards us came during that same December 2000 visit. Jackie, the consul from Caracas, informed us that a Prisoner Exchange Agreement, which would allow us to return to the UK to finish our sentences, was "in the final stages of being thrashed out". Pressed as to the timescale involved, she replied, "Look, if you guys are still here at Christmas time next year, I'll buy the turkeys." She would later deny having said that, but fourteen prisoners anxiously hanging onto her every word were very clear what they had heard, and what the implications were for our short term future. As it turned out, it was June 2003 before the agreement was signed, and the first British prisoner did not leave Venezuela under that agreement until November 2004.

In December, the group of foreign prisoners, which now numbered fifty if we included a number of Colombian citizens, began to make approaches to the prison director to clarify the situation about early release. The arrangement for Venezuelan citizens is that, providing they are of good behaviour and involved in either work or study, two days under the prison regime count as three days of the sentence served. Thus, a prisoner with a ten-year sentence who has spent three years and four months in prison will be deemed to have completed half of his sentence.

At that point, providing they have adequate support from their family and an offer of work from an established employer, they can apply for early release to a halfway house, from which they are expected to go out to work each day and can go home at weekends. Once two-thirds of the sentence has been paid, they may apply to live at home full-time, reporting to an after-care officer regularly until the sentence is purged. Clearly, any breach of the conditions for such early release will result in the person being returned to the prison, where they must remain until the expiry of their sentence.

With regard to foreign prisoners, the director assured us that no such benefits could be granted, that we would be required to physically spend every last day of our original sentence in the prison, and that the ominously titled Juez de Ejecución – who was, we were relieved to learn, the judge responsible for the execution of sentences rather than of prisoners – was completely firm in her view on the matter. There were two principal problems with allowing early release to foreigners. One was the fact that we could not count on the all-important family support on the island, not having family resident in Venezuela. The other was that we had no valid documentation, having entered the country on tourist visas which had now expired. The judge's view, therefore, was that by requesting early release, we would be asking her to be party to an illegal act.

We could see the validity of the argument from the point of view of the authorities, but were also aware that the Venezuelan Constitution demanded that all persons were to be treated as equal under the law, regardless of colour, creed, ethnic origin or nationality. The position held by the authorities in respect of us as foreign prisoners was clearly discriminatory under both national and international law. It hardly seemed beyond the power of mortal man to produce some form of temporary documentation that would cover our stay in the country until such time as we had paid our sentences in full.

As far as family support was concerned, this was in fact recognised as being home support rather than necessarily support of family members, and we were sure that most of us could overcome the obstacle of finding a family who were prepared to offer board and lodgings for a small remuneration.

The prison and judicial authorities, however, were unshakeable in their position, and we began to feel that the only resort we had to register our protest at this injustice, to call attention to our situation and to try and bring about a change in the attitude of the authorities, was to stage a hunger strike. We resolved that if we could not get favourable answers in any other way by the end of the first month of the year, we would declare a hunger strike of all foreign prisoners in San Antonio prison.

Christmas was a dismal affair. To all intents and purposes, the prison routine continued as usual, with the only concession to the festive season being a traditional Christmas meal, served on Christmas Eve and issued from the kitchen pre-plated on plastic disposable plates. The traditional food served in Venezuela at Christmas is *hallaca*, which is a kind of meat and chicken stew, with pulses, served in a maize flour envelope wrapped up in palm leaves and boiled. It is usually served with rice and a side salad. Cooked well, *hallaca* is quite palatable, and would adequately grace any working man's packed lunch, in the manner of a Cornish pasty. Those that were served to us, however, were heavy on the pulses, light on the meat, and carried much the same flavour as everything else that was issued from the dreadful, dark recesses of that diabolical kitchen.

Fortunately, there were no outbreaks of violence that December, and the prison remained largely calm as we prepared to harbour in the New Year. It was of course a time of great reflection, as I thought back to past Christmases and considered all that had been lost over the course of the last year. The Venezuelans were as usual full of confidence and hope, declaring that this coming year, God willing, everyone would be free. It was not a hope that I could realistically share, and it was with a heavy heart that I considered all that might lie before me in the year to come.

Not in my wildest imaginings could I begin to picture how terrible the events of the coming year would be, nor how I would begin to despair of ever overcoming the difficulties that lay ahead. Perhaps, for the sake of my sanity, it was just as well.

CHAPTER EIGHT

Tighten Your Belts

THE FIRST MONTH of 2001 passed quietly, the only incident of note being when Eric, one of the German workers in the kitchen, was sitting with his back to the wall in the central compound, having a smoke break, and had his ear lobe shot off by a stray bullet. No serious damage was done, and for the next week or so he walked around giving a fair impression of an ailing Van Gogh, with his head wrapped in swathes of bandage, but he was extremely lucky to escape with such a minor injury, and the incident was yet another reminder of the dangers that we all faced from day to day.

I was able to vastly improve my accommodation. One of the two rooms, or cells, in our block was occupied by Julio, as block leader. The other was "owned" by a friend of Mancho who suddenly decided that he wished to sell his room and move into the church. Mancho negotiated with him to offer the room for sale to me, and it was duly offered at a price of 20,000 bolivars, or about £20. This price included a bed, and I quickly concluded the deal, borrowing the money against the cash that I expected on the next consular visit. Suddenly, I had a ten foot by ten foot space to call my own! To show my appreciation to Mancho for arranging this deal, I donated my former bugaloo to him. It was not long before Mancho negotiated a deal with Marcos, a newly arrived, quite well-off,

Dutch prisoner, who bought a bunk bed and shared the tiny space with him. It was a move that was to have deadly consequences for Mancho within a few months, but for the moment all were content with the arrangement.

We foreign prisoners continued our campaign to get the authorities to accept the injustice that we faced in being obliged to remain in the prison for the entirety of our sentence, but we met with no success, and our resolve to enter upon a hunger strike grew. Accordingly, we held a meeting of all foreign prisoners on the seventh of February, on the open ground in the centre of the compound, to consider our next move.

"We've had enough of talking," someone called out. "The only thing they're ever going to pay attention to is action."

There was a general rumble of agreement.

"Are we all in agreement, then?" asked Juan, a Spanish prisoner. "Shall we begin a hunger strike immediately?"

"Yes!" came the resounding cry from the assembled prisoners.

We therefore decided that we would begin a hunger strike that afternoon. We returned to our pavilions, picked up our bed rolls and wash kits, and thirty-four foreign prisoners moved up to two adjoining rooms that formed part of the workshop. Carlos, a Venezuelan prisoner and member of the "management team", came with us as an expression of solidarity and to provide some degree of protection to us with his pistol against any surprise attack by prisoners from the other compound. We also suspected that he was there as an enforcer, to ensure that the strike proceeded according to the unwritten rules of Venezuelan prisons and to administer summary justice to anyone found to be breaking the strike.

Sympathetic visitors had previously taken out letters for the press explaining our actions and the reasons for them, and had undertaken to contact the various embassies to apprise them of the situation. It was a truly international group that gathered and began to lay claim to floor space within the two rooms. As well as the British contingent, we had Dutch, French, German, Spanish, Portuguese, Danish, a Canadian of Philippine extraction and Colombian prisoners, as well as our Venezuelan minder.

The rules for a Venezuelan hunger strike are fairly straightforward. One can drink as much water as desired, as well as sweetened black coffee, and can suck boiled sweets. Any other sustenance, vitamin tablets included, are banned. Given that we were not used to a great deal of food in any case, we did not suffer unduly from hunger pangs in the first few days.

We decided from the outset that we would handle certain aspects of the strike in a slightly different manner from that which we had observed when a group of the locals had held their strike a couple of months before. We determined to parade for the morning and evening head-count as long as we were able to stand and walk, as we had found the apparent inability of the locals to parade after two days to be pathetic and a demonstration of weakness that we were resolved to avoid. Similarly, we felt that their dramatic fainting fits were to be avoided, and decided that we would not ask for medical assistance unless someone became genuinely ill. Given that our intake of water was not limited, and that we could take as much sugar as we were able to buy or that was donated to us, we felt that we could maintain our strength for quite some time.

Once we were settled into our new quarters, a *vigilante* appeared to lock the barred doors, shortly after which the prison director appeared to give us a pep talk, advising us that what we were doing was a waste of our time and that we were endangering our health to no purpose, as the authorities could not move from the position that they currently held with respect to our release arrangements. We heard him out quietly but remained determined to continue with our action. It was clear from his manner, in any case, that the director was simply going through the motions and did not really believe what he himself was saying.

At the usual time in the evening, the Guardia Nacional appeared to carry out the head-count, and after the usual *numero* on the basketball court, they came to our quarters so that we could file out to the front of the building, be counted, then file back in again to be locked up for the night. Despite the anxiety about our situation, and the doubts as to how it would all end and how we would cope, we all felt a certain degree of relief to be freed for even a short period from the constant demands of sharing accommodation with the Venezuelan prisoners and their unending begging and negotiating. Not least among the pleasures was that of being away from the dreadful, repetitive Venezuelan rock music that they constantly listened to and which grated on the eardrums and nerves of anyone not brought up with it.

On the morning of the second day of the strike, a Thursday, someone brought us the local newspapers, and we were disappointed to read that the authorities had cunningly managed to take the wind out of our sails. The press releases had clearly reached the newspapers as planned, but when reporters contacted the prison, they had been told that the issues in dispute had been amicably resolved and that the planned hunger strike had been called off! It was this quote by the prison director that was given prominence in each of the newspaper articles about the incident.

We had no immediate way of refuting this barefaced lie, as we were effectively incommunicado until Saturday, when visitors would come into the prison. A group of us therefore set ourselves to preparing a letter to be sent out with a visitor on Saturday, refuting the claim by the director that the strike had been called off, once more detailing the reasons behind our taking this drastic action, and expressing our complete determination to continue with the action until such time as the authorities had taken action to correct the injustice that we as foreign prisoners were facing.

Over the following few days, we were visited by all the consuls of the nationalities represented in the hunger strike. We were able to explain fully to each of them what we were doing and why, and to ask them to bring our plight to the attention of anyone who might be in a position to bring pressure to bear upon the authorities. Each of the consuls expressed their neutrality, simply hearing our complaints and then departing, but we felt confident that there would be a considerable amount of communication going on behind the scenes in the following days.

On the Saturday, we were able to send out our prepared letter and hoped that the newspapers would be prepared to follow up on the story and would not allow themselves to be further fobbed off by any lies emanating from the authorities. Generally, morale remained high over the weekend, and a number of visitors approached the gates during the Saturday and Sunday visits to express their support. Some brought us a little sugar or some boiled sweets, in a very welcome gesture of solidarity.

On the Monday, we were visited by Doctora Yolanda Cardona, the judge in charge of sentenced prisoners on the island, together with her assistant and the director of the prison. At first, she reiterated the party line, that we would, as foreign prisoners, be required to spend each and every day of our sentence within the prison, but then, after hearing our arguments, and clearly taking account of our determination to proceed with our action to the bitter end, she conceded that the law could be interpreted in a slightly different manner to the position that she had previously held. She advised us that any foreign prisoner who was of good behaviour and recorded as being involved in work and/or study throughout their sentence, could expect to be released when they had completed two-thirds of their sentence, at which point they would be expelled from the country.

This did not give us equal treatment to Venezuelan prisoners but it was certainly a considerable step forward from the position that we had been in one week before, and so we decided to accept the compromise. In my case, it meant that instead of having to spend six years and eight months in the prison, I could reasonably expect to be released and deported after having served a little less than four and a half years.

The other complaint that we had was the length of time being taken to arrange the repatriation of those whose country already had an agreement with Venezuela for the mutual exchange of prisoners. This process was currently taking up to two years, although it should be possible to process the necessary paperwork in a matter of weeks. The director undertook to immediately begin rapidly processing the paperwork for those prisoners who qualified, beginning with the Dutch, who formed the largest group, then the Spanish, and so on. The judge agreed to play her part in accelerating the process and to invite the appropriate consuls to a meeting in order to obtain their support for speeding things up considerably.

Feeling that we had gone a long way towards achieving the aims of our strike, we spent Monday evening preparing a Minute of Agreement, detailing the various points that had been thrashed out with the judge and the prison director. This was presented to the director on the Tuesday morning, and when it had been returned to us, duly signed, we held a vote and agreed to bring our hunger strike to an end.

In a very fine gesture of reconciliation, the director ordered that a special lunch be prepared. Thus, two huge platters of grilled tuna steaks and two large pots of *bollos*, a kind of boiled maize dumpling, were carried up from the kitchen by four prisoners and laid on the grass in front of the workshop.

Unfortunately for me I was unable, despite seven days without solid food, to overcome a lifelong aversion to fish, and had to decline the principal part of the meal, contenting myself with chewing on one of the entirely tasteless *bollos*.

The following morning, the four men who had acted as representatives of the prisoners group in negotiations with the authorities were told that we were to go to the Palace of Justice to meet the judge and to ratify the agreement that we had reached with her. As befitting the make-up of the striking prisoners, we were an international group, consisting of a Spaniard, a Dane, a Dutchman and myself.

We were initially very nervous as we prepared to leave the prison, as rumours had been rife that now that we had allowed ourselves to be identified as playing a leadership role in the strike, we were to be transferred to one of the real hell-hole prisons on the mainland, such as La Planta, where twenty-five prisoners had been killed in a fire set by Guardia Nacional troops during a riot in 1996, and where 1,800 prisoners were crammed into a space designed for 500, or Sabaneta, where more than a hundred prisoners had been killed during a riot in January 1994.

Our concerns were not alleviated when the prison director met us at the main gate bearing with him our four files. Once we had been handcuffed and boarded the ancient and decrepit bus which, together with an equally venerable ambulance, constituted the prison's transport pool, our fears were considerably eased when the sergeant in charge of the Guardia Nacional team acting as our escorts announced, "I understand that you guys are going to a meeting with the judge, so if you behave yourselves, we will not give you any problems."

When we arrived at the Palace of Justice building after a half-hour drive, we were taken straight up the stairs, and our handcuffs were removed in the corridor before we were ushered into the judge's chambers. Once there, we were treated with great courtesy, offered coffee and biscuits, and invited to sit around a large conference table. Present at the meeting, in addition to ourselves, the judge and the prison director, were the President of the Court, the Spanish and Dutch consuls, and the judge's secretary. The judge was attired in a low-slung white top, which bore a small, printed Mickey Mouse logo between her pendulous breasts. When she was moved to anger or laughter, both of which occurred with alarming frequency, one waited with bated breath to see if Mickey would be able to continue to hang on, or if this time he would be shaken loose and fly through the air, before landing ignominiously in the centre of the table. I realised that I was probably feeling a little light-headed after a week without food.

A document had been prepared detailing the deal we had reached on Monday and largely based on the Minute of Agreement that the director had already signed. We all signed this, after which it was officially stamped and a copy placed in each of our files. The rest of the meeting was given over to the practical issues of how best the repatriation of those foreign nationals eligible could be expedited. It was agreed that the four prisoners present would act as a working party who would continue to meet at regular intervals with the judge, in order to review progress. All present undertook to do their best to avoid undue delays in processing of the necessary paperwork.

Feeling that something positive had been achieved, we filed out at the end of the meeting, after shaking hands with the judge and the President of the Court, to be clipped once more into our handcuffs before being escorted downstairs and onto our waiting transport for the journey back to the prison. There the harsh reality of our daily existence awaited us, our brief foray into civilisation and high-powered decision-making being over for the present.

During the following couple of weeks, a great deal was achieved, and the papers for all the Dutch prisoners were processed and sent off to the Ministry of Justice in Caracas. By the third week after the strike, the papers for the Spanish prisoners were almost completed. This process was not without its setbacks, however. While the political will existed in the courthouse to expedite the paperwork, the same could not be said for the prison. The standard of record keeping and administrative competence was abysmal, and the prison social worker, within whose remit the majority of the work fell, had no interest or inclination to move things along quickly. An incident involving Denis illustrated her approach.

One day, Denis was in her office to fill in some form or other. He was accompanied by a Dutchman who spoke perfect Spanish. While there, he decided to confirm that his name was in the book maintained to register those working within the prison, this being an essential part of earning the reduction of sentence previously described. The social worker replied that his name was indeed in the book. Denis told her that he would like to see it, just to make sure. At this point, she became irritated, and said, "I'm telling you that your name is in the book!"

"I'd like to see it please."

"Your name is in the book!"

Eventually, she was prevailed upon to produce the book in question, and soon discovered that Denis's name was not listed. She therefore produced a pen, wrote his name on the page and, unblushingly, turned the book around on the desk to show him.

"There you are! Your name is in the book!"

When the Dutch consul came into the prison to sign the repatriation papers for the Dutch prisoners, prior to the papers being sent off to Caracas, he was told by the prison sub-director that the papers were not available, as they had not yet come from the Palace of Justice. We knew, through a prisoner who worked in the prison office, that the papers had been delivered from the Palace of Justice the previous day. The usual black-is-white argument therefore ensued.

"But you received those papers yesterday."

"No we didn't."

"Yes you did."

"No, we didn't, absolutely not."

"That's a lie, yes you did."

"OK, I'll just go and get them then."

A WEEK AFTER we came out of the hunger strike, a truly momentous event occurred in my life. I was sitting in my room on the Thursday morning when Mancho came running in to tell me that I was needed in the director's office. At first, I assumed that it was something to do with the strike, but as I hurried to change into the long trousers and long-sleeved shirt required for a visit to the offices, Mancho said that he thought it was a telephone call.

Arriving outside the director's office door, I knocked, and he immediately called for me to enter. When I did so, my jaw nearly hit the floor. Sitting across the desk from the director was Maureen, a great friend of mine from Hartlepool, together with Tony, a friend of hers. I was totally overwhelmed, and I felt my eyes filling as I moved forward to greet them. Maureen had written long letters to me every month since learning of my arrest but there had never been any mention of any plans to cross the Atlantic to visit me.

The director said that they had been allowed to enter the prison to see me, in recognition of the distance that they had travelled, and that we could use the room normally used during consular visits to sit and have a chat for an hour. On Saturday and Sunday, they could come in to the prison during the normal visit times. I thanked him profusely and hurried to shepherd them out of his office. Joey, the Canadian prisoner, who was now spending his day in the no-man's land of the inner compound and boasted that he was one of the few prisoners in the world to be "homeless" in prison, came in to the room where we were sitting and rushed off to get coffee from somewhere.

We had so much to talk about.

"What's happening in Hartlepool?"

"You're looking very thin, are you not able to get enough to eat?"

"What's the food like?"

"How do you spend your days?"

It seemed that only five minutes had gone by when a *vigilante* came along to advise us that our hour was up and that my visitors would have to leave. I escorted them to the main gate and they promised to be back in to see me on the Saturday. I returned to the compound with my head spinning.

True to their word, Maureen and Tony visited again on the Saturday, bringing with them gifts from my friends back in Hartlepool. There was a radio with shortwave reception, which would allow me to listen to the BBC World Service, something that was to prove a huge morale booster, several books and a large dictionary signed "To Donald MacNeil from Billy W— 16-2-2001", which would over the following years do sterling service in settling arguments and disputes and which remains one of my most treasured possessions, as well as letters and cards. Most amusing was a T-shirt, bearing the legend "Donald – Margarita 2000-2006" and the Hartlepool "hanging monkey" logo.

For those unfamiliar with the story of the hanging monkey, legend has it that during the Napoleonic wars there was throughout Britain considerable fear of a French invasion, and a careful lookout was kept for possible spies coming ashore along the coast. Thus, when a French ship was wrecked near the coast off Hartlepool, the local fishermen were at pains to look out for anyone coming ashore from the wreck. It turned out that the only survivor washed up on the beach was a monkey, which had been kept as a pet by the ship's crew and which had been dressed in a French naval uniform.

The story goes that the locals seized the unfortunate beast, and being unfamiliar with either Frenchmen or monkeys, mistook one for the other, with the creature's unintelligible gibbering only serving to confirm in their minds that they were dealing with a foreign agent. An impromptu court hearing was held on the beach, the upshot of which was that the monkey was declared to be a French spy who merited immediate execution. Summary justice was carried out there and then, on the beach, and the monkey was hanged, with the mast of a nearby boat serving as impromptu gibbet.

Until recent times, the people of Hartlepool were deeply offended by the slight to their intelligence and knowledge of the world implied by any reference to the story of the hanging monkey, and a guaranteed way to start a fight with a Hartlepudlian was to call him a "monkey hanger". In recent years, though, the people of the town have begun to take a perverse pride in the story, and have countered their erstwhile detractors in the neatest possible way by adopting the tale as their own and humorously using the hanging monkey logo as being representative of the town.

In point of fact, a cursory examination of the circumstances would suggest that there is very little to support the truth of the tale. Hartlepool had, by the time of the Napoleonic wars, been an important seaport for several centuries, and so the people of the town would have been very familiar with the citizens, language and customs of all the seafaring nations of Europe, to a vastly greater extent than people living even a few miles inland. Monkeys have been kept on board ships as pets since ocean-going sailors first encountered them, and so it is unlikely in the extreme that there was no-one in the crowd who could recognise the captured creature for what it was, mass hysteria notwithstanding. Furthermore, I find it difficult to believe that any fisherman, notoriously superstitious as they are the world over, would allow the mast of his boat to be used to hang someone, blithely ignoring the possibility that such an action would lead to the boat and himself being haunted and cursed for all time.

Whatever the truth of the matter, it is an interesting story, and I was proud to wear my new T-shirt, and was more concerned that the dates 2000-2006 which it bore should prove to be an exaggeration than that the story behind the hanging monkey logo should prove to be so.

Maureen and Tony visited again on the Sunday and then again on the two visiting days during the following weekend, before flying back to Britain on the following Wednesday. They brought in chocolate, soap, toothpaste and a toothbrush, and toilet paper, all of which I had asked them for. They also brought some meat and cooking sauces, as well as tea bags, which helped to repair some of the damage done by the recent hunger strike.

During the second week of Maureen's visit, we received some horrifying news from the other side of the prison. A British prisoner who was obliged to live over there as a result of his various scams to relieve people of money and drugs had apparently been gang-raped by seven fellow inmates, and as a result was so distraught that he spent a couple of days handcuffed to the stretcher trolley in the vicinity of the offices, babbling away to himself. Maureen managed to get a message to the consul about this terrible incident, but as far as we were aware it was not followed up, and after a few days the prisoner returned to his previous quarters and appeared to make a recovery from his experience.

Maureen's visit resulted in my learning for the first time of the indignities to which female visitors to the prison were subjected before being allowed to enter the prison. After passing through the metal detector, each female visitor was required to enter a room, where she had to lower her underwear and then to do a couple of squat-jumps, before adjusting her dress and passing through into the inner compound. It was a degrading and humiliating ritual, and entirely ineffectual, as I never heard of a visitor being found with banned items during one of these searches, but was aware that a considerable percentage of the drugs consumed within the prisons were carried in by female visitors concealed within their bodies.

It was very sad to say goodbye to Maureen and Tony when they finally left at the end of visiting on the second Sunday, but their visit had been a tremendously uplifting experience for me, confirming that there were people who cared for me and helping to give me the strength to carry on. As I hugged them goodbye and watched them make their way out through the main gate, I could not have imagined for a moment that this would prove to be the last time that I would ever see Maureen.

CHAPTER NINE

Blood Strike

TOWARDS THE END of February, we had a visit from the British consul from Caracas, accompanied by the Head of Consular Services from London. He was able to give us a little more information on the progress of the repatriation agreement. He told us that things were moving extremely slowly and predicted that, based on current progress, the hope was that we would all have been shipped back to British prisons by the end of 2002. This was extremely disappointing news but at least we felt that there was something concrete in the offing and his visit reassured us that we had not been forgotten about.

One night, the local television station showed the film *Midnight Express*, depicting the trials of a young American imprisoned in Turkey for a drug offence. It was a film that I had watched several times previously, suitably appalled by the dramatic depiction of the brutal conditions within the Turkish gaol. On this occasion however, the film had a very different effect, and we howled our derision at the screen, making comments such as, "It's a holiday camp. Look, they've all got beds to sleep on." It was a sobering reminder of how truly grim our own situation was.

During the first days of March, increasing unrest began to manifest itself around the prison over the early release scheme.

At that time, there were a number of prisoners who considered themselves as being due for release, but nothing appeared to be happening and the current judge seemed to be very reluctant to take the decision to award people the release date that they merited.

The decision was therefore made that a prison-wide hunger strike would begin on the morning of Monday, March 12. This time, since the entire prison was involved, we all remained in our own quarters, which were kept locked throughout the day, and only left them for the morning and evening head-counts. Tensions were very high, as the normally excitable Venezuelans became even more unstable in the face of the additional deprivations of a hunger strike. Those that took drugs found that the drugs had more effect than usual, as a result of the lack of sustenance, and their behaviour became even more difficult to predict. The principal humanising factor within the prison, namely the regular and open visits, were suspended throughout the duration of the strike.

The first casualties of the strike took place on the second night, at around 1 a.m., when some prisoners in one of the pavilions on the other side of the prison were caught eating by other prisoners. In the shoot-out that followed, three people were injured. Two of those ended up in hospital, one of them in a coma, while the third was able to return to his quarters following treatment. The raid by the Guardia on the other side of the prison that followed the removal of the injured sounded, from our side, like the gunfight at the OK Corral.

Throughout the strike, thirty-six families maintained a vigil outside the prison gates and they were reported in the newspaper the following morning as having been able to hear all the shooting, followed by the prisoners pleading with the soldiers not to beat them, and then the screams as the soldiers ignored their pleas. Since the prison was built on a site that was remote from any habitation, it was very unusual for events within it to be so closely witnessed by anyone outside. It seemed that the progress that we had achieved in respect of human rights issues only applied to our side of the prison, with its large number of foreign prisoners, and could safely be ignored in the other compound.

The local television station interviewed the judge for an evening news item on the strike on the Wednesday, and she admitted that she was unable to establish which of the prisoners were eligible for early release, as no proper records were being kept in the prison. The director of the prison, a new appointment with only ten days in post, was quoted in a newspaper as saying that the prison was not really on hunger strike, since food was being smuggled in to the prisoners. This was a totally false and hugely inflammatory statement, as well as being utterly ridiculous. It appeared that he gave no consideration to the implications of the director of a supposedly secure establishment announcing to the world that enough food to feed four hundred people was being smuggled in every day, under his very nose, and that he was powerless to stop it, despite the contingent of Guardia Nacional troops attached to the prison having been increased to one hundred soldiers from the first day of the strike.

To be fair to him, such is the quality of journalism in much of Venezuela that the newspapers did not pick up on this point, and it is probable that neither did his superiors. The prisoners, however, were outraged by this and other similar disinformation designed to downplay the seriousness of the situation, and there can be little doubt that it had a considerable bearing on how the strike eventually culminated. As soon as the newspaper bearing the director's remarks began to circulate among the prisoners, the talk began to turn to a "blood strike".

Blood strikes are a time-honoured, if utterly gruesome, form of protest within the Venezuelan prison system. During a blood strike, protesting prisoners will inflict cuts upon themselves, sufficiently long and deep as to require major stitching, smearing the ensuing blood on their bodies in order to present the most horrific vision possible.

As enthusiasm for an escalation of the strike action to a blood strike grew, we foreigners could only look on with mounting horror. Should the decision be that a general blood strike was called for, we knew that we had only two alternatives: take part, or be shot out of hand. In the meantime, all we could do was keep our own counsel, being careful to neither advocate the barbaric action contemplated nor to appear to be taking a defeatist stance by not supporting whatever action would eventually be decided upon.

One factor which conspired to increase the possibility of an escalation to a blood strike was the fact that the Venezuelan President, Lieutenant Colonel Hugo Rafael Chavez Frias, was due to visit the Island on the Friday, accompanied by his usual retinue of national and international press, which would ensure the maximum possible publicity for such an action.

President Chavez had come to power at the end of 1999, bringing to an end some forty years of a cosy power-sharing agreement between the two principal right-wing parties in Venezuela. Once established in the presidency, Chavez had begun to implement wide-ranging social reforms, starting with the drawing up of a new constitution. His efforts met with huge and well-organised opposition from the traditional power bases, enthusiastically backed by their American allies. During these first years of his mandate, the country seemed to be in a permanent state of turmoil, with civil war a real and constant possibility.

As Friday approached, so our dread increased, and it was therefore with great relief that we heard the announcement on Thursday evening that the blood strike would indeed take place the following morning, but that participation would be entirely voluntary. I took great, if hidden, pleasure in "regretfully" declining the generous offer to take part in such a heroic action.

The blood strike began at nine in the morning, and soon our scaffolding pole was in almost constant use as we banged on the door in order to summon *vigilantes* to remove those who had sliced their legs open in our pavilion, the one next to us or the one behind us. In all, thirty people across the prison took part, and twenty-seven of those had to be taken to hospital. The preferred method was to slice open the back of the leg, from ankle to knee.

Soon, the press corps waiting at the airport to cover the arrival of the President got wind of the story, and we were able to watch on live television as our fellow inmates arrived at the hospital. Some of them were interviewed as they lay on trolleys awaiting treatment and were able to give an account of the reasons behind their action and the hunger strike that had preceded it. One of the prisoners required no less than eighty-five stitches on his self-inflicted injury. There is little doubt that it made great television, and the networks, almost exclusively owned by press barons bitterly opposed to President Chavez's regime, were delighted with the opportunity to cover this story in some depth.

That we were able to watch the story unfold was due to the fact that Marco, the fairly well-off Dutchman who now shared a bugaloo with Mancho, had managed to have a large-screen television delivered, which stood at the end of his bed. With the curtains of his bugaloo open, we were able to gather round and watch the unfolding drama. We little realised at the time that this television was soon to play a central part in a drama even more terrible than the one we were now watching.

The pressure upon the authorities brought about by these events was enormous and soon bore fruit. The Vice-Minister of Justice was helicoptered from Caracas to the prison, where he spoke to representatives of the prisoners. As a result of his promise that a Technical Commission would arrive at the prison on the following Monday, with the remit of gutting out the administration in the prison and organising the release of those who were due to be released within fifteen days of the Commission's arrival, together with his immediate action in ordering the release of seven prisoners, the strike was declared over. Those who had taken part in the blood strike returned to the prison later in the day, to be welcomed as heroes.

EARLY ON SATURDAY morning I was mopping the floor, as it was my turn to clean the pavilion in preparation for the entrance of visitors. Suddenly the door burst open and Harapo, a young Venezuelan who lived in the pavilion, came running in, pursued by two of the younger members of the "management team" bearing revolvers. Harapo ran into Fred's bugaloo, where he cowered in the corner, shouting and whimpering over and over again, "Don't kill me, please don't kill me." The next moment, his pleas turned to howls of pain as he was roughly pistol-whipped, before being dragged outside again and shoved into the church building. At this point, Julio appeared in the pavilion, surveyed the scene, and calmly ordered Fred to clean up his blood-spattered bugaloo before the visitors came in.

We never did learn what had led to Harapo's banishment, but he was one of three prisoners in our compound who were either pistol-whipped or stabbed that morning and then ordered into the church. Shortly afterward, on looking into the church through its barred gate, one could see one of the prisoners busy with sewing needle and cotton, stitching up the wounds of the new additions to the flock. Those were then placed out of sight, inside a bugaloo, so that by the time the first visitors entered the compound no trace remained of that morning's violent acts, and children were soon running in a carefree fashion around the compound. As usual on such occasions, I found it very difficult to get my head round the

137

dichotomy and was, not for the first time, reminded of a quotation from Euripides: *Those whom the gods would destroy, they first make mad.*

Early the following week, all foreign prisoners were called to the doctor's surgery, where the newly appointed director introduced us to a young man who announced himself as a doctor from Caracas. He stated that he was now in charge of the medical facilities in Venezuelan prisons and spoke at some length about the improvements that he wished to bring about. He acknowledged that medical services within the prisons were deplorable and announced that in future, supplies would be purchased centrally and then distributed to individual prisons. He promised that he would send a mobile clinic to the prison within two months, with specialists on board. I was in the meantime given the task of drawing up a list of the prisoners who required medical attention.

Much of the doctor's good intent was unfortunately doomed to failure before the improvements got under way, as he had apparently not taken measures to secure the full cooperation of the director and the prison doctor in his plans. Some of the foreign prisoners who were present at the meeting with the doctor also helped to undermine the initiative, as I was to learn when, the following morning, I was called to the director's office. The director could barely contain his pleasure as he thundered at me that they had discovered that while we were in the doctor's surgery the previous day, some medicines, hypodermic syringes and other medical supplies had been stolen from a cupboard in that office.

"I will suspend all medical services to the prison," he roared, "and it will be made clear that it is entirely the fault of the foreign prisoners."

I was furious at this, and the manner in which idiotic behaviour on the part of a few had played right into the hands of the director, allowing a situation to be created whereby all the work to break down barriers between foreign prisoners and the locals could be jeopardised. I therefore set about trying to retrieve what I could of the stolen supplies from those most likely to have been responsible. Some of the stolen supplies were indeed returned, but for weeks afterwards prisoners were declined medicines on the grounds that "they have been stolen by the foreigners".

Even when the promised medical supplies were delivered from Caracas, these were promptly sold by the doctor, who continued to drum out the excuse of "the foreigners have stolen them" as a reason for not prescribing treatment. Only when the mobile clinic arrived, and the specialists within began to treat various injuries and ailments, did the situation improve and we were able to put the incident behind us.

At the end of the week, I received a letter from my friend Robin, from Scotland. He had begun to write directly to the prison each month, which seemed to work reasonably well and meant that incoming mail did not have to wait for the next consular visit. On this occasion, he had enclosed a £10 note, referring to it in his letter, saying, "Do you have any idea how hard it is to get an English £10 note in Scotland?" Following an interesting few days of trying to exchange it for local currency, I wrote back to him, "Do *you* have any idea how hard it is to change an English £10 note inside a Venezuelan prison?" I suggested that it would not be wise to send any more money in this fashion, as the risks of it going missing were too high.

He also sent me a poster of Buachille Etive Mor, one of the most iconic of the Scottish mountains. A frame for this was immediately provided by my pal Mancho, and it took pride of place on the wall of my room above my bed, where it was the first thing that I saw when I opened my eyes each morning. A number of the Venezuelans commented on the beauty of the mountain and were particularly impressed when I told them that the water running down its sides was that used in the production of Scotch whisky.

The degree of corruption within the prison was evidenced towards the end of April, when four Bulgarians, who had been captured at the airport two or three weeks before while attempting to smuggle drugs out of the country, were allowed to leave. They were escorted out of the prison at eight o'clock one evening, complete with all documentation authorising their release, and presumably left the country immediately. The prison rumour machine was fairly confident that a sum in the region of $120,000 had changed hands.

A couple of nights later, we prepared ourselves for a *raqueta* when someone spotted a large group of Guardia Nacional entering the prison around midnight. We were soon able to relax, however, as their raid was not to be on the prisoner accommodation but instead on the prison offices. They left a short time later, carrying with them a number of computers and stacks of paperwork. We learned the following morning that the assistant director of the prison had been arrested, as had one of the *vigilantes*. Nothing further came of the matter, however, and these two members of the prison staff were back at work within the week, each driving a shiny new car.

The event did have some repercussions for the prisoners, as the temporary absence of the computers served, for a few weeks, as yet another excuse for paperwork not being processed for repatriation, or any other positive purpose.

During the last week in April, Denis's father and brother came to visit him. They were able to spend two weeks on the island and to visit him on every visit day during that time. They brought with them the news that Mick, the organiser of our ill-fated smuggling trip, was now dead, having been drowned in a diving accident in the Irish Sea while carrying out a deep dive on a wreck using mixed gases. Neither Denis nor I were in the least upset to receive this news, and considered that the human race was well rid of one of its least attractive members.

The visit was, as might be imagined, a tremendous boost to Denis's morale, although it was clearly difficult for his family to see him in such circumstances and the final parting was not easy for him or for them. Like all of us, Denis was suffering greatly as a result of the conditions of our confinement, and the visit served to accentuate the distance from home and family, and anything resembling a normal life.

CHAPTER TEN

Darkest Hour

A MESSAGE CAME in to the prison asking me to telephone Bill H, a friend from Hartlepool. I crossed into the inner compound, where the telephone was situated, and after waiting for some time in the queue, was able to make the call.

As soon as I heard Bill's voice, I knew that something terrible had happened, which was confirmed when, in a voice flattened by pain palpable even across the transatlantic telephone connection, he said "There is no easy way to tell you this, Donald. What has happened is that Maureen has died."

I immediately felt as if I had been kicked in the stomach, as a wave of anguish and grief assaulted me. Bill went on to give me a few more details: that she had been taking a bath while alone in her flat, had succumbed to one of the epileptic fits to which she had in recent years become prone, and had subsequently drowned. After thanking Bill profoundly for letting me know, knowing as I did how difficult it had been for him to give me such news over the telephone, I quickly brought the conversation to a close and hung up.

Leaving the telephone booth, I stumbled sightlessly across the inner compound and returned to my own compound, where I made my way to the far corner and spent the next couple of hours pacing backwards and forwards beside the perimeter fence, consumed with grief. It was so difficult to imagine that Maureen simply no longer *was*. A self-confessed free spirit, she had played an important role in my life in recent years, and since my arrest her lengthy, newsy letters, filled with optimism and her own zany take on life, which had unfailingly arrived each month, each one ending with her characteristic "Over, but never out, Mo", had become tremendously important to me.

Maureen's unexpected visit to the prison a few weeks before was typical of her, acting selflessly to provide that which she instinctively knew would be of most benefit to the other person. Her visit had been the high point of my time in prison, and now, so few weeks later, her death was the low point. I knew that whatever was ahead of me would be so much more difficult to bear without the massive moral support that she had provided. It is almost impossible to adequately describe the effects of receiving such news in that terrible place, but it was to mark the beginnings of a slide into a profound depression from which it would take me many months to recover. Not only had I lost an exceptionally good friend, but it was another reminder that the world was moving on and that many things might have changed by the time I was eventually released and able to return to Britain.

To their credit, my companions in the prison took account of my state of mind, and I was given time and space to myself for a couple of days, while I tried to come to terms with what had happened.

On May 18, we received a visit from the consul, accompanied by a delegation from the British charity Prisoners Abroad, including Alan Hooker, the case officer for Venezuela, as well as the director of the organisation. They were extremely kind and supportive and brought items of food and reading material that they knew we were in need of.

"We are very aware of how difficult your conditions are here, and are working on two fronts to tackle the problem,"

Alan Hooker told us. "We are urging the British Government to move forward as quickly as possible with the signing of a Prisoner Exchange Agreement with Venezuela, which will allow you to return to the UK to complete your sentences, and at the same time we are trying to bring pressure to bear on the Venezuelan authorities to improve conditions within the prisons."

We were able to give them a tour round the prison, allowing them to see for themselves the conditions in which we lived, the guard posts on the roof, etc. They assured us that the reports that had been submitted to them had been used as the basis of a report to the Foreign and Commonwealth Office, and that this had led to something of a spotlight being placed on our situation. This tallied with our own experience of the beatings having virtually ceased, at least on our side of the prison.

As a result of the heightened awareness of our circumstances, the Consular Service had also reviewed their policies and decided that consular visits should be more regular and would therefore take place on the first Tuesday of each month, barring unforeseen emergencies. The visit left us feeling more positive that there were organisations and official bodies both within and outside Venezuela who were concerned for our welfare.

On the evening of Saturday, June 2, after we had been locked in for the night, Miguel, who was the most powerful prisoner in the prison and to whom all the rest of the gangsters deferred, began to drink whisky, which had apparently been brought in during that day's visit. Miguel lived in the pavilion adjoining ours, and around seven o'clock he sent a message to Pavilion Five, behind ours, for another bottle to be sent to him. The route for any such delivery was through the back window of my room, which was close to the doorway of Pavilion Five, a building which lay at right angles to ours. A sandshoe attached to a long line, referred to by the locals as *el teleférico*, or cable car, would hurtle from my window and be retrieved by those standing in the doorway of Pavilion Five. Whatever was to be sent across would then be attached to the line, which would subsequently be hauled back by the person perched inside my window.

On this occasion, the carefully wrapped bottle was successfully retrieved and then taken out of my room to where there was a small hole, known as *el teléfono*, in the wall through which it could be passed into the adjoining pavilion.

Within half an hour, we began to hear loud banging coming from the other side of the dividing wall. It appeared that someone was carrying out major restructuring of the building. After almost an hour of this work, a sizeable doorway had been broken through between the adjoining pavilion and our accommodation, and through this came Miguel, clutching a bottle of whisky in one hand and a large, evil-looking, homemade knife in the other. He was accompanied by his band of about half a dozen young thugs.

Immediately upon entering, he made a beeline for the person who had been responsible for the transfer of his whisky and began to beat him about the head, mainly with the handle end of the knife, which consisted of the bare metal from which the knife had originally been fashioned. He unleashed his wrath upon this person, inflicting several deep wounds on his scalp.

Immediately afterward, Miguel entered my room and threw himself down, to sit on the bed beside me. He was a large, powerfully built man, about six feet tall and weighing at least sixteen stone, who exuded a sense of power and menace.

"Capitan," he began, "I know that you don't like violence, but there are certain things that have to be done."

He then proceeded with a long explanation of the action that he had just carried out. Speaking as he was, in fast, colloquial Spanish, his voice distorted by drink, and mesmerised as I was by the sight of the blood dripping from the knife which he was wildly waving around to emphasise the points that he was making, I struggled to understand what he was saying to me. Eventually, however, I gathered that the person who had just been punished had had the temerity to reward himself for his efforts in delivering the whisky by opening the bottle and taking a good swig of it, before passing it through the *teléfono*.

It was understandable that Miguel should be annoyed by such an act, at least as much for the lack of respect implied as for the act of taking the whisky. I certainly did not feel it was my place to point out to him that the punishment meted out had perhaps been a little heavy handed.

Now, however, Miguel began to expound on another theme.

"There is something else that we have come in here to do, tonight, and I know your views on the matter, but it is the law of the prison. Someone has to die!"

This time I was completely unable to follow the reasons given for the planned killing, only picking up the phrases "lack of respect" and "speaking out of turn". I was not even able to make out to whom he was referring.

Having ended his discourse and taken another slug from the whisky bottle, Miguel left my room, followed by his minders. Moments later, all those who normally occupied the floor space in the main room of the accommodation came scurrying into my room in a state of alarm. Next to enter was Marco, the Dutchman, repeatedly crossing himself and clearly in great distress. As the door to my room was pulled closed behind him by someone on the outside, he looked towards me and mouthed the word "Mancho". My heart froze, as I realised what was about to happen.

The dozen of us who were in the room sat in stunned silence, occasionally exchanging glances, as we heard dim sounds of a scuffle outside, and then a terrible silence, broken only occasionally by hints of quiet activity. When it was over, Miguel again entered my room, looking more subdued than

146

before but still implacable, this time with a revolver dwarfed in his massive hand. He signalled to the temporary residents to scarper, which they hurried to do. As his minders filed in behind him, Miguel once more sat down on my bed, and after taking a generous slug from the whisky bottle, began yet another diatribe, presumably justifying what had just taken place. I was in too much of a state of consternation and shock to be able to follow what he was going on about, as I tried to control my breathing, stop myself from vomiting, and prevent my entire body from shaking. I just wanted him out of the room. Eventually he ran out of things to say and, taking another slug from his bottle, wished me goodnight and headed out the door, trailed by his sidekicks.

Once they had all returned to their own pavilion through the hole in the wall, Julio came in, white-faced and shocked.

"Good God," he said. "I have been four years in prison and have never seen anything like that."

Mancho had been summoned from his bugaloo, which he shared with Marco, and told to sit in the middle of the floor. At a signal from Miguel, one of the minders then went behind him and manually strangled him. Once he was dead, his lips were first sewn together and then a bed sheet was torn into strips and plaited to form a rope. Once a noose had been formed at one end, it was put round Mancho's neck and his body was suspended from one of the concrete ventilation louvers in the window high on the front wall of the building.

The sewing together of his lips was significant in that it indicated that his death was a punishment for speaking out of turn, and as a warning to others. It turned out that the whole affair could be related to the wide-screen television set that Marco had brought in to the prison. Miguel had taken a fancy to it and decided to compulsorily swap it for his own much smaller television set. While raising no protest at the time, Marco was clearly unhappy with this, and complained loud and long to Mancho, who took up the banner and denounced the injustice to anyone who would listen. Word of this complaining had got back to Miguel, who decided that there was only one way in which the questioning of his actions could be nipped in the bud, and so Mancho lost his life. A clearer testament to the value placed on human life within Venezuelan prisons could hardly be imagined.

Few people slept during that dreadful night, with Mancho's body hanging next to the door. No-one lay down in the central floor space, all choosing to crowd into bugaloos or rooms for companionship and so as not to open their eyes to the corpse hanging above them. It is unlikely that anyone who was present that night will ever forget, or even fully come to terms with, the unspeakable horror of those events.

Eventually, the night passed, as even the longest night must, and we filed out, past the suspended corpse, for the morning head-count. About halfway through the count, one of the *vigilantes*, who had clearly entered the building for some reason, appeared on the parade and reported to the Guardia Nacional officer in charge. We were then counted again, following which we were told to sit down where we were. After about half an hour, the director of the prison appeared and was brought up to date with events. He asked for the occupants of the quarters in question to sit to one side. When he saw that we consisted of six Venezuelans and twelve foreigners, he ordered us to accompany him to his office.

Once in his office, the director advised us that we were each under suspicion of murder, stood to lose all our benefits and faced a possible five-year increment to our existing sentence. After we had each given him a statement saying that we had neither heard nor seen anything, we were allowed to return to our compound, where Mancho's body had already been removed by the *vigilantes*. One of the *vigilantes* had also discovered the new doorway that had been created in the wall between our pavilion and the one next door, and so the mystery of how Mancho had come to a violent end while locked up with the most pacific group of prisoners in the prison, if not in the entire Venezuelan prison system, was solved, and nothing further was ever done about his death.

Within half an hour of our returning to the compound, the main gate was opened for the entry of the Sunday visitors, and "normal" life resumed. Once more, I found myself wondering how long my sanity was going to stand up to the pressures placed upon it in this dreadful place.

Some months before, I had written a letter for Mancho, who could neither read nor write, addressed to his father, expressing his profound regret for all that had passed between them and hoping that things could be patched up and that the family would visit. There had been no response, but that Sunday afternoon Mancho's family appeared for the first time, having come in to collect any belongings that he had left behind. I felt sick at heart.

CHAPTER ELEVEN

The Listener

DURING THE SECOND week in June, the supervising judge, Yolanda Cardona, came to the prison, together with her secretary, to continue completing the paperwork for those who were due to be repatriated. She set up shop in the Guardia Nacional offices just outside the prison walls, and the four prisoners who formed the working party went out to meet with her there. Considerable progress was achieved in the space of a few hours, as she had brought with her all the relevant files from the court, and so it proved relatively easy to match up those with the prison files and fill out any blanks in either set.

Such concerted activity was clearly so unusual that she had decided to make it a photo opportunity, and brought with her a tame press photographer to record the event for posterity. We were promised copies of the pictures but these never did appear. The Dutch prisoners now had all their paperwork completed and were simply waiting for news of when their flight to Holland would take place. With the exception of a few details, the same was true of the Spanish prisoners.

Some of the Dutch were becoming very twitchy, having their flight back to Europe almost in their grasp but having been so brutally reminded of the fragility of their lives by the death of Mancho. Marco, in particular, having been so closely involved in the events leading to Mancho's death, was a nervous wreck and spent most of his time in his bugaloo with the curtains closed. When he did emerge, he shuffled around the prison looking as if he was trying to be invisible.

As more people came into the prison, the pressure on housing became serious. The church in particular was becoming massively overcrowded, as there was very limited living space within it. The prisoners noted that there was a large structure adjoining the church and extending out from the back of it. This had originally been designed as a dining room for the prison but was never used. A doorway was therefore broken through the adjoining wall to link the church with the dining room. When the director was made aware of what was going on, he came over to inspect the work in progress. The church members asked him for permission to dismantle the thirty or so solid concrete tables, each equipped with concrete benches, that made up the dining area, which was as large as any of the existing pavilions. The director flatly refused, threatening dire consequences if prison property was destroyed in this way.

Undaunted, those living in the church began to carry out their restructuring at night, and over the next two weeks the dining room was transformed into a large, open living area. Only a single line of tables in the centre of the floor were left in place, while the rest were broken down and removed. The rubble ensuing from the demolition was simply thrown out the windows, and each morning the larger pieces would be manhandled out through the doors, where they were soon put to use in bolstering the existing defensive structures.

Soon, bugaloos and partitions were being erected throughout the large new living space that had been made available, and the director had little option but to accept the *fait accompli* with which he had been presented. The church gained several new members at this time, due to the standard of accommodation now available to members.

Things were fairly active on the other side of the prison during those first two weeks of June 2001, with four people being gunned down and killed in two separate incidents. Living as we did in isolation from the other compound, we learned little of the history to such events and could only presume that they had accumulated bad debts or had been challenging the power of the gangsters in charge over there. We always felt that San Antonio was like an overheated pressure cooker, requiring very little in order for it to go out of control and explode completely.

On the afternoon of July 2, an event took place that sent shock waves through the group of foreign prisoners in San Antonio. That it should happen had been long predicted and was to some extent inevitable, given the manner in which prisoners were treated, but the reality still brought everyone up short. The first foreign prisoner died.

The Canadian prisoner, a forty-four-year-old of Philippine extraction known to all as Joey, who had been living for some time around the inner compound of the prison, began to complain of severe pain on the evening of Thursday, June 28. He had a long history of stomach ulcers. Unfortunately for him, the doctor had visited the prison on Thursday morning and was not due to visit again until the following Tuesday, and so he was told that he would just have to wait until Tuesday morning.

Over the course of the next couple of days, his pain and discomfort increased, he was unable to sleep, and he spent the nights sitting on the floor adjacent to the duty vigilante, moaning with pain and asking for help. Each day, he asked the most senior person on duty to please get him to a hospital but his requests were always denied.

As a further misfortune of timing, the Canadian consul was

off the island for celebrations connected with Canada Day and the embassy in Caracas was closed for the long weekend for the same reason. It therefore proved impossible to obtain help from outside in order to bring pressure on the prison authorities to get proper medical attention for Joey.

On Monday morning, Joey once more went to the offices to ask the assistant director for help but was ejected from the office area. Returning again at the beginning of the afternoon, Joey pleaded with the assistant director to get him to hospital, as he "knew that there was something seriously wrong". Again he was told that he would not be taken to hospital and would have to wait until the following morning to see the doctor.

At this point, Joey collapsed onto the floor and the assistant director burst out laughing, pointing out to the other *vigilantes*.

"Look at this one. What a great actor."

Within a few minutes, however, they realised that something was indeed seriously wrong, but by that time it was far too late and Joey was showing no signs of life. He was quickly stretchered out of the prison and taken to hospital, but was found to be dead on arrival.

Although such a tragedy had been almost inevitable, we were all still shaken by Joey's death, and many of the foreign prisoners who did not qualify for repatriation began to apply for transfers to a prison on the mainland. The prison of choice was Santa Ana, near the Colombian border, which was reputed to be one of the most reasonable of the country's dreadful prisons. Despite submitting letters to the judge requesting transfer, all were aware that the processing of such requests was likely to take an inordinate amount of time and that they would personally be responsibly for the payment of all costs associated with the transfer.

In the middle of July, a new director was appointed to the prison, the fourth within the space of one year. His was, apparently, an interim appointment, as he spent only four weeks in the prison before being replaced by a sixty-year-old former army officer. This last proved to be one of the most reasonable of the directors that we had experienced. Clearly well used to commanding men, his bearing and manner commanded respect and he was the first director in my experience who was prepared to enter our compound without an armed guard of soldiers to protect him.

His style was demonstrated shortly after his arrival, when he entered the compound during a *raqueta* following the shooting of two prisoners within the compound. Dismissing the Guardia Nacional troops, he motioned the assembled prisoners to gather round him so that we could all hear him. Then in a quiet but clear voice, he said, "At the moment, I am busy trying to bring the paperwork up to date for those who are due for early release. If you want to kill each other, it's up to you, but you should be aware that when a violent death occurs, I have a bunch of paperwork to complete, press interviews to give, and so on, and it is approximately two days lost from the paperwork that I would prefer to be getting on with. I ask for your cooperation in keeping the situation quiet so that I can get on with trying to help you. That is all."

Standing alone, surrounded by more than a hundred dangerous and unstable prisoners, he looked old and frail but with a huge amount of dignity and common humanity. By sheer force of personality, he was able to dominate his audience, who listened in attentive silence to what he had to say and who could be seen digesting the sense of his message. His period in charge proved to be one of the most stable during our time at San Antonio, although there were considerable undercurrents of unrest and naked ambition at work among the ranks of the prisoners, which were later to erupt in bloodshed and chaos.

Around this time, Kurt the German, who had by this time moved in to the inner compound as a result of his inability to live at peace with the locals in our compound, was diagnosed as being HIV positive. It was hardly surprising, given the wild tales he told of sexual exploits during a visit to Thailand. When I heard the news, I went across to offer my sympathy but was surprised to find him in upbeat mood.

"This is good news," he exulted. "Now, they will have to let me go from this hellish place, and I can go back to Germany, be cured and all will be well!"

With a heavy heart, I pointed out that no cure had yet been discovered or developed for the HIV virus in any part of the world, but I am not sure that he believed me. In any case, the future was less important to him than was the hope that the German government would step in, in response to his newly diagnosed condition, and arrange to have him removed from the prison of San Antonio. It was another demonstration, if such were needed, of the intense pressure that we all felt in that place, that someone would welcome a diagnosis of HIV as a means to escape it.

THROUGHOUT THE MONTHS of July and August, the food served in the prison became even worse than usual and the ration smaller. It transpired that the prison had run up debts of six million bolivars with their food suppliers, who had decided to refuse to supply any more until at least one million (about £10,000) of the debt had been paid off. As the prison did not have this kind of money, they resorted to buying tinned tuna and sardines, rice and spaghetti for cash, on a daily basis, and serving them up in the various permutations that this limited supply allowed. Given my aversion to fish, it was a very lean couple of months indeed for me. As letters written by me demonstrate, I began at this time to seriously doubt my ability to see my sentence through to the end. There seemed to be too many things conspiring against my survival.

Two main elements contributed to my state of mind at this time. One was a natural reaction to the terrible events of the preceding months, and the other was the fact that the locals had realised that I was a good listener, with the result that my room had become a kind of therapy clinic, with a stream of visitors every day who just wanted to talk about their lives, their fears and frustrations and their regrets, in the knowledge that what they said to me would remain in confidence.

"When I was sixteen, I saw someone I knew, about the same age as me, being killed horribly," one young man told me. "He was in a rival gang, and was captured by our group. They held him down and took a chainsaw to him, starting with his hands, then his feet, working inwards. I couldn't do or say anything, or I'd have been next. It was awful. I was just willing him to die to end the torture. I can still hear him screaming."

"I have killed men," another told me. "Now though, I see their faces whenever I shut my eyes. I can never get a night's sleep unless I fill myself up with drugs. Now I'm afraid I'm going to die in this place. I'm scared."

"I've lived on the streets since I was seven years old," recounted yet another. "I never knew my father and my mother couldn't cope with five of us. I was put out to survive as best I could. I have never spent one day in a school; it's always been just survival, doing whatever you can to get by."

Most of them had lived through some horrific experiences, despite their youth, and had been involved in some dark and evil deeds. I found myself carrying an ever-increasing burden of the pain and suffering of others without myself being able to enjoy the luxury of a safety valve to vent my feelings. It did give me a unique insight into the life experiences of Venezuelan prisoners, who appeared to have been destined almost from birth to a life on the fringes of society, and with each stage in their lives pushing them further along the path towards criminality. Many young men shed tears as they recounted incidents from their past or expressed their fears for the future, before pulling themselves together and exiting to take up their duties on the guard post or whatever, assuming their usual devil-may-care façade.

I felt inadequate in the face of this avalanche of misery, but it seemed that just providing an attentive, sympathetic and non-judgemental ear was sufficient, as they returned time and again, and even very senior figures among the prisoners took to pouring out their troubles to me. There were times when I felt that I would lose my mind as I was exposed to a seemingly endless parade of pain, depravity and deep fear, but my efforts undoubtedly earned me considerable respect among the local population.

One less desirable result of this growing respect was that the custom developed that whenever one of the management team had, for some reason, to enter the church, where weapons were not allowed, he would first come into my room and give me his pistol to keep under my pillow until he came back out again. As might be expected, their weapons training was appalling, and on more than one occasion I was alarmed to see someone pull a revolver out of his waistband, look at it, and say, "Oh, silly me, I had it cocked all the time." Accidents were a reasonably regular occurrence, and the gangsters were almost as much of a danger to themselves as they were to anyone else.

As there was now a reasonably large population of young foreigners in the prison, my room also became the first point of call when, as not infrequently happened, disputes broke out between them and the locals. At least once a day, I would be confronted by two outraged faces, with the local saying, "Capitan, would you please tell him . . ." Normally, these disagreements were based on something trivial and it was easy enough to settle things down.

One very young British prisoner called Lance, from southern England, seemed to lurch from crisis to crisis, constantly getting himself into hot water. Things came to a head one day when Ramon, who sold drugs, and was a senior member of the management team in the prison, came to me to say that he had reached the end of his tether with Lance, who had run up a considerable bill with him and appeared to be making no effort to pay it off, despite working each day washing clothes to make money.

"I am going to have to stab him," exclaimed Ramon. "I've given him every chance, but he is just not cooperating."

I promised to have a word with the errant youth. Shortly afterwards, Lance himself came in, saying, "I've decided to move out of the compound and go to work in the kitchen. I can earn three thousand bolivars a week there, and I'm going to use it to pay off everything I owe."

I was horrified at this development, and told Lance plainly, "If you do that, you'll almost certainly be dead within the week. If Ramon sees you leaving the compound, he'll think you're trying to avoid paying him, and there's no way on God's earth is he going to stand for that.

"Besides," I pointed out, "look what's happened to every other nutter who's gone into the kitchens. They've all become crackheads within a couple of weeks. I don't see anything to show that you'd be any different, so apart from wrecking your life, you'd just get deeper in debt and never be able to pay Ramon back. One way or another, you're negotiating your way into a body bag unless you wisen up."

I advised him that his only realistic option was to move into the church, continue working and pay off his debt a bit at a time. I offered to run a bank for him, so that he could deposit whatever money he earned by washing clothes with me each day, and we would pay Ramon in 10,000 bolivar increments. Following a great deal of argument and discussion, Lance eventually accepted the seriousness of his plight, agreed to the proposal, and we decided to sound out Ramon.

Ramon proved amenable to this suggestion, and the arrangements were put in place. To his credit, Lance paid off his debt, as agreed, over the following few months, although his time in the church was not without its episodes of high drama, and Lance would come into my room on a regular basis to air his grievances, which ranged from, "Cappy, I've been trying to tell them that it's not fair that I should have to take part in the morning service, because I work hard all day," to, "Cappy, the guy who shares my bugaloo plays with himself all night and I can't get to sleep." All I could offer in response to the latter complaint was, "And what the hell do you expect me to do about it?"

As I watched Lance in his daily struggles to cope, in an environment where he was totally out of his depth, I often wished that he could change places with whichever unscrupulous bastard had taken advantage of his naivety to send him to South America on a drugs run.

One incident involving Ramon provided considerable amusement, although the possible consequences were dangerous enough. Fred, who had made little effort to learn Spanish, began working with Ramon, who was responsible for tending the garden at the back of the accommodation blocks. As the cultivated ground was the main deposit for both drugs caches and the storage of weapons, ammunition and explosives, it was important that Fred be able to follow instructions to the letter.

One day, an exasperated Ramon entered my room with Fred in tow. They sat down, upon which Ramon, who spoke fast, very colloquial Spanish, turned to me and said, "Tell him, Capitan, he has to work at learning Spanish. Also, if there is something he doesn't understand, he must say so and not just nod his head and say, 'Yes.'

"Watch this," he continued. Turning to Fred, he smiled and nodded encouragingly, while asking him, in conversational Spanish, "Would you like me to blow your fucking head off?"

Sure enough, the response from Fred was an answering smile and nod, and the words, "Yes, yes!"

Turning back to me in fury, Ramon said, "See what I mean, Capitan? It's crazy. If he doesn't stop it, he's going to get himself killed."

I promised to pass on Ramon's concerns as forcibly as I could, and to encourage Fred to work harder at his Spanish. The two continued to work together until they were finally transferred out of the prison and managed to overcome their language difficulties, eventually achieving a considerable degree of mutual respect.

In order to pass the time in the evenings, Fred and I decided that we would have a go at building a model boat. I had noticed that bundles of lollipop sticks, which seemed to have been produced and sold specifically for modelling, were regularly brought into the prison by visitors for various projects of the locals, and was pretty sure that we could construct a reasonable craft using them. I therefore drew, as best I could from memory, the plans for a three-masted schooner, scaled them, and we then set about scrounging and borrowing the necessary materials to begin construction. White wood glue was in plentiful supply, as it was used in the workshops, our modelling knife was a piece of razor blade embedded in a stick, and we improvised with clothes pegs and elastic bands as vices in order to hold joints together while they set.

Working with such primitive tools, the construction was to take months, but it provided a very useful diversion for us week after week. Like so much else in San Antonio, the project was not to have a happy ending, but Fred and I happily worked away throughout the autumn of 2001, engrossed in what we were doing.

Miguel was released from the prison at the beginning of September, leaving the reins of power in the hands of his stepson, another leading gangster on the island, who had been in the prison for just over a year. This decision was to have dreadful consequences for San Antonio prison and everyone in it.

CHAPTER TWELVE

Sinking
The Good Ship Hope

IN MID-AUGUST, we were once more united with our companions from the DISIP police station. Having been held in the police station for more than a year they were eventually taken to a trial, at which Alexis, his son Adrian, and Oliver were found guilty and sentenced to prison terms of fifteen years. José had been freed.

Alexis moved into the church, where Denis was also now living. Adrian and Oliver moved into my room, Adrian sleeping in a hammock slung across the room, and Oliver taking the top bunk of a bunk bed, the bottom bunk being occupied by a middle-aged Hungarian prisoner called Carlo, who had entered the prison some months before and whom Miguel had sent to live with me, as he spoke no Spanish and only a few words of English.

In the space of a few weeks, some sixty additional prisoners had come into our compound, making an already crowded living situation intolerably more so. Tensions inevitably rose with the pressure of numbers, although for several months incidents of outright violence were few. Permission had been sought, and obtained, from the director for prisoners from the women's annex to visit the compound for a few hours twice a week, accompanied by their guards, and this measure undoubtedly helped to maintain a degree of calm and a sense of semi-normality within the compound.

A Scottish prisoner, Aileen, offered to bring a meal across to Denis and I each time she visited, charging us cost price, and so twice a week we were able to supplement the miserable rations from the kitchens with a decent meal which actually tasted of something other than cockroach.

One negative development, in September 2001, was the return to the prison of the officer in charge of the Guardia detachment, after an absence of several months. During his absence, the detachment of troops had been under the command of his second, who had proved to be a fair and reasonable officer. Now, however, "Scarface", as he was known among the prisoners, was back, newly promoted to captain and seeming to be as full of spit and venom as before, if not more so.

Immediately upon his return, Captain Ramirez began to mount frequent *raquetas* and the attitude of his men became more aggressive and provocative. Whatever training course he had been on had obviously involved the use of metal detectors, as he now brought one of those in during each and every *raqueta*, and many new holes began to appear in our walls as he "discovered" the steel reinforcing rods running up through the concrete at regular intervals. Much to his obvious chagrin and frustration, none of these searches turned up the weapons for which he was looking.

One day, near the beginning of November, the captain decided to change his tactics. After entering for a raid, he and his men ordered all the prisoners to leave the compound and we were assembled in the inner compound, where we were left to be guarded by four soldiers while the captain and the remainder of his men entered our compound bearing spades, shovels, picks and machetes. After we had sat baking under the hot afternoon sun for four and a half hours, the director returned to the prison from some meeting that he had been attending. Immediately upon taking stock of the situation, he marched into the compound and ordered the captain to get out and to take his men and gardening equipment with him. Somewhat sheepishly, they retired, taking with them their haul for the day: half a kilo of marijuana and a knife. We returned to our compound to a scene of utter destruction. All over the compound, banana plants, mango trees and other vegetation had been hacked down and considerable areas of the grounds dug up.

Another new tactic employed by the captain was the disruption of visits, delaying the entrance of visitors to the prison in the mornings. On several occasions, it was only the intervention of the director that allowed the visit to go ahead. Clearly, there was little love lost between the two men and we were all quite sorry when, at the end of November, the old man left the prison, to be replaced by a younger man.

One morning, we awoke to the sound of heavy rainfall. As we prepared to exit for the morning head-count, water was seeping in through the door, and when it was opened a deluge entered, quickly reaching knee height. We waded out into this murky, effluent-laden water, to be met by the sight of the Guardia Nacional troops wading around wearing green capes over their battledress. By the time we reached the basketball court, the water was thigh deep, and we ludicrously lined up as usual while the Guardia waded around carrying out the count. Nothing must interfere with the precious *numero*. After the headcount, by which time the torrential downpour had ceased, we were able to move up onto the high ground around the workshop and wait until the water level dropped, which it did very quickly.

It seemed that a river running close beside the prison had burst its banks, which had caused the flooding within the gaol. As the waters receded, several small, flat fish were found around the grounds, a windfall that the locals were quick to take advantage of. Soon frying pans were in action in every pavilion as they prepared to enjoy the unexpected feast.

When I returned to my room, I found that the mucky slime left behind by the water as a high water mark lay just a couple of inches below my mattress. It took all the rest of the day to clean the filth left behind by the invading waters.

TOWARDS THE END of November, the prison was visited by the British Ambassador to Venezuela. He carefully listened to our tales of life within San Antonio, and toured the prison to see our living conditions for himself. By the time he left, he had clearly been impressed and considerably shocked. The news he had for us about repatriation, however, was not good: he announced that it was his understanding that a bi-lateral agreement would be signed by the two governments "within eighteen months". After that, each applicant's submission under the agreement would require about a year to eighteen months to process. While disappointed by this news, we appreciated his honesty in laying before us a realistic timetable.

Meanwhile, other nationalities were faring very much better. All the German prisoners were transferred to a prison near Caracas in early November. Half the Dutch prisoners were flown back to Holland to spend the remainder of their sentences under the custody of the Dutch penal authorities. The other half of the Dutch contingent were expected to follow shortly afterwards. One Danish prisoner had been released in November under the agreement arrived at with the judge following the hunger strike. The other Danish prisoner had not earned sufficient work credits to be released, although his release was expected shortly. The Spanish prisoners were awaiting final arrangements for their repatriation.

Of the European Union countries represented in the prison, only the French were in a worse position than the British. As long as the infamous Venezuelan terrorist known as Carlos the Jackal was serving a sentence in a French prison, it was unlikely in the extreme that a repatriation agreement could ever be reached between the two countries.

During the last week of November 2001, all prisoners were weighed and measured and had their fingerprints recorded digitally by machine. During that process, I was very surprised to discover that I had lost twenty-two kilos (just under three and a half stone) during my imprisonment. My normal weight had been eighty-two kilos, or just under thirteen stone, and now I weighed slightly less than nine and a half stone. I had of course been aware that I had lost a lot of weight during the previous eighteen months, but was shocked by the amount. I sincerely hoped that we would not have to face another hunger strike, and I would certainly not recommend the San Antonio Diet Plan to anyone hoping to lose a bit of weight.

The new director was a stark contrast to his gentlemanly predecessor. He also entered the compound unescorted, but with a pistol stuck into his waistband, and he would sit and chew the fat with the management team for hours on end. He seemed determined from the outset to prove himself to be some kind of gangsters' friend, and used slang and curses at least as much as they did in his everyday speech. Within a few days of his arrival, he announced that "we will not be taking any more shit from the boys in green" (a reference to the Guardia Nacional). He extended the lock-up time until six in the evening, stating that the Guardia would have to "like it or lump it". He also gave permission for the prisoners from the women's side to visit the compound for a few hours each day. His attitude was soon to take a dramatic reversal, however.

By the beginning of December, the efforts that Fred and I had put into our model ship were paying off. Having mastered the techniques necessary for its construction through trial and error, we had built the hull and deck, shaped masts and spars, constructed deck houses and hatchways, and added details such as a steering wheel, anchor windlass, lifebelts and a stand. The hull had been painted black, the decks and spars varnished and the masts mounted with standing and running rigging. We had cut sails out of old cloth, of a suitably tan colour, and attached these to the mast.

The building of the vessel had attracted attention and admiration from around the compound, and each day a stream of visitors would come in to review progress. Fred and I had decided that we would try to finish the ship by the second week in December, then try to sell it in order to buy a bottle of whisky with which to properly celebrate Christmas.

These plans were brought to an abrupt end on December 13. That day, a prisoner from the other side of the prison was killed in "no-man's land" by a prisoner from our compound, using an automatic pistol. It was an opportunistic attack, taking advantage of a rare opportunity when one of the management team from the other side had placed himself in a part of the prison where he was vulnerable.

Immediately, the siren sounded and we all hurried to our usual assembly point at the rear of the basketball court to await the inevitable *raqueta*. As we made our way to that point, we could hear some of the usual gunfire behind us as a group of Guardia troops prepared to jump across the wall and enter the compound. A couple of shots were then fired into the compound from the guard tower outside the perimeter wall which overlooked the basketball court, presumably to encourage some stragglers to hurry along.

Up until that point, things had proceeded as we would normally expect, but now all hell broke loose and we all threw ourselves into a prone position as a hail of high-powered rounds whizzed through the air just over our heads. Heavy and sustained fire continued as we tried to work out what the hell was going on. We then realised that a full-scale gun battle was being fought between the Guardia Nacional troops trying to enter our compound and the Guardia Nacional trooper in the external guard tower.

Apparently one of the rounds fired from the tower initially had been aimed high and had passed over the roof of our pavilion, narrowly missing one of the entering soldiers. Jumping to the, perhaps natural, conclusion that they were being fired upon from the roof of the pavilion, the entering troops returned the fire, emptying magazine after magazine in long bursts of automatic fire, the angle of fire ensuring that their rounds went whizzing around the guard tower, where the incumbent responded by letting off a stream of bullets in the direction of the roof of the pavilion, from where he assumed he was being attacked. The battle went on for about ten or fifteen minutes, which seemed to us like hours, during which countless rounds were fired. Prisoners working in the kitchen would later describe seeing *vigilantes* running across the compound carrying bags of spare ammunition to the soldiers.

Once I realised what was happening, I could only pray that none of the Guardia Nacional troops was hit, as the result would almost certainly be a massacre of the prisoners. In any event, I worried about the state of mind of the troops when they eventually did enter. A part of me wondered if it was a situation pre-arranged by the Guardia captain to provide him with an excuse to order his men to open fire upon the defenceless group of inmates. It was utterly terrifying to lie there, wishing that one could disappear into the ground, being completely helpless to do anything to alter whatever course events would take over the next few minutes.

Eventually, the firing died away, either because the lookout in the tower had realised what was happening or because he had run out of ammunition. In any event, a couple of minutes of calm ensued, following which the first pair of Guardia troops could be seen cautiously making their way round the end of the pavilion. When the first reached the corner of Pavilion Four, he fired a long burst of suppressing fire into the doorway of Pavilion Five before making his way onto the basketball court, while being carefully covered by his second.

"Where's the rifle?" he shouted as he came forward. "Where's the fucking rifle?"

Several prisoners pointed up towards the guard tower, and one shouted, "It's up in your own fucking guard tower, you shower of fucking idiots!"

Still, he did not seem convinced, and maintained a watchful distance until the rest of his colleagues entered, accompanied by the prison director, who came running in with pistol drawn.

By this time, reinforcements had come into the prison from Guardia Nacional posts throughout the island, and we were soon surrounded by a large number of troops who, led by the gangsters-friend director, began to kick and beat us at random using boots, swords, baseball bats and rifle butts. The director appeared to be beside himself with rage, having apparently taken the events of the afternoon as a personal insult and a challenge to his authority.

Having kicked and beaten us into ranks, sitting with our heads down and stripped of all clothing, and taken a head-count, the Guardia troops limited themselves to maintaining guard over us while the director began a rant. He knew, he said, that it was an automatic pistol that had been used in the killing of the prisoner earlier in the afternoon, and he was now giving orders to the captain of the Guardia Nacional that they were not to leave the compound until that pistol had been found and confiscated.

For the next three hours we sat there, hearing crashing and banging coming from our accommodation, as the Guardia Nacional troops took advantage of the licence that they had been given to them by the director and caused the maximum damage possible inside the pavilions.

After three hours of destructive searching, the pistol had not been found and the prison director had to admit defeat and retire from the scene, while we were escorted to our pavilions by the troops and locked inside to survey the damage to our quarters and recover from what we all recognised as having been a close brush with death.

The first thing that met my eyes when I entered my room were the pathetic remains of the model ship that Fred and I had worked on for so many long hours, lying smashed on the floor, beyond any hope of repair. The rest of the damage – upturned beds, coffee, sugar, cooking oil and flour poured indiscriminately onto the floor among clothing and bedding – was by now routine, but this was a wanton act of sheer vandalism that had nothing whatsoever to do with the search for an automatic pistol and everything to do with small-minded spitefulness. With maximum dimensions of fourteen inches by five, the model would not have had space enough for even the magazine of an automatic pistol and its weight would make it obvious that the hull was empty.

As I thought back over the planning, the frustration, the work and the pleasure that had gone into its construction over so many weeks, my heart sank and I moaned with despair, and then called out to Fred, "Come and look what the bastards have done." He was equally devastated to see what had happened to our work, saying, "I don't fucking well believe it."

By the time I had finished putting the room back together, my despair had been converted to quiet anger, and so I spent the rest of the evening mounting a small shelf on the wall, on which I carefully arranged what was left of the ship model. I then stuck a notice beside it, written in both English and Spanish, and reading:

Here lies the wreck of the good ship 'Hope',
Destroyed by enemy action on the 13th December 2001,
When she was attacked by the notorious Capitan Scarface,
And his band of pirates.

Throughout the pavilion, bullets had penetrated the walls in about seven places during the fire fight. One had entered low down on the back wall, fatally wounding a fridge in a room shared by four Colombians. The following day, when we were allowed out of the pavilion, we found many bullet holes and scars on the outside of the walls, and indeed the front corner of the building had suffered so many hits that it had been rounded off! The gate was pockmarked with lumps of lead, and two palm trees in the front grounds had bullet holes right through them.

From that time onwards, the Guardia Nacional wore full riot gear each time they entered the prison, even for routine headcounts, and their weapon of choice changed from the previously ubiquitous Fal to the Uzi sub-machine gun, with its devastating six hundred rounds per minute rate of fire.

It was a frightened and demoralised group of prisoners who passed that festive season in San Antonio, and we all wondered what the New Year would bring. We did not have long to wait before we found out.

CHAPTER THIRTEEN

The War Of
The Pavilions

THE PRISON REMAINED tense. The Guardia Nacional
maintained their nervous disposition, and all it took was a
prisoner to shout out, "Asusta me!" (Scare me!) when the head-
count parade was breaking up for all weapons to be loudly
cocked and safety catches to be switched off. Naturally, this
behaviour played into the hands of the prisoners, who delighted
in provoking this response at every opportunity.

One morning, a young Venezuelan arrived late for the
head-count, and as he was hurrying across the parade ground,
a knife fell out of his shorts. A Guardia Nacional trooper
borrowed a pump-action shotgun from one of the *vigilantes*,
then called for the young man to pick up his knife and
ordered him to hand it over. Holding the shotgun in one
hand, the soldier held out the other hand for the knife as the
young prisoner reluctantly moved forward holding out the
knife in his hand while trying to maintain the maximum
possible distance from the soldier. As soon as the soldier had
a hold of the knife, he pulled the trigger of the shotgun,
unleashing a cartridge-full of plastic crowd control pellets
onto the ground between the two of them, while the
youngster tried to make good his escape. As they are designed

to do, the pellets bounced into the air, and many of them hit the young prisoner's legs, causing painful burns. The growl of protest emanating from the group of prisoners as a response to this act of cruelty was immediately met with the sound of sliding bolts as the remaining Guardia troops cocked their weapons.

Incidents such as this kept the pot simmering, and the rumour machine was working overtime with suggestions that five members of the management team were about to be transferred to one of the grimmer prisons on the mainland. The director had decided that his days of being best pals with the gangsters were over, and kept himself to his office. Visits by the female prisoners to the compound were drastically curtailed.

The British Consul paid us his routine visit on January 24, bearing the usual letters from home together with any money that had been sent by family or friends. We were greatly surprised when he returned to the prison the following day and astonished when he explained the reason for his unscheduled visit. Mr Weller explained that, following his visit to the prison, the British Ambassador had requested, and the Venezuelan Government had agreed to, the transfer of all British prisoners who so wished to one of the more peaceable prisons on the mainland. We could choose between one of two, namely Santa Ana prison in Táchira state, near the Colombian border, or the prison in Mérida. Transfer would be carried out by military aircraft within ten days.

As we had all heard very good reports of Santa Ana prison, all the male prisoners chose that one. The female prisoners all chose to remain where they were, in recognition of the fact that the female annex at San Antonio was one of the most reasonable in the country, with a tiny number of prisoners in comparison to any of the female prisons on the mainland.

Mr Weller had brought forms for us to sign, formally

requesting the transfer, and my hand shook when it was my turn to sign the form. It was wonderful and amazing! Just when I had resigned myself to being stuck in this dreadful place for years to come, without possibility of alternative, here we were being offered an almost immediate exit from the horrors of San Antonio. I was overcome with gratitude for the role played by His Excellency Ambassador Dr John Hughes, who had taken the trouble to visit the prison, had possessed the humanity to understand and appreciate the plight in which he found us, and had then concerned himself to find a solution to our difficulties and to apply that solution, using the power of his office to do so.

On the Friday following the news of our impending transfer, the prison director advised us that, as from Monday, we must be ready to leave the prison "at half an hour's notice" and that the transfer would certainly take place before the following Wednesday. By the end of the following week, however, there had been no further news, and alarmingly we became aware that the director was now selling seats on the transport to foreign prisoners who could afford to buy them. With the appearance of each new candidate for the transfer, there was inevitably further delay, as that person's paperwork had to be prepared and the authorisation paper sent to the courthouse to be signed by the judge.

When challenged about this activity, the director blithely stated that he was offering additional places on the transfer "purely on humanitarian grounds" and that it was necessary to make a charge for this for the simple reason that, although the British Consul was correct in saying that a military aircraft had been arranged at no cost, no mention had been made of the cost of fuel for the aircraft or the expenses of our escorts. With sinking hearts, we realised that the dead hand of Venezuelan corruption was at work and that the whole arrangement was likely to become embedded in a quagmire for as long as the director felt that there was more money to be milked out of the deal.

At the beginning of March, while we continued to wait anxiously for news of when we were to leave the prison, we were visited by a small working party of officials from London, who had been in Caracas ironing out the final details of the Prisoner Exchange Agreement with the Venezuelan Ministry of Justice. There were representatives of the Foreign and Commonwealth Office, as well as officials from the Home Office Prisons Department. They brought the good news that the accord was now ready to be signed and that the signing would take place the next time a suitable British Government Minister visited Venezuela, which they hoped would be in the early summer.

We were able to show them round the prison and they were shocked by what they saw. The overcrowding and the poor sanitation were bad enough, but those members of the working party who worked for the British Prison Service were horrified to find themselves strolling amongst prisoners openly displaying weapons and to see gun-toting prisoners on the roof. They were also horrified to see the damage remaining from the Guardia Nacional activities of December 13. One member of the group had tears in her eyes as she surveyed the remains of "Hope" and heard the story of how the wreck came about. They assured us that any applications for repatriation coming from the Island of Margarita would be processed by them in record time.

Each day became an endless nightmare of Chinese torture as we waited for any firm news on the transfer and each day were disappointed. To make matters worse, tensions within the prison reached an all-time high, and I received an increasing number of visits from those close to the management team, who all expressed their concern that things were not going well and that something terrible was about to happen.

These predictions came true when, one afternoon in the middle of March, the top man, Miguel's stepson, was gunned down in front of the pavilion by members of his own bodyguard. During the *raqueta* that followed, the dead man's brother and five of his immediate supporters were allowed to move out of the compound and they took up residence in a small room adjacent to the offices, while awaiting transfer to another prison. As he left the compound, the dead man's brother, his face contorted by grief and rage, turned around and swore vengeance on those responsible for the murder.

Julio had tried to defend the dead man, and it was widely expected that he would be next to die. However, Julio knew something that no one else did, and that was that he was due to be released the following day. In the morning, he not only managed to leave the compound safely, but he had previously smuggled his pistol out of the compound and before leaving the prison he delivered this into the hands of one of the leaders on the other side of the prison. The following day, the top man of one of the pavilions on the other side of the prison was killed, in what is euphemistically known in Venezuelan prisons as a "change of government".

The whole prison now moved onto a war footing. The gangsters who were now in charge within our pavilion, and who had led our own change of government, realised that they were likely to face revenge attacks and did their best to prepare for them. Additional guards were posted throughout the day at key vantage points around the perimeter. Those who lived within the compound were banned from exiting except for some crucial purpose and then only with specific permission from the man in charge, a measure which served to increase the difficulties that we were facing in our attempts to move forward our transfer to another prison.

On the night of April 1, around one in the morning, an attack was mounted on our compound from the other side of the prison. Prisoners in one of the pavilions on the other side had made a hole in the exterior wall of their accommodation, and two of them exited via this hole before climbing onto the roof and reaching our compound by way of the kitchen roof.

From the roof of Pavilion Five, one of them threw a grenade through the louvered window of one of the cells. In the last moments of their approach they had been spotted from the doorway of Pavilion Five and several shots were fired, which was our first indication in Pavilion Four that something was going on. Despite the gunfire, they were able to press home their attack and then retreat once more across the rooftops, and seconds later there was an almighty bang as the grenade exploded.

There had been only one prisoner in the room where the grenade entered at the time, sleeping in a hammock. He was very severely injured by blast and shrapnel. Immediately, the residents of Pavilion Five began to fire guns into the air, and those in our pavilion began hammering the door with the scaffolding pole to alert the *vigilantes* that there was a severely hurt prisoner who needed evacuating. Understandably nervous as a result of the shooting and explosion, the duty *vigilantes* refused to enter the compound until they were backed up by a squad of Guardia Nacional troops, who provided cover while the injured man was stretchered off and then ordered all prisoners to the basketball court, where we were strip-searched and a head-count carried out.

The moment that we were allowed back into our pavilions, work began on improving the defences. Access already existed between the two parts of Pavilion Four, having been created during the dreadful events of the previous June. Now, passageways were knocked through between our accommodation and the church and from the church into Pavilion Five, giving the defenders free access to move between all the

177

accommodation blocks of our compound. After a couple of hours, another attack was mounted across the roofs, but this time the two attackers were spotted by very alert and nervous lookouts and the attack was driven off. There was no reaction by the prison staff or the Guardia Nacional to this second burst of gunfire.

The following morning, those not actively involved in guard duties began working on creating additional lookout posts within the buildings, so that a proper lookout could be maintained at night. In my room, a slit-hole was punched through the wall, high in the corner, which overlooked the kitchen roof. A chair was mounted on the wall, and from that time forward there was an armed lookout posted in that position from six o'clock in the evening until six o'clock in the morning. This was one of a total of seventeen lookout posts distributed around the accommodation blocks throughout the night. The rule about no weapons being allowed into the church was waived, as the church was the nearest part of the accommodation to the enemy camp. The lookouts were changed every two hours, and the person in charge of the lookouts entered every ten minutes or so to shout at them to maintain an alert watch, thus rendering sleep impossible for the occupants of the room.

The tension within the prison was unbearable, and the level of drug taking among the locals grew to enormous proportions as they tried to cope with the sense of imminent danger. Suspicion and paranoia were at an all-time high. On the evening after we were attacked, a service was held in the church, commencing around seven in the evening. There was very loud hymn singing, accompanied by the beating of drums. It soon became clear that this activity, which went on for hours, was designed to act as a cover for the noise of a hole being hammered into the exterior wall of the church building. The hammer blows were being coordinated with the beating of the drums. All pretence that the church was a centre of peace and tranquillity within the prison had now been abandoned.

After several hours, a hole had been created in the exterior wall big enough to allow a crouching man through. Final preparations were now made for a retaliatory raid against the maximum security block on the other side of the prison. About three in the morning, a group of five prisoners left through the hole in the church wall, armed with pistols and one grenade, to attack the block just a short distance from the rear wall of the church.

The rest of us remained in an agony of suspense, waiting for the expected explosion. After some minutes, we heard several bursts of gunfire but no exploding grenade, and within a few minutes more the raiding party came charging back, excited and breathless, to announce that they had failed. Apparently, in the heat of the moment the person charged with launching the grenade had found it impossible to pull the pin out but had thrown it into the building in any case, while coming under fire from the defenders within the block. No one had been injured on either side during the attack. Thus, the only thing achieved by this raid was to present the other side with a free grenade, whilst reducing the stock of weaponry on our side of the prison by the same one grenade.

A few minutes later, the Guardia entered the prison and could be heard around the grounds, shooting liberally, presumably firing at shadows before they came to open the pavilions and ordered us out for a head-count. Once the count had been completed, the sergeant in command of the detail spoke briefly to the assembled prisoners. He strongly recommended the use of knives as opposed to guns in the resolution of disputes, particularly at night, as the Guardia would then be limited to coming in to pick up the pieces in the morning, and would not need to be disturbed in the middle of the night!

After the routine roll call in the morning, a few troops remained within the prison, unnoticed by the prisoners, and they began prowling around the back of the buildings, finding the hole in the church wall through which the raiding party had left and re-entered the night before. When two of them entered through the hole, they came across a South African prisoner, who had been detailed to keep watch beside the opening. This individual was forced at gunpoint to lie down on the floor and then one of the Guardia troops climbed up onto an adjacent, three-foot-high, table and jumped onto his chest, leaving him winded, in great pain and with several broken ribs. This prisoner had to be hospitalised later in the day.

Meanwhile, work continued apace to convert our pavilions into a fortress. Fred and I had a chat about it and decided that, much as we had no wish to participate in this war, we should offer our advice on defensive measures that could be taken, purely for our own protection. Having discussed the situation, we then made a number of recommendations to the "management". These included the clearing away of plants and bushes close to the exterior of the buildings to remove protective cover from anyone sneaking up on the buildings during the night, the laying of a stone pathway around the buildings to create noise should anyone tread on them, and the hanging of light bulbs outside the buildings to illuminate the exterior. From that time onwards, the interior of the buildings was kept in darkness during the night. We also suggested that soft drinks cans be strung on lines and laid across the kitchen roof to increase the chances of detecting anyone approaching from that route. For my own room, I obtained some plain fencing wire, cut it into lengths and fitted it inside the louvers of my window, in the hope that any grenade hitting it would be repelled and would simply fall outside, to explode harmlessly outside the building.

There was an air of unreality to the whole situation which was very disquieting. The prison authorities seemed to have retired from the scene and were just leaving us to get on with it, being apparently oblivious to the interior of the prison being cannibalised at will in order to create an armed camp. The sense of danger, though, was real enough, and each night was a torture of expectation as we awaited the next attack from the other side. Regularly a shot would ring out as a nervous lookout let loose at a cat or a pigeon that had moved on the roof. Sleep was something to be snatched, a few minutes at a time, and I spent many hours at night preparing coffee for the lookouts in my room or just talking to them to make sure that they did not fall asleep. It had been made clear that anyone caught sleeping while on lookout would be shot out of hand, but some of the youngsters found it very difficult to stay awake for their two-hour spell of duty in the middle of the night. I drew heavily on my years of experience at sea following a watch-keeping routine and sometimes having to endure days on end with little or no sleep, to cope with the exhaustion engendered by the "war".

One night, as I made my way through the darkened accommodation on my way to the toilet at around two in the morning, I paused to properly look at surroundings that had become familiar to me over the preceding weeks. There were three lookouts sitting high on the walls, aiming their pistols out through their gun slits. One covered the front of the building, and the other two aimed out the side, at the parts of the kitchen roof that could not be seen from the post in my room. At one end of the room, sitting on the floor, were six or seven Venezuelans, squatting around a candle made from a bit of rag floating on cooking oil in a small can. They were engaged in a heavy session of smoking crack cocaine, and their faces appeared contorted both by the effects of the drug and by the feeble light emanating from their candle, which belched evil-smelling black smoke into the surrounding air. As I took in this infernal scene, a wave of despair washed over me and I could only think, what the hell am I doing in this place? Will I ever leave here alive?

If the frustration that we were facing as we awaited our transfer was terrible and difficult to cope with, that of the Danish prisoner Hans was infinitely worse. In December, a couple of weeks after the other Danish prisoner had left the prison to return to Denmark at the end of his sentence, I was sitting beside Hans one evening when he received a telephone call from the Danish consul, who had phoned to a mobile phone held by one of the prisoners. The Consul had called to say that all the arrangements were now in place for Hans to go home too. He was told the times and flight numbers of his flights the following day and assured that his mother had been advised of the good news and would meet him in Copenhagen airport. A few minutes later, Hans received a call from the Danish ambassador in Caracas, confirming all that the consul had told him and arranging that the ambassador would meet him in Caracas and see him safely aboard the flight to Denmark. Within half an hour, Hans's mother phoned him to express her great joy at the prospect of being reunited with him in a couple of days' time.

As might be imagined, Hans was euphoric, and began to rush round, organising himself and giving away all of his possessions that he did not intend to take with him. Early the next morning, he was devastated to be told by the prison director that it had all been a mistake and that his exact date for release had not yet been established.

By the time Hans eventually left the prison in March, he was a broken man, with a massive cocaine habit, his mind almost gone, and was unable to sustain a sensible conversation. I had grave doubts about his ability to survive for long in society.

*

THE POLITICAL SITUATION in Venezuela was also becoming extremely tense. Since the end of 1998, the Government had been led by a populist, left-wing president, Lieutenant Colonel Hugo Rafael Chavez Frías, who had been elected with a clear majority and enjoyed massive and growing support among the ordinary people as a result of his efforts to improve the lot of the poorest sections of society.

His regime was not at all to the liking of the United States Government, long used to having US-friendly regimes in place in Central and South American countries and to arranging the removal of those regimes that did not suit their needs, as they had done in Nicaragua, Chile, Haiti and elsewhere. As a major oil exporter, holding the fifth largest oil reserves in the world and the largest reserves of natural gas in the whole of the Americas, Venezuela was clearly in their sights, and in the years 2000 to 2002 they had spent at least two million dollars bolstering up any opposition groups who were prepared, by fair means or foul, to act towards the overthrow of the Chavez regime. This activity was detailed in a book, *El Código Chavez* (*The Chavez Code*) by a lawyer specialising in international law, Eva Golinger. Many of the damaging revelations contained in her book were obtained from the US Government through its Freedom of Information Act.

There were two reasons that we in the prison were concerned about the worsening political situation in the country. One was the generally held fear that, in the event of a civil war, among the first casualties would be prisoners, as the Guardia Nacional would enter the prisons and wipe them out. There had been precedents for this kind of behaviour in South America. The other reason concerned the proposed transfer of prisoners to Santa Ana prison. We had been told that this transfer would be carried out by agents of the Ministry of Defence, acting in cooperation with the Ministry of Justice.

Clearly any major disruption to the normal workings of government would result in the transfer becoming an extremely low priority, if it was not shelved altogether. If there should be a regime change, we would depend on the British ambassador making fresh approaches to officials of the new regime to solicit our transfer, which was hardly likely to take place until the new regime was well settled in, which could be many months down the line.

It was with considerable dismay, then, that we learnt on the afternoon and evening of April 11 that things were going very badly in Caracas. There had been an opposition march earlier in the day, which was supposed to be heading for the headquarters of the state oil company, PDVSA. As the march progressed, an increasingly aggressive group of speakers began to whip up the crowd into a frenzy and began to suggest that the route of the march be changed and that they march on the presidential palace of Miraflores, where several thousand of the President's supporters were already gathered.

Before the march reached the palace, shots rang out and twenty people were killed or injured. Almost immediately, a group of high-ranking military officers appeared on the screens of all the private TV channels and one of the officers, acting as spokesman, read out a declaration lamenting the deaths that had occurred amongst the members of the opposition march, blaming President Chavez for the deaths and calling for a military uprising against him. When, months later, CNN correspondent Otto Neustald admitted to having recorded this statement by the senior military officials in the early morning, before the march had even begun, it added to the growing body of evidence that the affair had been stage managed by those who were plotting to overthrow Chavez.

In the meantime, the same group of senior officers were inside the presidential palace, trying to persuade the President to resign and assuring him that there would be extensive bloodshed if he did not. After many hours of such persuasion, at around three o' clock on the morning of April 12, Chavez agreed to leave the palace in order to avoid a massacre outside it, but refused to resign. He was taken away under escort to the military headquarters of Caracas, Fort Tiuna, before being flown by helicopter to a military base on the coast, called Turiamo, and then, on the 13th, to the military installation on the island of La Orchila.

Back in Caracas, meantime, a leading industrialist, Pedro Carmona, had been sworn in as interim president and had immediately announced the closure of the legislative body, the National Assembly, as well as all the principal organs of state. It was announced that President Chavez had resigned after having sacked his entire government, although no document was produced to verify this claim.

In the confusion of the prison of San Antonio, I listened with growing dismay to the confusion taking place in Caracas. It was very difficult to get a clear picture of what was happening due to the degree of news control that was going on. The state broadcasting service had been forced off the air shortly after the coup began and the private channels confined themselves to celebrating the downfall of the "tyrant" Chavez and a return to "democratic" rule, apparently oblivious to the fact that all the institutions of democracy had just been declared by the new president as being closed until further notice and that he had announced his intention of ruling by decree, effectively establishing a dictatorship. I anxiously twiddled the tuning dial on my radio, switching between local FM radio stations, a national radio station on medium wave, which was carrying a CNN news stream, and the BBC World Service on short wave, to try and get a grasp of what was really happening.

On Saturday, April 12, something extraordinary began to happen in Caracas. Throughout the day, the inhabitants of the poor townships, or *barrios*, that surround the capital began to

185

descend on the capital city in their hundreds of thousands, demanding the reinstatement of their president and the legitimate Government. The private broadcasters began to play non-stop music, carrying no news items, a sure sign that things were not going their way. It is estimated that as many as two million people rampaged through the streets of Caracas that day, threatening full-scale insurrection if Chavez was not returned to power. Troops loyal to the Government emerged from Fort Tiuna and began moving towards the presidential palace, at which point the plotters lost their nerve and abandoned the palace.

Meanwhile, President Chavez had managed to arrange for a note to be smuggled out of his place of imprisonment, categorically denying that he had ever resigned, and shortly afterwards the Parachute Brigade mounted a rescue operation on the island of La Orchila to bring him back to the capital. He re-entered the palace of Miraflores just before four in the morning of April 14, and the coup was over.

I listened to the reports of the President's reinstatement with mixed feelings. On the one hand, I was pleased that the American-backed coup had failed and that civil war had been avoided, but on the other hand, I was convinced that a considerable restructuring of the armed forces and other government departments would now take place and that the Ministry of Defence would be far too occupied for the next few months putting its own house in order to worry about the transportation of a few foreign prisoners from one part of the country to another.

In the meantime, our own private war proceeded unabated. Something of an arms race was taking place, as it had become apparent that Miguel, the gangster who had previously been in charge of our compound and the death of whose stepson had triggered off the wave of violence, had decided to take a hand in matters from outside the prison. He was now established once more as a gang leader on his old territory in one of the barrios on the island and was arranging for weapons, including grenades, and ammunition, to be smuggled in to the opposing forces on the other side of the prison. By the middle of April, our side had been reduced to three grenades and four sticks of dynamite, as well as a large number of handguns and ammunition. Having seen the grenades and dynamite, which were both looking the worse for wear as a result of long storage in unsuitable conditions, I was not at all sure that they did not represent at least as much danger to their prospective user as they did to any group being attacked. There seemed to be some difficulty in our side of the prison obtaining fresh supplies, and a Venezuelan was shot and killed just outside the fence one night during the second week in April while attempting to deliver grenades to our compound.

The imbalance in "war stock" was made even worse during the third week in April, when the Guardia Nacional captain entered our compound for a *raqueta* with quite a large force of troops. Once we were all sitting in our usual positions on the basketball court, the captain made a call on his mobile telephone, and while still listening on the phone, he entered Pavilion Five. Shortly afterwards, he emerged, smiling triumphantly, still clutching the telephone to his ear and bearing two pistols and a large bag of ammunition, which he handed to one of his subordinates. As he made his way towards an outhouse which had previously been used as an arms cache, the truth became apparent. On the other end of the phone was Miguel who, as former top man in the compound, knew the hiding places intimately. The atmosphere was electric as we observed the captain's progress.

Fortunately, those currently in charge had had the foresight to move at least some of the weapons to previously unused hiding places, or there was a very strong possibility that we would have been left defenceless. Eventually, after an hour of further searching and when it became clear that the captain and his men were approaching another location where they were likely to find something, one of the management team decided that enough was enough. He loudly announced that he was hungry and was going to return to his pavilion to get something to eat. This was the signal for the rest of the prisoners, who all stood up, large numbers of them announcing that they too were hungry.

We stood in a group in the middle of the basketball court, with the result that the captain and his men came rushing over to confront us. With his men deployed in a line in front of the group of prisoners, he began loudly to order everyone to sit down, while his nervous twitch became ever more pronounced. When his orders were ignored, he drew his pistol and his men cocked their weapons. It was a moment of unbelievable tension, but the prisoners stood their ground, even when the troops began to fire warning shots into the air.

Then, slowly but inexorably, the group of prisoners began to walk forwards, towards Pavilion Four. The captain was furious, demanding that we stop, and I was expecting that at any moment he would order his men to fire on us, but instead they gave ground and began to step backwards before the advancing group of prisoners. The psychologically critical moment had passed and the prisoners advanced with more confidence towards the retreating troops, until eventually the corner of the building was reached and we were able to move along the front of the building and enter the pavilion.

The troops then began to leave, bizarrely carrying away with them the entrance gate to the compound. Clearly, we were being left as vulnerable and exposed to attack by prisoners from the other side of the prison as it was possible to arrange. Once again, I found myself wondering how long my mind was going to be able to cope with this constant attack upon my nerves, with every situation seeming more horrible, dramatic and dangerous than what had gone before.

The ever-irrepressible Venezuelans weren't going to allow such a setback to get them down, though, and a large group immediately headed up to the workshop, where they proceeded to writhe a large grill off one end wall which, when carried down to the gateway, proved to be just the right size for the gap. Within less than an hour of the gate having been removed, a new one was in its place and secured. Another group had meantime climbed onto the roof and began to wildly fire off shots, to demonstrate that we were far from unable to defend ourselves against any attack.

In truth though, the losses were a serious setback, particularly when added to the previous loss of the grenade together with the pistol that Julio had managed to smuggle over to the other side. It seemed only a matter of time before our resources had diminished and the other side's built up to the extent that they would feel confident in mounting a full-scale attack on our compound. I longed to be away from this hellish place but had no confidence that there was any prospect of such an event in the near future.

FOR THE REST of April and the first couple of weeks of May, both sides remained heavily defended and poised to attack the other side if an opportunity arose. It was an unending nightmare of tension and fear, not knowing from one minute to the next when the whole thing would explode out of all control.

On the morning of Monday, May 20, a group from our side of the prison carried out an attack in broad daylight on the maximum security block and were able to throw a grenade into the building. One person was killed and five injured in the explosion. The attacking band managed to escape without injury to themselves, although a large number of shots were fired by both sides.

During the *requisa* that followed, once we had been strip-searched on the basketball court, we were ordered to move up to the workshop and sit down inside. As we entered the workshop, the escorting Guardia troops encouraged us to look behind us, to where we could see that a machine gun had now been mounted in the external guard tower, with a clear range of fire towards the entrance to the workshop. Clearly, the captain had decided that there would be no repeat of the mutiny that had cut short his previous search.

Following a two-hour search, during which nothing was found by the troops, we were allowed to return to our quarters, where we were locked in for the rest of the day, being allowed out only for meals and for the evening head-count.

Two days later, on the morning of the 22nd, word went around the prison that a new director had appeared, the previous one having mysteriously absented himself from the scene a couple of days before. Around nine o'clock in the morning, this person entered the compound, accompanied by a group of *vigilantes* who were all new to us and who were all armed with Uzi sub-machine guns. It appeared that this new director was some kind of a trouble-shooter sent from Caracas with his own group of *vigilantes* to restore some kind of order to the prison.

"Let's go and speak to him and tell him we're sitting here waiting for a transfer that never seems to be going to happen," said Denis. "Maybe he can do something for us."

"What's the bloody point?" I replied wearily. "None of these bastards gives a damn about us. Unless the directive comes from headquarters in Caracas, there'll be bugger all done at local level. Talk to him if you like, but I think it's just a waste of time."

Denis was convinced that it was worth a try and that there was nothing to lose by asking, so he approached the new director, who was familiarising himself with the compound.

Denis explained to him that we were a group of foreign prisoners who had been promised a transfer to Santa Ana at the end of January, and that we were now beginning to despair of the transfer ever taking place.

The director listened patiently, then said that he would need to check in order to see what paperwork there was on the matter in the office and would let us know the result. One hour later, we were all called to his office, where he advised us that our transfer had been approved and that the necessary paperwork had been ready since February! Clearly a man of action and decision, he then proceeded to make us an offer.

He and his men had arrived that morning in two vehicles and he was prepared to make the vehicles available to us to leave the prison later that day, provided that we were prepared to pay for the return ferry trip to the mainland for the two vehicles, the petrol for the twenty-hour drive to Santa Ana, and the food for ourselves and our Guardia Nacional escort.

Several frantic phone calls served to establish the total cost per head as 120,000 bolivars, roughly £120. I telephoned the British Embassy in Caracas and asked if it would be possible for the honorary consul to visit the prison in the next few hours, bringing with him any money due to British prisoners. Since a number of the prisoners would not have enough money to cover the costs of the journey, I further asked if it would be possible for the embassy to lend those people the money against future prison comfort payments from the charity Prisoners Abroad.

It was quickly agreed that Mr Weller would shortly bring to the prison what money there was in prisoners' accounts and that the embassy would indeed lend the residue, which would be forwarded to San Cristóbal for delivery to the prison of Santa Ana, by the honorary consul there, first thing on Friday morning before the escort was due to start back on the return journey. On that basis, we told the director that we were delighted to accept his deal.

I could scarcely believe that everything was falling into place so neatly after so much waiting and so many disappointments. A part of me was waiting for the bombshell to drop and the whole arrangement to fall apart, but I really did not know how I would react if that were to happen. It would have been too cruel after all that we had suffered in that place, particularly over the past year.

As the day went on, nothing happened to upset our plans. We hastened back to the pavilion to pack our few possessions, trying not to show too forcibly our joy and relief at the thought of leaving that hellhole within the next few hours. At two o'clock in the afternoon, the consul came with the money, which we were able to pass on to the director. As the consul had not visited us for two months, I had sufficient cash to be able to pay for my trip.

Around four o'clock, we were called over to the office with our bags, and so we said goodbye to our companions in the pavilion, with whom we had shared so many dreadful experiences for so long, before gleefully making our way out of it for the last time. It felt as if all my Christmases had come at once, but a part of me was still terrified that something was going to go wrong at the last moment.

In the office area, we were locked into a central cage, where we were to remain until the evening head-count was over. Once the Guardia had completed the count, we were taken out of the cage, four at a time, to a side room, where our bags were quickly checked before we were handcuffed in pairs and led out to the main gate. When all sixteen of us who were to be transferred were ready, we were escorted out through the main gate. At last, I could begin to believe that this was really happening.

Immediately outside the main gate, my heart sank when I

caught sight of the transport that we were supposed to use. They were two light utility vans, each of which would take perhaps six people at a push. There was simply no way that we were all going to fit in. I fully expected that at that stage those in charge would simply shrug their shoulders and order us back into the prison, but they thankfully seemed determined to go ahead with the transfer now that it had been set in motion.

After a brief discussion between our escort and the director, the dilapidated prison bus was brought into action. Six people were ordered to climb into one of the vans and the remaining ten boarded the bus. Three soldiers entered each vehicle. We then drove off into the town of Porlamar, eventually stopping outside a police station, where we collected a slightly larger vehicle than the vans that had initially been provided. Those of us who had been on the bus were transferred to the new vehicle and the little convoy set off for the ferry terminal.

As we tried to make ourselves as comfortable as possible on the floor of the small vehicle, we were driven at high speed for about forty minutes, but to our dismay we arrived at the ferry terminal as the last ferry of the day was pulling out. Once more, the spectre of being driven back to the prison rose horrifyingly in front of us. After an acrimonious exchange between our guards, and a couple of telephone calls, the decision was made to drive us to another ferry terminal, where a smaller vessel was due to leave for Porta La Cruz, on the Venezuelan mainland, in approximately one hour.

It was with huge relief that we digested this news and settled back good humouredly for the journey across the island to the new terminal. After a short wait at the terminal, the vans drove aboard the small, nearly empty ferry, and we were allowed to get out and sit in a small passenger lounge near the aft end.

Still nervous, I listened carefully to the sounds around me and only began to relax when I heard the engine beat increasing and saw the lights on the pier beginning to move against the rear windows of the lounge. We were on our way! As we moved further out into the bay, I breathed a huge sigh of relief – at last we were rid of that corner of hell that had been our home for the last two years. My thoughts and sympathies went to those who remained there, and I wondered how the war would develop and what new horrors it would bring for them in the months to come. I also thought of the fifty prisoners who had died there in a little under two years, and all the dreadful events that I had witnessed. I hoped that I would never set eyes on the Island of Margarita again. As things turned out, I would have to pay the island a brief visit before I finally left Venezuela, but that was to be three and a half years down the line, by which time the mental scars had had time to heal somewhat.

After a two-hour crossing, we approached Porta de la Cruz and were ordered to board the vehicles again. Leaving the ferry, we began what turned out to be a thirty-hour drive to our new prison, following the coastline westward for many miles before turning inland and beginning the long climb up into the foothills of the Andes. We stopped twice for something to eat, each time being herded into a roadside café while handcuffed together in pairs. Our guards became more aggressive and belligerent as the drive continued, and we realised the reason for it when we looked through the small window in the front of the rear part of the vehicle and noticed that they were sniffing cocaine and sharing a bottle of whisky. At one point, as we drove at some sixty miles per hour along a country road, the vans drew level with each other so that a bottle of whisky could be passed from one cab to the other.

Needless to say, the driving also grew more erratic as the journey went on and we managed to take wrong turnings on a couple of occasions, being forced to double back some miles each time before encountering the correct road. As we climbed into the mountains on the Thursday evening, it began to rain heavily, and we discovered that our compartment was far from waterproof. Despite getting cold and wet, and being unable to prevent our bags getting soaked on the floor, we consoled ourselves that every mile along the road was another mile further from the purgatory of San Antonio.

Eventually, at about 1 a.m. on Friday, we drew up outside what was clearly the gate house of Santa Ana prison. Our escort completed some paperwork and we were waved through, and a short drive took us to the main entrance of the prison, where we were ordered out of the vehicles. This was our new home.

CHAPTER FOURTEEN

Tomorrow And Tomorrow And Tomorrow

OUR FIRST IMPRESSIONS were that everything seemed clean and well ordered, as well as being on a much larger scale than we had been used to. We were expected, and a *vigilante*, who was very noticeably only armed with the short ceremonial sword called a *penilla*, told us that all the paperwork would be processed in the morning and that meantime we would be housed in the observation block, which was used to accommodate new prisoners. We followed the *vigilante* into the large central patio and then down some steps, too tired and emotionally exhausted to take much stock of our surroundings.

The *vigilante* unlocked the gates of a large dormitory on the ground floor of a building and ushered us inside. In the dim light, we could make out a large, open area, with what seemed to be about forty or fifty prisoners sleeping on foam mattresses on the floor. We were immediately conscious of an atmosphere of order and quiet, such as we had not experienced for a long time. Something else which struck us was the temperature, which was several degrees cooler than we had been used to, with a chilly breeze passing through the unglazed windows. We hurried to find space on the floor to unroll our mattresses and settle down for what remained of the night. A couple of people spoke to us as we organised ourselves, but they did so quietly and with courtesy, and all talking quickly ceased as we got our heads down.

"Here, everything is peaceful and well organised," they told us. "No-one will bother you here. It is not like the other prisons. Here, it is possible to live quite well."

It was noticeable that none of them asked us for anything, which was in itself an entirely novel experience for us. Despite the newness of the surroundings, I quickly drifted off, grateful for the opportunity to sleep, having spent so many weeks with almost no sleep at all.

I awoke around 5.30, as others were stirring, and we were soon called to the gate for *numero*. Some things were clearly the same. The procedure for the head-count was different though, much simpler and more relaxed. We simply had to exit the accommodation, shouting out consecutive numbers as we passed through the gate. The *numero* was conducted by two unarmed Guardia Nacional troops, accompanied by a *vigilante*, and once they had checked the number of prisoners against a list that they carried, we were allowed to enter again, calling out consecutive numbers as we passed through the gate as a double check. As we sprawled on our mattresses again for another hour's rest, we felt that we had arrived in a different world.

SHORTLY BEFORE EIGHT, a *vigilante* came to the observation block and ordered all of us who had been transferred from San Antonio prison to go with him to the administration block. As we followed him up the concrete path, we had a better opportunity in the daylight to take in our surroundings.

The prison covered an extensive area, and prisoners were housed in three large, two-storey blocks built in a line near the south perimeter fence. A fourth two-storey building was on higher ground to the east, while the north side was taken up by the administration block, which was also large and consisted of two storeys. In the centre, in the area known as the patio, there were two basketball courts laid side by side, one of them marked out for five-a-side football and volleyball as well as basketball. There were also two areas laid out for the playing of *bolas criollas*, a game similar to boules, which Venezuelans are extremely passionate about. Beyond the buildings, on lower ground to the west, was a full-sized grass football pitch bordered by a baseball pitch. We understood that there were just over two thousand prisoners held in the male prison, and there was a female prison alongside containing two hundred and fifty prisoners.

While we were waiting in a side room for the admission process to begin, a couple of Colombians who had been transferred from San Antonio about a year before came and spoke to us. They welcomed us to the prison, congratulated us on getting away from Margarita, and assured us that we would be received into good accommodation in *letra*, or dormitory, 2A.

At this point, the British consul's assistant arrived. She was a Venezuelan known as Zulay, who spoke passable English and told us, "I will be your main point of contact here with the British authorities. I do the prison visits for the consul. I will try and help you as much as I can." She had brought with her the money from the embassy, which we were able to hand over to the sergeant in charge of our escort detail, who immediately set off to return to Margarita. A short while later, we were ordered upstairs to complete the paperwork. This involved visiting about four different offices, but was carried out with reasonable efficiency by the prison staff. They must have thought us all very strange, as it had to be very unusual for them to deal with a group of convicts who were smiling and laughing and were clearly delighted to be admitted to the prison! The whole process took about three hours and we were then able to go down to the dormitory assigned to us.

Letra 2A was one of two dormitories on the ground floor of the central block. A doorman sat behind the entrance bars and opened the gate for us to enter. We discovered that anyone who didn't live in the *letra* would not be allowed past this gate until they had explained their business to the doorman and he was satisfied that they had legitimate reason to enter. Each of the dormitories in the prison operated in the same way.

Immediately inside the entrance gate, there was a shower room on each side of the passageway containing a line of six showers, and then as one passed further along there was a toilet area to the right and a roomy washroom to the left. Beyond was a door fitted with coloured glass panels and equipped with a Yale type lock. Passing through this, we entered the dormitory area itself. It was a large, airy, open-plan space equipped with bunk beds. It was divided into cubicles by waist-high partitions, with three bunk beds to each cubicle. The central passageway was tiled, and a line of four plastic tables, each with four chairs, was arranged along one side of it. Three large ceiling fans ran down the centre of the room and the windows were all glazed. The whole dormitory smelled and looked clean, although it housed just over one hundred prisoners, and the beds were all tidy, with a couple of metal lockers standing by each bed. The first cubicle on the right as one entered had been converted into a shop, selling basic foodstuffs and toiletries and with an urn of coffee on the go throughout the day. Opposite this cubicle was a water cooler and a rack containing a dozen demijohns of fresh mineral water.

We could scarcely take it all in and were astounded at each discovery. We expressed doubt that we were even in the same country. How was it possible that two prisons within one country could be so different? It was only now that we began to fully realise how terrible were the conditions in which we had lived for the last two years.

We were introduced to the *cabo*, or head man in the *letra*, and began to understand a little about how the prison was organised. There was the usual management team of hard men who ran the prison, but they, together with everyone else in the structure of the prisoners' organisation, played a dual role. To the prisoners, they were the *gremio*, or management, and were the law within the prison, holding the power of life and death over prisoners. While writing this book, I read in a Venezuelan newspaper that on the morning of April 19, 2006, ten prisoners were executed in Santa Ana prison by order of the *gremio* as a result of a power struggle.

To the prison authorities, though, they were known as the prisoners' committee, and met regularly with the prison director and other officials to organise sports competitions, cultural events, educational courses and other aspects of prison life.

Each *letra* had its *cabo*, appointed by and representing the *gremio* and who was responsible for the smooth running of the dormitory. He could eject people at will or otherwise discipline them as he saw fit if they did not conform to the required standards of behaviour and hygiene within the *letra*. The *cabos* were known to the prison authorities as dormitory representatives, and met with officials to discuss such mundane matters as the provision of cleaning materials and the organisation of sports teams to represent each *letra* in the competitions that were regularly held.

The small group of people who comprised the *gremio* were in a very strange position. They wielded a huge amount of power and influence within the prison and accumulated considerable wealth for themselves through their control of such activities as the drug supply and money lending inside the prison, as well as by taxing almost all commercial activity within the walls, but each knew that his days were numbered. As soon as they were released from the prison, there would be former prisoners awaiting them outside who bore grudges for treatment meted out to them within the gaol. During my time in Santa Ana, four members of the *gremio* came up for release. Not one of them survived longer than forty-eight hours on the streets before he was gunned down by rivals.

We were introduced to our *cabo*, known as Fabio. He informed us that we would each have to pay 2,000 bolivars per week to live in the *letra*. This money was used to pay the doorman and two cleaners responsible for keeping the toilets and other communal areas clean, as well as any other minor expenses related to the dormitory. An account of how the money was spent was posted each week on the *letra's* noticeboard. From time to time, there would be other payments required for such things as the purchase of sports uniforms and the decoration of the *letra* for Christmas, but these would be announced with a fortnight's notice.

In exchange for a small deposit, he issued us each with a key for the inner door, and advised us that we would each be allocated a bed space later in the day. We were now free to roam the grounds and explore our new home, and Denis, Fred and I set off to do just that. Immediately behind our block, and forming the ground floor of a second-floor dormitory, was an area with two full-sized snooker tables, behind which there was a well equipped weight-lifting room, with a sign on the door detailing the small charge for membership. On each side of this building was a sizeable area of grass.

Walking through the front of the block brought us onto the main walkway linking the three accommodation blocks. Like all the walkways in the prison, it was covered with a corrugated iron roof. A delicious aroma of cooking assaulted our nostrils, and we became aware that there were cafes in front of each of the blocks. In all, there were five cafes where one could sit at a table and eat a two-course lunch for 1,500 bolivars, or about £1.50. There were also half-a-dozen fast food outlets, selling such things as *arepa* with cheese, or *empanada*. Roving vendors wandered up and down, selling little plastic cups of coffee from large vacuum flasks at 100 bolivars a time. Others sold ice poles or freshly prepared tropical fruit drinks. There were three mini markets in the prison, selling a much wider range of stock than the little shop in the *letra*, and where one could buy everything from fresh meat to medicines.

Two laundries were in operation, equipped with industrial washing machines, each of which offered a pick-up and drop-off service to your dormitory at a very reasonable price. The more we saw, the more difficult it became for us to absorb that we really were here and that this was not some kind of crazy fantasy.

All of the sports facilities were being fully utilised and there seemed to be an air of purposeful energy about the place that we found amazing. The whole establishment seemed to have more of an air of a busy college campus than of a prison. On the walkway leading up to the workshops, which was the large building to the east of the central patio, we came across about twenty people who clearly belonged to the native Indian tribes, busy carving away at blocks of wood. Some of the work being produced was magnificent, with wonderful eagles and pumas as well as religious statues. All were being created using the most rudimentary of tools, together with a great deal of skill and huge patience.

Entering the workshops themselves, we came across a scene of frenzied activity and the roaring and screeching of power tools and machines. On the ground floor, there were several woodworking workshops, engaged in the production of everything from cup holders to double beds, all bearing elaborate carvings in the flamboyant South American style. Two small hardware stores on the ground floor provided the raw materials to support all this activity, and a couple of bakeries were also in operation.

On the second floor, a number of small workshops were engaged in the production of shoes, and people could be seen in each of them, hard at work, cutting shaping gluing and sewing. Almost all the activity in the workshops was being organised by Colombians, who made up a large percentage of the prison population and whose organisational abilities and desire to turn a buck were largely responsible for the well ordered nature of the prison.

To say that we were impressed with everything that we had seen would be a huge understatement, and we found ourselves wondering increasingly not just if we were in the same country but if we were even on the same planet. As we left the workshops, the bell for lunch sounded, and we went round to the dining hall which ran along the front of the workshop. As the first people emerged, carrying their food, we were almost pleased to see something that brought us back down to earth. The disgusting mess scattered across the plates looked and smelled even worse than the dreadful food that we had become used to in San Antonio! At least some things about the Venezuelan prison service were consistent.

On the way back to the *letra*, I decided to buy a pair of jeans from a young prisoner who was selling them cheap in front of our block. I was astonished to find that my waist size had gone down from thirty-four to twenty-eight. I hoped that in this prison I would be able to regain some of the weight loss, and determined to find a source of income to allow me to buy and cook my own food.

When we got back into the dormitory, the *cabo* was ready to allocate beds, and I found myself on a top bunk, while Denis had another top bunk in the same cubicle. As I unpacked my bag, I realised how much everything in it stank. Despite having been careful to wash my clothes and sheets regularly, they all were pervaded with the disgusting smell of San Antonio. It was another thing that we had grown so used to that we didn't even notice it until we were placed in a new environment.

That evening, after *numero*, those of us who had been transferred from Margarita sat around one of the tables and swapped stories as we began coming to terms with what we had gone through and adjusted to the new life that was beginning for us. We were all infused with a sense of relief, together with excitement and anticipation.

"I thought we'd never get out of that place in one piece," said Fred. "It scared me to death, being in there."

"Remember the night the grenade went off?" asked George. "That really shook me up. I thought we were all done for after that."

"I'm hungry," said Frank. "Who's going to buy me something to eat?"

"I've still got to keep pinching myself to prove I'm not dreaming," said Denis, ignoring Frank's habitual moaning. "This place is like another world."

We did not realise it then, but for some the transfer from San Antonio had come too late, and the experiences there had taken too much of a toll. As a result, there would be a number of casualties along the way. Such thoughts though, were far from our minds as we settled down to sleep for our first full night in Santa Ana. The lights went out at nine, and immediately all televisions, radios, music systems and conversation were muted to allow those who wished to sleep to do so. It was another fine example of the order that we had come to after the chaos of before.

OUR SECOND DAY at Santa Ana was a Saturday and

therefore visit day. Preparations were impressive. The entire centre patio area took on the appearance of a large street market as stalls were set up all along the pathways, selling all kinds of goods that had been made in the prison during the previous week. They included shoes, hammocks, deckchairs, leather belts, wallets and purses, egg boxes, cup holders, jewellery cases, clocks, folding chairs and tables, as well as oil and water colour paintings.

When 9 a.m. came, and hundreds of visitors began to swarm in through the entrance gate, the cafes swung into full production and the fast food stalls prepared for an onslaught of customers. The cries of the ambulatory vendors of coffee ("Café, café, tinto, tomar tu tintinto, café, café!"), aromatic teas ("Aromática, tomar aromática!"), ices ("Helados que se venden, fresa, mora, naranja!") and snacks "Empanadas, perros calientes!") could be heard ringing out around the prison as they touted their goods, their shouts blending with the sound of the ubiquitous *vallenato* music emanating from loudspeakers in all the cafes to create a carnival atmosphere. Hairdressers and shoe shine boys began to ply their trade. In a prominent position on the patio, there was a children's play park, complete with swings, roundabout and slides.

Within a couple of hours, the prison population had at least doubled as visitors poured into every corner. Some came in simply to pick up bargains from the various stalls, which they would then sell on during the week in the pavement markets of the nearby city of San Cristóbal. Throughout the day, steady trading took place in the street market, the cafes and food stalls did a roaring trade, and within each pavilion groups of visitors were busy cooking and enjoying a family day with their imprisoned relatives. Couples retreated into curtained-off lower bunks to enjoy a few minutes of privacy together while older children or friends looked after their younger children.

At 2.30 p.m., a bell could be heard sounding across the patio and the visitors began to make their way to the exit, with the last of them leaving the prison by three. Once the visitors had gone, we were herded back to our dormitories for a quick head-count to make sure that no prisoners had sneaked out among the visitors, and then all prisoners were allowed to roam freely around the prison once more, until 5 p.m.

After the evening *numero*, it was party time for most prisoners, enjoying the food and treats brought in to them by their visitors as they looked forward to more of the same on the following day. The smoking of drugs was not allowed inside most *letras*, being confined to the toilets, but many prisoners regularly got drunk on *michi*, which is a foul tasting, colourless alcohol distilled from a rice mash. Each *letra* in the prison was equipped with its own homemade still, and this fiendish-looking apparatus would be set up each Friday evening in the toilets and would operate throughout the night to produce the "fuel" for the weekend parties. Inevitably, loud arguments and the occasional fight were the results of these drinking sessions, as *michi* seems designed to induce aggression in even the most peaceable individual. A few well chosen words from the *cabo* were usually enough to settle things down.

Sunday followed a similar pattern to Saturday, with visitors inundating the prison throughout the day. The evening, though, tended to be much more subdued, as people nursed hangovers and contemplated not seeing their loved ones again until the following Saturday. Each Sunday evening, the *cabo* collected the rent from each prisoner and accounts were expected to be settled by those who had taken credit from the shop and other small businesses within the *letra*. The process of collecting debt on a Sunday evening usually resulted in many loud arguments, with excuses and recriminations being hurled backwards and forwards.

As I was soon to discover when I began to run my own little

business in the *letra*, the question of debt was always a delicate one. If you did not give credit, there would be no custom; give too much, and you would go out of business pretty quickly. To stop someone's credit would almost certainly result in a bad debt, yet to give a person unlimited credit would be extreme foolishness. Someone pointed out to me during my first few days in Santa Ana, "Be careful here. In San Antonio, people steal with knives, and guns. Here, they steal with their tongues." It was to prove very good advice.

On Monday morning, the prison once again reverted to a place of work and sport, with furious activity in the workshops to prepare for the next weekend's market.

Towards the end of our first full week in Santa Ana, Sonny, a Nigerian who had transferred with us from Margarita, was called to the prison infirmary to be given the devastating news that the blood test that we had all been given on our admission to Santa Ana had shown him to be HIV positive, undoubtedly as a result of liaisons with prostitutes who from time to time had entered San Antonio at weekends. He was told to return to the *letra* and collect his bedding, taking it to the infirmary, where he was to be confined for the rest of his time in the prison.

Meanwhile, a couple of the young British prisoners who had been transferred from the island were showing some difficulty in coming to terms with the apparent freedoms in our new prison. Having lived so long under the oppression of guns and knives, they began to get the impression that they could now act as they wished with impunity. What they did not take account of was the fact that guns and knives most certainly did exist but were held and controlled by a select few. We had all been advised by our Colombian acquaintances shortly after our arrival, "You will not see guns or knives here, or if you do see a gun or knife, it will probably be the last thing you ever see."

George came back from the dining room one day, saying, "It's great here. I went up for my lunch and there were hundreds of people quietly standing in a queue. I just walked straight to the front and no-one said a dickey bird!"

"Listen, George," I said. "Just think about it for a minute. How many murderers do you think were in that queue of a couple of hundred prisoners? How many real thugs? Do you think they're standing quietly in a queue because they've suddenly all turned into boy scouts? Or is it that they know they've either got to toe the line or risk getting very seriously hurt? How do you think they feel about some poncey gringo strolling past them to the front of the queue? Enjoy your honeymoon period, but wind your neck in or you're going to get into serious bother."

George was determined to go his own way however, and celebrate the 2002 World Cup in style in his new surroundings. Discovering that it was remarkably easy as a foreign prisoner to obtain credit, he went on a tremendous spree, eating breakfast and lunch in cafes and eventually running up a food and drugs bill that he had no earthly hope of repaying. Before many weeks had passed, he had scuttled into the prison's drugs rehabilitation unit to obtain temporary relief from his creditors.

Ahmed, a British prisoner of Middle Eastern origin, also got caught in the debt trap, although he seemed to go in with his eyes wide open and with no intention of paying his way. He had been in prison for six years by this time and spoke rapid, fluent, colloquial Spanish. During his time in San Antonio he'd been involved in various scams, which had led to his being banished to the other side of the prison from us. He once ended up in the maximum security block there for a period after he had persuaded the officer in charge of the Guardia that he could provide a course in English for the troops. No sooner had he obtained the notebooks and pens that were to be used for the course than he sold them to buy drugs for himself, to the outrage of the officer in command.

Now, he used his huge powers of persuasion to obtain maximum credit from wherever it was available within Santa Ana. He even managed to persuade some of the vendors that his uncle was an Arab prince who would shortly be visiting him with a large sum of money. Offering repayments of forty, fifty and in some cases one hundred per cent interest, he played the vendors beautifully, using their own greed together with their desire to get one over on the daft foreigner to reel them in. He eventually ran up debts that amounted to millions of bolivars around the prison and managed to keep all the balls in the air at the same time for a remarkably long time before eventually being locked up in the maximum security block. It is likely that many of his debts never came to the surface, as his debtors were too embarrassed to admit how easily they had been suckered by a gringo.

Another prisoner who had been transferred with us from Margarita, a huge Nigerian called Ike, also began to show symptoms that appeared to be a direct result of the mental anguish that he had suffered while in Margarita. Over the course of weeks, he gradually became more distant and withdrawn, his unusual behaviour culminating in his appearance one evening stark naked and chanting psalms and hymns learned as a child at a mission school in Nigeria. It was obvious that his mind had cracked following the years of stress endured on the island. With a great deal of persuasion, the guards succeeded in getting Ike to accompany them to the prison hospital, where he seemed to make a recovery after some weeks and was released back into the mainstream prison. He remained unstable, however, and seemed to suffer a relapse every couple of months, resulting in his regular readmission to the prison hospital.

It is fair to say that all of us who had been in that dreadful place displayed, to a greater or lesser extent, the after effects of our traumatic experiences. Most reported disturbed sleep patterns, horrible nightmares or flashbacks, and I personally began a slide into a terrible, profound depression that it would take many months to recover from. I now refer to it jokingly as my "winter of discontent", but at the time it was far from being a laughing matter, as I became immersed in a kind of despair, spending hours in moody contemplation, endlessly reviewing scenes from my life and engaging in destructive, over-critical self analysis.

During this period, I appeared to function reasonably normally but had no desire to engage with people other than at the most superficial level, and managed to drive away those closest to me with my caustic, and at times hostile, approach. Even the writing of letters became an unbearable burden to me and I would often be reduced to scribbling off apologetic one-liners when the call went out that the British consul was visiting. Once more, it was the lighthouse on the other side of the ocean that was my salvation. The letters from Robin in Scotland arrived each month without fail, and I regularly received mail from friends in Hartlepool.

The fact that these people continued to write, month after month, despite getting little or no response from me, eventually enabled me to reassess my self-worth in a more positive light, to begin the long climb back from the depths of my despair and to begin to engage with the world again. Depression was something that I had suffered bouts of throughout my adult life, but neither before nor since was there ever anything to compare to those early months in Santa Ana. Indeed, it was not until I finally left the prison and was able to spend many hours with Denis, going over our experiences in San Antonio and thus learning to come to terms with them, that I finally began to feel that I could put the negative feelings behind me and become a whole person again.

After I had been in Santa Ana a couple of weeks, I was approached by an Austrian prisoner.

"I've got a good opportunity for you," he said. "There's a small business that will be available shortly, as the owner is about to be released. Come and have a look at it, and talk to the owner. See what you think."

José's cottage industry consisted of a large fridge fitted with a lock, a two-ring cooking stove and a liquidiser, together with various tubs, buckets and plastic containers. All was for sale, together with his double bunk, which was equipped with a lockable cash drawer. The job was to make up and sell drinks made from fresh tropical fruits, jellies and tubes of ice frozen in the sizeable freezer compartment. As José pointed out, if you are in the business of selling water, or air, to people, it is very difficult to lose out.

It was agreed that I could spend a week working with José, learning how to make the various drinks, and then decide whether I was interested in taking over the business when he left the prison. Eighteen litres of one main drink was produced each morning in a large plastic tub and sold throughout the day in plastic cups. A popular product was a typical Venezuelan drink called *papelón con limon*, or *agua panela*, which is easy to make, requiring no cooking, and is very refreshing. *Papelón* is a solid block of the raw, hardened sugarcane pulp known as *panela*, dark brown in colour, and is widely used in Venezuela as a sugar substitute in the preparation of drinks. The block is first broken up into small pieces and then added to a large tub of water together with the juice of about ten lemons and some refined sugar. All is then thoroughly stirred until the *papelón* is dissolved completely, then a tube of ice is added before the tub is placed in the fridge ready to sell.

Over the next few days, I learned to make drinks from *lechosa*, which is also known as papaya, as well as guava, tamarind, *guanábana* and passion fruit. Another drink which was very popular, although more expensive and produced in smaller quantities as an alternative to the "juice of the day", was *avena*, which is based on oatmeal but prepared very differently to the porridge to which British people are accustomed. The oatmeal is blended with milk, sugar and water, together with a little cinnamon and a few drops of vanilla essence, and makes a surprisingly refreshing and wholesome drink. It is generally prepared raw, although it may be cooked if desired, giving a fuller consistency to the drink.

The under-the-counter drink was *masoto*, a fermented rice drink prepared by cooking rice in water with *panela*, cinnamon and cloves, blending it in batches then sieving it into a large tub, where it is left to mature in a warm place, becoming mildly alcoholic after a few days. As it is used, more can be added and mixed in to keep the brew going. Periodically, one of the *vigilantes* would demand to sample the *masoto*, and if it had become too potent he would supervise the dumping of the entire batch. This could often be avoided by paying the *vigilante* a 2,000-bolivar fine.

Having learned the trade, and on being informed that the whole was for sale at a very reasonable price, I agreed to buy the business from José on condition that he would help and advise me for a couple of weeks, or until he left the prison, whichever was sooner. One of the advantages of running a drinks outlet was that it was counted as being six days' work each week for the purpose of earning an earlier release, whereas most other forms of work counted as five days.

My experiences in dealing with the locals on a commercial basis, though, were not destined to help in any way towards relieving my depression. If anything, the case was quite the reverse.

NOW THAT I had a business to run, my routine became very different, and certainly a million miles away from my experiences in San Antonio. I normally woke up around 5.30 a.m., enjoying for a few minutes the peace and tranquillity of the darkened dormitory, lit only by the external security lights, while listening for the sounds of flowing water which would indicate that the water supply had been turned on. I then rose and made my way through to one of the shower rooms for a coldwater shower. There were normally only about four or five people up and about around that time.

Returning from my shower, I would pick up a coffee from the coffee vendor and relax until six, when the lights were switched on and everyone began to make a move. The arrival of the staff for the morning head count was signalled by a warning bell rung by the *cabo*, and on hearing it everyone would hurry towards the doorway. *Numero* was normally over and done with in five minutes and the lights were once more extinguished. Once the three buildings had been checked by the Guardia, the *vigilantes* returned to open up the *letras* to allow those who wished to collect their breakfast at the dining room to do so. The majority of people in 2A chose to buy their own food and cook it in their cubicles, and so most people stayed in bed at least until the lights came on again at seven.

Once the lights were switched on it was permissible to make noise, and so I would switch on my radio to listen to the BBC World Service news and Caribbean report, to keep up to date with events in the outside world. At around 7.30, I would make my way through to the washroom to wash up any dishes from the evening before and to fill my tubs with fresh water, as running water was only available for certain hours each day and had to be stored otherwise.

With the time approaching eight o'clock, shouted warnings would be given, following which the *letra* was locked from the inside for half an hour to allow the two cleaners to work their way through the dormitory. Once the cleaning was over, I would normally take a walk outside and pick up an *empanada* and coffee for breakfast from one of the stalls on the patio. *Empanada* is a corn flour pastry stuffed with meat or chicken and is a hugely popular snack in South America; in Venezuela they are normally deep fried, and in the prison that was generally done outside over an open fire of scrap wood from the workshops, which was sold by the bagful.

At 9 a.m. it was time to set up shop, and so I would return to the *letra* and prepare my drinks for the day and a batch of jelly if required, and fill up bags with water for ice. The ingredients for my products were bought through a wholesaler who visited the prison each week and supplied all the shops and businesses within the gaol. Each Thursday, this lady was ensconced in an office in the administration block set aside for the purpose, where she would take orders for produce to be delivered to the rear of the workshop area on the Friday morning. On Monday, she would be back in the office to collect payment for the goods delivered the previous week. The management team, or *gremio*, always took considerable interest in the flow of goods and produce into the prison, and one of their most senior figures and principal enforcer, a guy known to us foreigners as "Chains" due to the weight of gold that he habitually wore, was invariably present when goods were being brought in or money collected. I was never sure what percentage of the wholesaler's turnover was taxed by the *gremio* but remain convinced that they enjoyed a considerable income from it.

One distinct advantage of the involvement of the *gremio* in the commercial activities was that the traders could move around the prison carrying large sums of cash without fear of being robbed. On a Monday morning, the owners of the larger supermarkets might be walking across the central patio with over one million bolivars in their pockets, but could do so with impunity. The consequences for anyone trying to carry out a robbery would be an instant application of summary justice, and they certainly would not live to enjoy the fruits.

That breaches of the unwritten, but strictly adhered to, prison rules would bring instant retribution was amply demonstrated when, a few weeks after my arrival in Santa Ana, a couple of young, new prisoners, held up a female visitor at knife point, relieving her of 5,000 bolivars in cash towards the end of the visiting hours. The last of the visitors had not yet left the prison when the two of them were gunned down. Although they were killed in full view of a couple of *vigilantes*, the gunman was never identified and no further action was ever taken.

The downside of the interest taken by the *gremio* in the business transacted by the wholesaler was the pressure that it placed on those operating businesses within the prison to ensure that their bills were paid on time and in full. Although a certain amount of leeway was allowed, the repeated carrying over of debt was severely frowned upon. Individuals who bought goods and products on credit within the prison, however, did not feel the same sense of pressure in ensuring that they paid their bills on time, and thus each Sunday evening was a fraught time for those with businesses as they tried to collect the money that was due to them.

Although everyone who traded within the prison suffered more or less from the same problem, I found that trying, as a foreigner, to run a business was a double nightmare. I did not have a large enough turnover to absorb other than a small amount of credit and bad debt, and many Monday mornings were filled with anger and anxiety as I tried to scrape together sufficient to cover my bill with the wholesaler. Most of the locals who lived in those more affluent dormitories within the prison were extremely proud of their self-proclaimed status as "serious people", a phrase which carries particular significance in South American Spanish as indicating a person who can be relied upon in any circumstances. They did not appreciate my pouring scorn on such claims, pointing out that their attitude to debt belied any right to assert themselves as serious people, and that Mickey Mouse was to my mind a serious person in comparison with half the people whom I dealt with each day.

"Show me the serious people in this goddamn *letra*," I would rant on a Monday morning, when the Sunday's takings had been particularly bad. "As far as I am concerned they're just a crowd of thieves, liars and low-down swindlers."

By the middle of 2003, my relationship with the people of *Letra* 2A had deteriorated to the extent that I felt it wise to move to another dormitory, following months of a steadily worsening atmosphere. Part of the problem was undoubtedly my own attitude towards those people following my experiences in Margarita. I resented those arrogant young clowns swaggering around, enjoying the best of food that their parents and family brought in to them at the weekend. Just give them a week in San Antonio, I thought to myself, and they'll be scrambling to pay their debts on a Sunday evening just for the privilege of being back in Santa Ana, where their life is so easy. It was unfair, of course. Those guys had no concept of what we had been through on the island, and could only judge prison life from their own experiences, genuinely believing that they were having a hard time of it. My attitude was not helped, however, by the knowledge that some of the worst offenders were those whose parents were paying considerable sums to the *gremio* each week to ensure that their dear little sons were protected from harm within the prison.

Once any business with the wholesaler had been transacted, I returned to the *letra* to prepare for the lunchtime sales. It was one of the busiest times of the day, as lunch is the main meal in Venezuela, only a supper normally being prepared in the evening. The early part of the week tended to be quiet, though, as those who had not paid their bills avoided me or at least avoided asking for further credit. Towards the end of the week, they would generally appear once more, with assurances that their family was definitely expected to visit at the weekend and that there would for sure be no problem about paying off all that they owed this coming Sunday.

Once lunchtime was over, I generally locked everything up and headed out for a stroll around the grounds. Being at 3,000 feet above sea level, in the foothills of the Andes, Santa Ana was surrounded by mountains and some of the views were spectacular if one could manage to keep the perimeter fence out of focus. There was a pleasant enough walk around the large football field, which took one well away from the noise and bustle of the central part of the prison, and a cooling breeze was present on most days. I could lie back in the grass and for a few minutes escape from the harsh realities of prison life.

By 4 p.m., it was time to make my way back, as the running water would again be available for an hour or so and people would be returning to the dormitory, perhaps looking for drinks after playing sports all afternoon or working in the dusty atmosphere of the woodworking shops. All prisoners had to be back in their *letras* by 5 p.m. in any case, as they were locked up at that time until briefly opened around 5.30 for the evening head-count.

Once the evening *numero* was over, I prepared an evening meal for myself, then normally spent the evening reading and standing by to serve any drinks that were needed. The prison had a small library which included a few books in English, although I was by that stage able to read most things in Spanish and generally borrowed books in that language in order to practise my language skills.

Most of the locals who owned bottom bunks had a television, plugged into the prison's cable TV network, and they used to pass the evenings watching the dire Venezuelan and Colombian soaps, or listening to *vallenato* music on CDs.

At 9 p.m. the dormitory lights would be switched off and the volume of all TVs and music systems was reduced to a minimum to let people sleep. I generally switched off my bedside light at this stage and tried to sleep, but most nights I tossed and turned for hours, unable to drop off, or slept briefly only to waken after a couple of hours, unable to get to sleep again and waiting for 5.30 in order to begin the whole routine all over again.

I was conscious of a tremendous sense of pointlessness to the time that I was imprisoned in Santa Ana. It was just a case of going through the same, mind-numbing routine, day after day, week after week and month after month, without respite. What, I thought to myself, is being gained here, what are the advantages to society in continuing this endless stream of boring days? The sheer mundanity of life within the prison made the absence of freedom seem even more poignant than it had done in San Antonio.

One tremendous advantage of the prison, though, was that the system which allowed prisoners to work towards their early release actually functioned in Santa Ana. Each week, a *vigilante* would tour the accommodation with a register to confirm that each person running a business was actually working. A daily register was kept in the workshops so that the attendance of each at their place of work was recorded. The information from the registers was transferred each month to prisoners' files in order to keep them up to date and to streamline the process of applying for early release once the appropriate point had been reached.

The judicial system in the state of Táchira, where we were now based, made no distinction between foreign prisoners and locals for the purposes of early release, and so it was possible for a foreign prisoner to leave the prison and live in the local community under licence until such time as his or her sentence had expired.

Unfortunately, the administration of the paperwork during our transfer from Margarita had been dealt with in the usual chaotic fashion, with the result that some of us were regarded as fully transferred, with all case paperwork and control of the case in the hands of the local judges. Others were not so fortunate, and power over these cases remained with the judge on Margarita. For example, Denis was now the responsibility of a judge in Táchira, who had full power over his case, including his right to early release, whilst my case remained under the control of the judge on the Island of Margarita. The British consul tried on several occasions to correct this anomaly, but to no effect, and eventually the rules were altered to make the transfer of cases between one state and another impossible, and so I remained dependent on the judge on Margarita for all decisions over my case, to my eventual great cost.

In a similar manner, the records dealing with work carried out within San Antonio prison had been transferred for only some of the prisoners and not for others. It was to be July 2005 before I was eventually able to arrange for a copy certified as original of that certificate to be placed before the court on Margarita, with the result that I spent a great deal longer time in prison, and then in Venezuela itself, before being allowed home than should have been the case.

Each prisoner was personally responsible for ensuring that the appropriate steps were taken to move the process forward towards eventual release. Any prisoner who did not make the necessary applications to the prison administration might work faithfully each day, but would be left to serve every last day of their sentence, and possibly beyond. When a, highly unusual, audit was carried out in Santa Ana prison in November 2005, it was found that there were five prisoners who had served more than the total of their sentences, but who had never been considered for release. Sadly, it was also found that three of those prisoners had no desire to leave the prison, as they had nowhere else to go, and after many years there, now considered Santa Ana as their home.

As Christmas approached, a small group of us who had transferred from Margarita collaborated in preparing a three-course meal on Christmas Day, and celebrated the day in a very civilised manner. But as we considered the year to come, many of us had our thoughts set on 2003 as being the year when we could look forward to leaving the prison. In my case, it was to prove a year full of disappointments and stress.

CHAPTER FIFTEEN

Eviction

WHEN WE LEFT Margarita, I had brought with me the drawings that I had produced as plans for the model ship that Fred and I had built. Now, Fred approached me with the idea that we should repeat the exercise and build ourselves another ship to replace the "Hope", which had come to a sad end at the hands of the Guardia Nacional.

While being unable to rouse much enthusiasm for the project, I agreed to provide any technical advice required and to carry out the detailed work, such as some of the painting and the rigging of the vessel, work which was too fine for Fred's failing eyesight to cope with. Due to the ease with which the necessary tools and materials could be obtained in Santa Ana, the construction was completed in the space of a very few weeks, and the final painting was carried out by Frank, who had considerable artistic skill. It was almost inevitable that the name painted on the stern should be "Phoenix" and the model was eventually presented to Denis, who brought her back home with him across the Atlantic. She now enjoys a prominent place in his new home.

Enthused by his success in building Phoenix, Fred now came up with an idea to build a model motor yacht, whose deck would lift up to reveal a fully furnished interior. I duly produced the scaled drawings and Fred set to work, building a very presentable gin palace yacht, a project that required many weeks as a result of the detail required, particularly in the interior.

Meanwhile, my relationship with the locals who lived in *Letra* 2A continued to deteriorate. I had made the error of involving the *cabo* in my attempts to get bills paid, and this now rebounded on me.

"You are under the *cabo's* wing," debtors would declare. "Miserable old gringo, using the *cabo* as debt-collector."

Denis had, towards the end of 2002, moved to a dormitory upstairs in the same building, *Letra* 2E. The accommodation there was arranged in a different manner, with each double bunk being built into its own cubicle, built up to greater than head height, and each fitted with an entrance door that the prisoner could lock, either from the inside or from outside with a padlock. He spoke warmly of the advantages of this increased level of privacy and the generally more mature, responsible attitude of the inhabitants of his *letra*.

By the end of May, I had had enough of my struggles with those with whom I currently lived, and I approached Denis to ask if it would be possible to join him upstairs, living on the top bunk in his cubicle. He readily agreed, and so I spoke to the *cabo* of *Letra* 2E and asked if he would permit me to join his residents, which he did without hesitation. My next move was to advise my own *cabo* of my decision and then visit the administration building, where I reported to the senior *vigilante* in charge of allocation to inform him that I wished to change *letras* and that the *cabos* of both were in agreement.

Once the paperwork was completed, I returned to 2A and arranged to move my fridge and the rest of my bits and pieces upstairs. Then I left, with few regrets but a quantity of bad debt, and made my way to 2E to avail myself of Denis's hospitality. In retrospect, it was a move I should have made long before, when things first began to turn sour.

Denis was at this time well advanced in the process of gaining his freedom, as a result of his case being handled by the Táchira court. The first step in the path to freedom was known as *Destacamento de Trabajo* and involved the prisoner living in a kind of halfway house, operated by the prison authorities, from Monday to Friday and going home at weekends. He had been working since shortly after his arrival in the prison with a Colombian who had a workshop where he made small items to sell at weekends, such as cup racks, clocks and egg boxes. These were sanded, painted with fanciful designs and then varnished. Being fully involved in their production, Denis spent each day in the workshop and the weekends manning the stall at which these goods were sold to visitors. Denis had also for some months been building a relationship with a young Colombian woman, who regularly visited her father in the prison and who then continued to visit Denis after her father's release.

Daisy had expressed her willingness to act as "family support" for Denis, which the authorities regarded as a fundamental necessity to enable the release process to go ahead. Thus, all the pieces were in place to allow Denis to push for early release under *Destacamento* as soon as he qualified for it in August 2002. I, meanwhile, would have to wait until the certificate arrived from San Antonio acknowledging that I had worked during my twenty-two months there. It was to prove to be a long wait.

When Denis left the prison in August, it was a difficult time for me. We had been through so much together and now he was moving on, while I had no idea as to when I would be able to leave. As he prepared to go, Denis spoke to me, saying, "I hope you are able to get your paperwork sorted out soon, and that I'll see you out there in San Cristóbal before too long. I'll try and get in touch, once I've got things sorted out." We shook hands, and I wished him luck in this next step of the journey towards freedom.

My main hope was that the repatriation agreement, which had been signed in April 2003 and for which I had applied in May, would produce results within the promised six months to one year and that I would be able to finish my sentence in a British prison.

On Denis's departure, Fred moved up to *Letra* 2E, as he also had become disenchanted with the occupants of our previous dormitory. He and I now shared Denis's former cubicle and settled down to pretty much the old routine. I was still selling drinks and ice from the fridge but only in small quantities and for cash, just sufficient to ensure that my work qualified for a reduction of sentence. Having had my fingers burned once, I had no more desire, as a foreigner, to run a business within the prison.

Our routine came to an abrupt end when, one morning during the last week in September, the *cabo* called a meeting of all the prisoners in the *letra* and informed us that the dormitory was to be shut down for two weeks to be completely refurbished. We each had the rest of the day to find ourselves alternative accommodation in another dorm and would need to be ready to move out, with all our baggage, by 5 p.m. It was an astonishing position to be put into within a prison, and it seemed that the surprises would never cease. Each time we thought that we had seen it all, something new would happen to amaze us.

Fred and I went outside and sat in one of the cafes, drinking coffee, while we considered what to do. Neither of us wanted to move back to our old dormitory, even for a couple of weeks, and there were few alternatives that did not have their own problems. Then I came up with an idea.

"Why don't we see if we can rent a cell?" I asked. All the accommodation in building three was arranged in cells, each *letra* having about twenty cells arranged along the walls, with the remainder being a large open area where many people slept on the floor.

"That seems a reasonable idea, if you think we can get one," replied Fred. "How will we set about getting a cell, though?"

Santa Ana had about half a dozen young prisoners whose job was to find people who were needed in the offices for any reason, including consular visits. Known as *aviones*, or aeroplanes, they "flew" around the prison calling out the names of those whom they were seeking. The nature of their job meant that they knew most things that were going on in the prison, and were thus useful sources of information. I flagged down a passing *avión*, slipped him a 1,000-bolivar note and said, "Tell me, do you know if there are any cells for rent in Building Three at the moment?"

"I believe Douglas has a couple," the young man replied. "Talk to him."

Douglas was the enforcer for the *gremio*, the guy known to us foreign prisoners as Chains. He was only about five and a half feet tall, and around thirty years old, but he was built like a tank. He had a tremendous aura of power and self confidence and walked around the prison, trailed by his several body-guards, as if he owned the place, which to all intents and purposes he did. I had got to know Douglas through my dealings with the wholesaler and had always got on reasonably well with him, although he was a pretty scary character and not to be messed with.

"Where is Douglas just now?" I asked.

"He's up around the classroom area."

Fred and I strolled up to the administration block, where the classrooms were, and came across Chains standing in a corridor talking to someone. His five bodyguards were distributed around the corridor, and I indicated to one of them that I wished to speak to the man himself. Once he had finished with his current business, Chains turned to me and said, "Well, Capitan, what can I do for you?"

"We're looking to rent a cell, if you have one available.

Something not too expensive, and just for a couple of weeks, while our *letra* is being sorted out."

"I have one in 3H that I think will suit you. You need to take it for the month, and it's thirty thousand bolivars a month, paid in advance."

"OK Douglas, I'll take it."

I happened to have the money on me at the time, so I counted out the bills. He then ordered one of his bodyguards to accompany us to 3H and show us the cell.

Building Three was an area that I had always avoided entering, as it was the most densely populated of the three prison buildings and those who slept on the corridor floors were undoubtedly at the rougher end of the prison population. However, we now had little to worry about, as being in a cell known to belong to Chains would ensure that no-one would dare to bother us.

The cell was about ten feet square and had its own water supply, led to a kitchen sink and drainer. It was equipped with one single bed, which Fred kindly agreed that I should have, since I had been responsible for brokering the deal with Chains. Once the heavy steel door was shut, the sounds from outside were muted, and it furnished us with the greatest level of privacy that we had enjoyed since being imprisoned. The big drawback was the communal toilet and shower near the entrance to the *letra*, which was pretty much on a par with what we had been used to in Margarita.

Fred and I spent a couple of hours transporting our belongings to our new accommodation. I left the fridge where it was, as the risk of it being damaged by taking it up and down stairs was too high to justify moving it, especially as we only expected to be away from our *letra* for two weeks. As things turned out, our new cell was to be home not for two weeks but for two and a half months. During that time I was of course, making no money from the fridge, and things began to go wrong with the delivery of the money that was sent to me each month from Scotland. Ensuring that the rent was ready for payment to Chains each month therefore became a bit nerve-wracking, but fortunately Fred had some money sent to him from England and was able to help me out. I had no money left over to buy food though, and my weight once more began to decline.

During the second week in December, our *letra* was declared as having been completed, and Fred and I hurried to move back in. The work that had been done was very impressive. All the cubicles had been rebuilt with hardboard partitions, giving them a uniform appearance as opposed to the haphazard collection of building materials that had been used in the past to create partitions. The whole dormitory had been professionally rewired, with electrical cables properly led in conduits and terminating in electrical sockets in each cubicle. A fresh coat of paint had been applied throughout, giving a fresh, clean appearance. Similar work was to continue in the prison over the following few months, with each *letra* being refurbished in turn. The shops did a roaring trade in electrical plugs, which were now in use for the first time in the prison.

Frank also moved into the *letra*, sharing a cubicle with an Indonesian prisoner whose speciality was cooking up spectacular meals. Philippe, a prisoner from Surinam who had also been in Margarita, joined us in the *letra* and ran the small dormitory shop.

As 2003 drew to a close, I still seemed little further forward towards release, and it was clear that the repatriation arrangements were taking much longer than we had been promised. Indeed, towards the end of November I was called to the prison offices to sign the application for repatriation once more. It seemed that the papers that I had initially signed in June had gone missing somewhere in the Ministry of Justice in Caracas. I hoped against hope that 2004 would bring better fortune, and that I could either leave the prison through early release or through repatriation.

MY BOAT-BUILDING partner Fred, who had initially been sentenced to a term of five years, was released by order of the judge in Margarita during the second week in January, under the arrangements for the second level of early release known as *libertad condicional,* or conditional freedom. This involved reporting to a probation officer every couple of weeks but otherwise being free to live in the community. Daisy had kindly agreed to act as his domestic support, and he went to live with Daisy and Denis for a month until he could organise his own place. Denis had by then also qualified for conditional freedom, and he and Daisy were living in a rented apartment in Santa Teresa, one of the quieter parts of the city of San Cristóbal. They had kept in touch with us by letter and telephone.

While I was naturally delighted to see Fred head off into freedom, it was a wrench, as it meant that the two people to whom I had been closest throughout my imprisonment were now away, and I felt more lonely and isolated than ever. Fred's release was also important from my point of view, however, as it was to the best of our knowledge the first time that a judge from Margarita had signed the necessary papers allowing a foreign prisoner to join the early release programme. It seemed that the new judge now in post on the island was content to allow the prison authorities in the state of Táchira to follow their normal practice with regard to foreign prisoners.

I prepared a letter for the judge, detailing the time that I had spent in prison and arguing that I should now qualify for release, not just under the first or second levels of early release but also under the third and final one, known as *confinamiento,* which was the least demanding of the early release regimes, and requesting that my case be transferred to the Táchira Court. Everything depended on being able to present the court with a copy, certificated as being original, of my record of work from San Antonio. The consul had managed to obtain a copy, which she had brought in to me in November, but this was not valid, as it did not carry the necessary stamps and signatures to confirm that it was a copy of the original document.

I sent off the letter to the judge during the third week of January but received no reply. The postal service in Venezuela is virtually non-existent, and it was necessary to send any letter which one hoped to arrive at its destination within a reasonable time, if at all, through a courier service, at a cost of 10,000 bolivars a time. I was later told that the judge had replied to my letter but that the reply must have got lost in the post. In any case, the reply was to the effect that the regulations had changed so that it was no longer possible to transfer cases between states, and so my application for early release would have to be dealt with in Margarita.

Meanwhile, a session with the legal adviser in the prison led to the conclusion that I would shortly be eligible for early release, simply taking into account the time I had spent in the two prisons added to the extra time that I had earned through my work in Santa Ana, and I therefore began going through the process to obtain a certificate for this work. At this stage, I was spending most mornings in the administration block, attending to the various steps necessary to have my record of work prepared for presentation to the committee whose job it was to calculate what it was worth in terms of reduction of sentence. When not busy with that, I was queuing to use the telephones in order to establish what was going on in Margarita to advance my case for early release.

My efforts were not aided by the fact that my money supply appeared to have simply dried up, although I knew that Robin was faithfully sending money to me on the same date each month. For three months in a row, the consular assistant, Zulay, a short, stocky individual with paler skin than most

Venezuelana, came into the prison with no money for me. It was usually easier to converse with her in Spanish, as she struggled with anything in the least complicated in English.

"Donald," she would comment on each occasion, "you're looking very thin. You're losing a lot of weight. You must look after yourself better."

"Have you brought me any money this month, Zulay?" I would ask, only to be told, "No, there was no money for you this month."

"In that case," I would reply, "I'll be looking a lot thinner the next time you see me."

Eventually we discovered that the person on the Venezuelan desk in the Foreign Office, to whom Robin had always addressed the postal orders he sent for me, had been transferred to Switzerland, and for some months my money had been getting forwarded to Switzerland, before being sent back to London, then on to the embassy in Caracas, before being forwarded to the consulate in San Cristóbal. I supposed I should be grateful that the lady in question had not been transferred to Timbuktu.

Had it not been for the intervention of my pal Chains, who told the prisoner in charge of the telephones that I was to get unlimited credit on them and who also lent me some cash, my efforts towards gaining early release would have been put on hold for a few months. I was not, however, happy at being in debt to that formidable character.

MY CERTIFICATE OF work done in Santa Ana, together with the calculation of how much it was worth in terms of my sentence, were completed by the end of the first week in March, and I immediately had them sent out to the court in Margarita by courier mail service. These papers would now be considered by the judge, whose next step would be to recalculate my sentence, taking the new information into account, and send me back a certificate which would show on what date I qualified for early release. I could prepare an application for early release at that time. The whole system was so cumbersome that it was a wonder anyone ever managed to get released from Venezuelan jails.

At the beginning of March, Daisy came in to visit me, bringing with her some food as well as drawing materials, as I had begun to take an interest in drawing as a way of passing the time, which was hanging increasingly heavily. Daisy promised that she would do anything that was needed to move my case forward with the courts, and would act as my domestic support. Denis was still unable to visit, as he was awaiting some form of identification document which he could show to the prison authorities in order to allow him to enter on visit days. By the middle of April, he had been able to obtain what he needed from the consul in San Cristóbal, and began to visit regularly, which was a huge boost to my morale. I could well imagine the sacrifice it took for him to enter the prison again, as it was not something that I could envisage myself doing under any circumstances once I was allowed to leave.

When the beginning of May came round and there was still nothing back from Margarita, Denis persuaded his judge, who was the senior judge in Táchira State, to call me down for an interview so that I could explain my predicament. So it was that on May 12, I saw the outside of Santa Ana prison for the first time while being driven in a coach, along with fifty other prisoners, on the forty-minute drive to the courthouse in San Cristóbal.

When it came my turn to speak to the judge in his office, he listened sympathetically to my case and then instructed me to dictate a letter to his secretary, detailing my situation. He then prepared a covering letter, to be sent to the judge on Margarita Island along with mine, basically suggesting that she get her act together and do something about putting my situation to

231

rights. Denis, who was waiting outside the judge's office, immediately took the letters so that he could send them to Margarita by courier, while I returned to the prison.

Around this time, Robin sent me a copy of the first part of Jeffrey Archer's trilogy about his prison experiences in Britain, following his conviction for fraud. I was amazed to read what he described as "Hell", for example, his shock at finding that his cell was not equipped with curtains. I could only wonder what the noble lord would have made of a Venezuelan gaol.

On May 22, Frank, who had served seven and a half years of a ten-year sentence, was released under *libertad plena*, or complete freedom, which meant that he was free to return to Britain immediately, having been deemed to have fully served his sentence. This was in accordance with the agreement that we had made with the judge on Margarita following our hunger strike of 2001, whereby any foreign prisoner serving two-thirds of their sentence, and having been working and classed as having been of good behaviour throughout the period, would be released and allowed to return to their country of origin.

His delight at being released and allowed to go home after such a long time can only be imagined. Never one to be hugely sensitive to the feelings of others, he danced around the dormitory, chanting, "I'm going home, I'm going home! I'm out of this shithole!"

I was by this time on tenterhooks, expecting each day to hear some positive news about my release date and continually being disappointed. It is one of the most terrible aspects of Venezuelan prisons that one has to battle for the right to be released and you never know until the last moment when that is going to happen.

At the end of May, I contacted the consul on Margarita and asked if he would be able to go into the court for me, pick up the judge's decision on the recalculated sentence and send it to the prison of Santa Ana by courier. Zulay could take the cost of the courier post from my money the next time she received it. He agreed to do this, but a week went by and nothing appeared, and so I telephoned him again.

"Oh," he said, "I really thought it would have been there by now, I sent it to Caracas the day after you called me."

"Caracas?" I said, filled with dismay. "I thought you were going to send it direct to the prison here."

"Ah, well," he said, "I spoke to Lourdes, who is in charge of prisoner affairs in the embassy in Caracas, and she wanted it to cross her desk before it was forwarded to you."

I telephoned the embassy and spoke to Lourdes, who confirmed that she had received the documents a week before but had been "very busy" and unable to send them on. Her main concern seemed to be the question of how and where I had got the telephone number of the consul in Margarita and to try and give me a smack on the wrist for having dared to contact him.

"All communication must come through either Zulay or me, you have no right to contact any other officials in the country," she said.

I could scarcely believe what I was hearing, and cut her short. "I am making this call on borrowed money, as the Consular Service have proved themselves unable to get my money to me for the past three months. I did not know that a problem existed with my contacting officials in individual consulates, and now that I know, it will not happen again. Now, can you please get the documents to me that I need, as I am long overdue for release and can't move forward until I have these papers?"

"OK, I'll send them this afternoon."

At times, I began to think that I was caught up in a conspiracy to make it as difficult as humanly possible for me to obtain my release.

Eventually, the documents arrived in the prison and I was

able to use them as the basis for an application for early release, under the benefit of *libertad condicional*, which I duly sent off to the judge on Margarita. Her next step should have been to ask for reports from the prison psychologist and the Probation Service to support my application for release, but it was only when Daisy travelled all the way to Margarita at the end of June and laid siege to the courthouse that those requests were produced.

Returning to San Cristóbal, Daisy handed the requests for reports in to the Probation Service office in the town on July 3, only to be told that requests for any given month had to be received before the first of that month, and that my case would therefore go into the August batch. A further problem was that the Probation Service staff took their vacations during August, so I would not actually be interviewed before the beginning of September. By this time, I was punch-drunk from setback after setback and began to feel that this nightmare would go on for ever. It was very difficult to deal with the everyday hassles and stresses of prison life while having this enormous strain hanging over me all the time. I think it was only the regular visits by Denis and Daisy, together with the knowledge of the extraordinary efforts that they were making on my behalf, that kept me sane.

ONE MORNING, I got up as usual around five, and as I was making my way through to the toilet, met a sixty-year-old named Maracucho, one of three prisoners who slept on mattresses in the corridor. He had obviously just returned from an early visit to the toilet, and he plonked himself down on his mattress to resume his sleep. I was not surprised that he might be tired, as I had heard his voice long after lights out the previous evening, clearly having a high old time on cocaine and *michi*.

Half an hour later, I was enjoying a coffee outside the grills of Philippe's little shop, standing next to Maracucho's mattress when the *cabo* came up to me.

"Capitan, I think Maracucho's dead!"

Thinking he was joking, I smiled and said, "I wouldn't be surprised, after his carry-on last night."

"No, really," he exclaimed, "I think he's died."

Still half thinking that it was a joke, I looked down on what I had thought was a sleeping figure, lying face down. Sure enough, he was unnaturally still, and when I bent down I could feel no pulse, although the body was still warm. Pulling his head away from the mattress, it was clear what had happened. He had fallen so deeply into a drunken coma that he had suffocated on his own mattress.

At that moment, the staff arrived for *numero*, and after we had all filed out of the dormitory one of the *vigilantes* and a Guardia Nacional trooper went in and satisfied themselves that the man was dead. They then asked for four prisoners to help and the body was removed from the *letra* to the top of the stairs by the simple expedient of a person getting hold of each corner of his mattress and carrying him out. Once we were all locked into the dormitory again, some *vigilantes* arrived with the stretcher trolley and the body was taken away. It was a stupid and futile death, and his only legacy was the fact that the *michi* distilled in *Letra* 2E would for some time to come be known as *mata Maracucho*, or Maracucho killer.

On Tuesday, August 29, I was called to the prison administration block for the psychological and Parole Service interviews. Both went smoothly and I was promised that the reports would quickly be completed and sent off to Margarita. Once more, Daisy came to the fore, besieging the Probation Service offices and managing to ensure that the reports were ready for postage within twenty-four hours, and then sending them to Margarita by courier mail.

The courier service would normally have been able to deliver

235

them to the courthouse within forty-eight hours, but now nature decided to play a hand in the affair, and Hurricane Ivan, one of the fiercest tropical revolving storms of the 2003 hurricane season and which had caused massive destruction on the island of Grenada, passed close to the north of Margarita, disrupting transport services to the island for a couple of days.

I knew from my reading of the Pilot books four years before that Margarita had not been affected by a hurricane since 1947, but was not hugely surprised that it was being battered now. Anything that could possibly go wrong in the process of my release would do so. I prayed that the judge would drive carefully for the next few days.

Filled with excitement that now all the pieces were firmly in place, I allowed a few days to pass and then began to haunt the archive section of the administration offices, calling in at least twice a day to see if there was any news. On the afternoon of September 15, I wandered up there around 2.30, to find only one official present. He was sitting at a desk, deeply engrossed in reading a document, and I waited by the door for a minute or two before politely knocking. He looked up from his reading, his face expressionless, and said, "Ah, you again, come in and sit there," indicated a chair in front of his desk and then returned to his reading.

As I sat there waiting for him to finish, so that I could ask if there was any news about my case, he suddenly began to read aloud, but quietly, as though reading to himself. At first I gazed into space, then a few phrases caught my attention: "You are to report to judge number one in the court of San Cristóbal within twenty-four hours; you will follow any conditions imposed by that judge; you are to make yourself known to the Probation Service, and report to them as required . . ."

I was electrified. Could it be? After all this waiting, had it finally happened?

"Is that about me?" I managed to stammer, feeling that my heart was about to burst through my chest.

"Well, if you are Donald Iain MacNeil, then I guess it is." Then he chuckled, and handed me the document.

I pretended to read it, although in truth my eyes were unable to focus properly and my hand was shaking so much that the words were a meaningless blur. Then I heard the official say, "Of course, it's far too late today to do anything about it. Just come along first thing in the morning, and we'll sort it all out."

"Don't say that," I pleaded. "It's only a few bits of paper to sort out. Please let me go this afternoon. I'll go and pack my bag while you're doing it, and I can be back here in fifteen minutes, ready to sign the papers and go."

As he chuckled again, I realised that he had been having me on and that he had intended all along to let me go straight away.

I sped out of his office, then pulled up short when I saw Zulay, the consular assistant, inside the glass fronted allocations office talking to a couple of *vigilantes*. I took a deep breath, and walked in.

"Hello, Donald," she said when she saw me.

"Hello, Zulay. I wonder if I can hitch a lift with you down to San Cristóbal this afternoon?"

She looked puzzled for a moment, and then the implications sank in.

"Are you getting out at last? Well done! Of course I'll give you a lift into town. I'll be about an hour, seeing all the British prisoners, so wait for me at the main gate once you are ready."

I made a quick telephone call to Denis, telling him to expect me in about an hour, and then I scuttled off to my *letra* and threw my few bits and pieces into a bag. Denis had been taking odds and sods with him on each visit for the past few weeks, in anticipation of my release, and so I was left with only a couple of changes of clothing and my wash kit. I had sold my fridge and my cubicle a few weeks before, and so there was nothing left to do but say a few hurried goodbyes, then trot back up to the administration block to complete the paperwork, which took no more than a few minutes.

The records official then gave me an authorisation sheet, as well as a copy of the release order signed by the Judge, and directed me to the main gate, where there were another couple of forms to be filled in. My thumbprint was stamped on their exit sheet and I was then allowed to proceed through the gate in order to wait immediately outside for the consul.

Feeling weak at the knees, I sat down with my back to the gatehouse and sat back to savour the unutterable joy of freedom, taking deep breaths of the pure fresh air, which seemed so different to that just a few yards away on the other side of the fence.

After waiting for thirty minutes or so, I heard Zulay approaching the other side of the gatehouse. And as she was signing out, I heard her inquire, "I'm supposed to be meeting a British prisoner here, has he arrived yet?" I chuckled to myself when I heard the sergeant on duty reply, "No madam, I'm afraid you've got that wrong. The prisoners are those inside the fence. The gentleman that I believe you are looking for is a free man, and he is waiting for you just outside."

Now I knew that the worst nightmare of my life was finally over and a new era was beginning.

— CHAPTER SIXTEEN —

In The City

I SAT BACK in Zulay's car as we drove round the outskirts of the prison. Already it looked alien to me, and I could hardly bring myself to believe that I had spent two years and four months within its fences. I knew that nothing would induce me to ever enter its gates again, and I contemplated once more the selflessness that had led to Denis visiting me regularly over the previous few months.

We passed through several small villages as we descended from the mountains, and I gazed with childlike eyes at my surroundings, soaking up this unfamiliar concept of freedom. Life suddenly seemed full of possibilities and challenges.

Zulay knew where Denis lived, and after a drive of about forty-five minutes, we pulled up outside the pizza restaurant that lay on the ground floor of the apartment building. We could see Denis waiting on the balcony outside his flat and he hurried down to greet us. I thanked Zulay for the lift and said goodbye, promising to call in to see her in the next couple of days so that she could sort out some form of identification document for me.

Denis led me upstairs to his flat, whose front and back doors were open to allow the fresh, cooling breeze to pass through. The flat was small but well appointed, with tiled floors, and had been recently painted. As he showed me the bedroom that was to be mine, Denis said, "I expect you'd like a beer, then."

"Would I ever!" I exclaimed, throwing my bag onto the floor beside the bed, and so we hurried down to street level, crossing the road to get to an adjacent *licorería*, where Denis ordered two bottles of the most popular local beer, Polar Ice, and we drank a toast to freedom. Never had a drink tasted so sweet. It was my first beer in four years and four months.

The beer soon went to my head, and after just two I was talking like a budgie, going over the events of the day and of the previous couple of weeks since I had last seen Denis. We returned to the flat and prepared to go down into the city centre to meet Daisy, who was working until seven o'clock in a drapery store and of course knew nothing of my release. It had long been arranged that on my first night of freedom, we would go out for a Chinese meal at a restaurant that I constantly heard being advertised on local radio, the Nan King.

Catching a bus into town, Denis and I alighted on 5th Avenue, close to Daisy's workplace. The street was packed with people, and we had to carefully pick our way around the many street vendors who had goods spread out on the pavement. Entering the shop, I spotted Daisy near the rear of the store. As I approached her, I picked up a bolt of cloth from a nearby shelf, then tugged her sleeve and said, "Excuse me, miss. How much do you want for this?" As she turned towards me, her face took on a look of puzzlement, then surprise, and finally delight as she realised who it was, and she gave me a big hug to welcome me into freedom.

The shop was in the process of closing, and so the three of us made our way out to the street, where we hailed a taxi and made our way to the Nan King, where we enjoyed a delightful meal and I continued to savour the sheer delight of being a free man again.

The following morning, I was required to report to the courthouse, and so Denis and I accompanied Daisy on the bus to work, and then walked the few hundred yards to court. The officials there had no paperwork on me as yet but they opened a file, taking a photocopy of my release order, and then told me to report to the Probation Service office at the other end of the town. The Probation Office had not received any paperwork from Margarita either, and so they simply recorded my visit and asked me to continue coming in once a week until the documents arrived and they were able to deal with me officially. We returned to Santa Teresa, where Denis introduced me to the local Internet café. I opened an e-mail account and sent messages back to friends in Britain to let them know that my freedom had finally been approved.

One of my priorities was to get my teeth sorted. I had suffered from a lifelong phobia of dentists and my teeth were thus in fairly poor condition when I was arrested, and had deteriorated considerably since. I now took the attitude, after all I've been through, what the hell can a dentist do to me that I need to fear? I therefore walked in to the nearest dental surgery and made an appointment for an examination and estimate. The dentist proved to be a delightful, friendly woman, and I was to spend an hour each day on her treatment chair for the next three weeks while she worked her magic on my decayed molars. At the end of the treatment, she had restored my smile, and the bill came to just over £150, which was paid thanks to a whipround amongst my friends back in Scotland, who were delighted to learn that I had at last done something to sort out my terrible teeth.

The sting in the tale came when, encouraged by my positive experiences in the dentist's surgery, Daisy decided to have an impacted wisdom tooth that had been giving her trouble for some weeks extracted by the same woman. On the last day of my treatment, therefore, Daisy entered the surgery and had her tooth removed, but she was to suffer greatly as a result. Afterwards, her jaw swelled up and locked, and following a month of unsuccessful treatment with antibiotics, she was admitted to the city's General Hospital, where she was to spend a month. It eventually transpired that the dentist had dislocated her jaw in extracting the tooth, a fact that was not spotted until the very end of her long treatment process.

Visiting Daisy in hospital gave Denis and I an eye-opening insight into the workings of yet another of Venezuela's public institutions. It was a sobering experience. Each patient had to buy their own medicines, syringes, dressings and surgical packs. The officially recommended post-surgical wound-cleansing antiseptic was a well-known brand of mouthwash. When the nursing staff came round the wards to administer medicines, the first question was always, "Have you bought your medicine today?" If the patient or their relatives had been unable to do so, the staff simply moved on to the next bed, leaving the deprived patient unmedicated, no matter the seriousness or gravity of their situation or the degree of their suffering. Some months later, a doctor who was studying English with me told me that she was shortly moving to Europe to work, as she simply could not cope any longer with trying to practise medicine under such conditions.

One day, on entering the hospital, we noticed a stand in the foyer where a middle-aged man was selling books. On strolling across to examine his products, we found many medical volumes and a few English language courses. We chatted to the guy for a few minutes, and he then asked if I might be interested in working for his company selling the English language courses at a local trade fare to be held in January. He gave me the name and telephone number of the head of sales and suggested that I contact him. This led to my first job on leaving prison, as a book salesman.

In the meantime, as a regular visitor to the Internet café in Santa Teresa I had got to know the staff, and one of them one day sent a lady over to talk to me who was looking for English lessons. Her name was Morna and she was a biologist who had done some TV work. She already spoke English to a reasonable standard, and basically wanted conversation practice in order to improve her pronunciation and grammar. It was agreed that I would visit her home on three days per week to give her English lessons. After a few weeks of this, Morna mentioned to me that a local language academy was looking for English teachers, and so I decided to present myself as a candidate.

The Alpha Centre was only ten minutes' bus ride away from Santa Teresa, and after I had completed a test and interview they agreed to take me on as a full-time English teacher, starting early in the new year. Now that I had a job, it only remained for me to find myself a place to live, as I clearly could not go on impinging on Denis and Daisy's lives for ever.

By this time, I was regularly meeting Fred, who had left the prison in January and who now rented a small, single-storey, two-bedroom house just a couple of blocks away from Denis. When Fred announced his intention to move down into the town centre, I readily grabbed the opportunity to take over the rent of his current house, moving in at the beginning of December. After all the trials and setbacks of the last few years, it seemed that everything was falling nicely into place for me to have a reasonable life while serving out the last part of my sentence.

Santa Teresa was a nice area to live in, built on a hillside rising up above the main part of the town. The views of the surrounding mountains were spectacular, particularly in the early evening, when dramatic thunderstorms roiled around the peaks. There was rarely any trouble in that part of the city, although the need to take due care was highlighted by the fact that even the local bakery had a security guard armed with a pump-action shotgun. You had to take great care in the city centre however, and the sprawling *barrios* on the outskirts of the centre, largely consisting of corrugated iron huts jumbled cheek by jowl on precipitous, landslide-prone slopes, were simply no-go areas for any foreigner, or indeed for anyone who did not actually belong there.

Christmas 2004 was a very different affair to the four that had gone before, and on Christmas Day, Daisy, Denis and I enjoyed a barbecue in front of my house, cooked on a somewhat retro barbecue stand constructed from an old car wheel hub mounted on three reinforcing rods and with a grill on top. On New Year's Eve, Daisy went across the nearby border to visit her family in the town of Cúcuta, while Denis spent the night at my place and we toasted the coming of the New Year to each of the various time zones that we were now acquainted with. We both looked forward with eager anticipation to finally being able to return home in 2005.

At the beginning of January, I attended the week-long training course in sales techniques at the book sales firm, before starting work at the Trade Fair, which ran for ten days. I worked in a team of five, manning a large stand specialising in English learning material. We worked alternate days at the fair, being expected to distribute sold material and follow up on contacts during the days when we were not involved in direct sales. The days on the stand were long and hard, and I did not have a great number of sales, lacking the fluency to be able to deliver a rapid-fire sales pitch to the passing crowd. I did have some successes, though, and the line, "Hello, do you want to learn to speak English?" was often enough to stop someone in their tracks long enough for one of the other vendors to home in on them and confirm a sale. Most of all it was great fun and I made some good friends amongst my sales team-mates.

The day after the fair was over, I started my career with Alpha, teaching English to fee-paying students. The days were long, typically starting at 8 a.m. and finishing at 8-8.30 p.m., with an hour and a half off for lunch, but the work was not difficult, with a maximum of three students per half-hour session, and it enabled me to put behind me the horrors of the previous few years.

Each Saturday, I finished at 2 p.m., and Sunday was free, so I generally went round to Denis's place on a Saturday afternoon, and we would drink a few beers and put the world to rights, spending hours standing on the balcony and discussing what we had been through, what it all meant now in terms of our attitudes to life, and how we would cope with the future. Acting as each other's "therapists" we both found to be hugely beneficial, and it led to the development of a deep and lasting friendship, based on mutual understanding, trust and, at times, brutal honesty.

The week before Easter, I was invited to spend the weekend in a small farmhouse in the mountains. The grandparents of one of the girls on my sales team at the Fair lived high in the mountains, above the small town of Queniqea, about three hours' drive from San Cristóbal, and she had invited the five members of the sales team to spend the weekend in one of the cottages that they owned. We travelled by bus along the steep, narrow mountain roads to the delightful little town, and then had to walk for an hour up a steep hillside before arriving at the cottage, where we soon got a fire going in the wood-burning stove, then sat outside to enjoy the sight of the sun disappearing behind the dramatically shaped mountain peaks.

We spent the days exploring the mountains, and in the evening, returned to the cottage for some traditional meals, accompanied by *calentado*, a hot drink similar to mulled wine. On the Sunday afternoon, we walked across the mountain slopes for about twenty minutes to pay a visit to our host's grandparents, a wonderful couple in their nineties who had brought up eleven children in their home in the hills and who were as full of vigour, fun, and the joys of life as many people half their age. They would not trade their simple existence on the mountain for anything, and I couldn't blame them. Their only regret was that all their sons and daughters had moved away to the cities and they had no-one to keep up the work of sugar cane production on the land. I was sorry to leave that wonderful spot when it became time to return to the city. Although I was anxious to return home, I felt fortunate to be able to see another side to Venezuela and its people, to set against the almost totally negative experiences of the previous four years.

Denis knew that the date on which he would be free to go home was December 7, 2005. Having spent sixteen months more than him in prison, my end-of-sentence date should have been considerably before that, but the time that I had spent in San Antonio had still not been considered by the court for the purposes of sentence reduction, and so I was recorded as being due to finish my term on February 12, 2006. The only way to bring that date forward was to furnish the court with a copy, certificated as original, of my record of work while detained in San Antonio.

When I contacted Santa Ana prison, they assured me that they did not have an original copy and neither did the consulate. The court officials in Margarita assured me that they did not have one in my file there. Finally, in the middle of May, I was able to speak to a newly appointed director of the prison of San Antonio, who assured me that she would look for the necessary paper in my file if I sent her a fax explaining all the details. During the second week in June, I was assured by the director that the document had now been delivered to the courthouse.

In May, Denis obtained a new passport from the British Embassy, who had altered their previous position that they would only issue passports on completion of sentence. Desperate to return home, he now had a very difficult decision to make. Technically, there was nothing to stop him boarding a plane in Caracas, to return to the UK. He telephoned his father, to ask his advice.

"Son," he said, "I can't wait to get you back home, but I think it's better to stick it out for another few months, and then you will be free and clear and will not spend the rest of your life looking over your shoulder."

Denis decided to stay where he was. It was a decision that was to stand him in good stead, for months later his judge absolutely guaranteed him that his certificate of *libertad plena*, or full release, would be signed on December 7, saying, "I'll make sure you have that paper on time because I appreciate what you have done. I know how difficult it is for you as a foreigner to stay here and how easy it would have been to go."

On June 12, I received my passport from the Embassy. I expected to be going home by the end of July or the beginning of August, and so I did not face Denis's dilemma. There now followed a marathon of telephone calls to the court officials on Margarita, as I attempted to move my case forward. In June, I was told that the court had not received the document in time for it to be considered by the relevant committee at their June meeting. At the end of July, I was told that the committee had been unable to meet that month and that my case would now be considered in August.

At the beginning of August, I handed in my month's notice to the Alpha language centre, fully convinced that I would be on my way home by the beginning of September. I continued to have some contact with the Centre after I left, assisting in the production of new teaching materials with Elizabeth, the principal teacher. I helped out by proofreading books one and two of the series, and contributing some articles to the third book, as well as recording the accompanying CD. While carrying out this work, I spent several very happy weekends with her and her delightful family at her spacious home above the little village of Michelena, about an hour's drive from the city of San Cristóbal. I first visited her home to take part in a lavish leaving party that she and the staff put on for me at the beginning of September.

When I telephoned the court at the end of August, I was told that the court had been all but closed down for the month for vacations, and so my case would not now be presented until the committee met again towards the end of September! I could not believe it; this seemed to be a repeat of the nightmare that I had endured the previous year, when I was trying to obtain authorisation to leave the prison.

My call to the court at the end of September elicited the information that my case had been considered but that there was no further reduction in sentence due to me. I was now in despair; this could not be happening all over again. After many frantic phone calls, I eventually tracked down a court official who was prepared to listen to my case and then to sit with my file in front of her while I went through the various documents that should be contained in the file. Eventually, I heard a gasp.

"Gosh, you're right. The time in Margarita has never been calculated for the purposes of reduction of sentence."

"OK, so when can my case be put before the committee again, so that this mistake can be put right?"

"The committee doesn't meet again until the end of October."

"I see, well, I'll look forward to some good news at the end of October then."

When I called at the end of October, I was told that, for various reasons, the committee had not been able to meet and that my case would therefore be dealt with in November. The date was later put back to December 13. This was getting completely beyond a joke. Throughout the autumn, I had tried on various occasions to get some help with my problem from the Embassy but met with complete indifference from Lourdes, the official who would need to sanction any action proposed. I became convinced that my chances of getting home before Christmas were slim.

Denis and Daisy left San Cristóbal to return to the UK on December 7, and it was a poignant moment when we said goodbye, as I still did not know for sure if I would be back in Britain for Christmas. One thing I did know is that I had two very close and dear friends for life, and that we would be seeing a great deal of each other in the future, whatever happened.

In the meantime, Denis and I had been contacted by a British television company, who proposed the filming of a drama documentary about our story. Following our previous experience four years before, when we had been demonised by Tom Mangold in a *Panorama* programme, we were both tremendously reluctant to consent to taking part in a television programme, and it was only after many hours of telephone conversations, during which we became convinced of the benign intentions of the production team towards us, that we agreed to take part.

The film crew's schedule called for them to film an interview with me in San Cristóbal on December 12, and then to move on the 13th to the Island of Margarita to film the drama part of the programme. It was agreed that they would film Denis back in the UK. For once, the coincidence of timing seemed to be working in my favour, and the film crew agreed that I could travel with them to Margarita to give me an opportunity to "camp out" on the doorstep of the courthouse and collect my release papers personally. I obtained a letter from my parole officer authorising me to travel to Margarita at the beginning of December.

Thus it was that I found myself, on the afternoon of December 13, stepping out of an aircraft onto the soil of the island that I had hoped never to set foot on again. It was a strange experience, and the heat and humidity immediately woke within me memories and feelings that I would much prefer to have remained dormant. I remained edgy and unhappy throughout my stay on the island, even after I had made a telephone call on the morning of the 14th and been able to confirm that the committee had finally met, considered my case and awarded me the time that I was due. I was told my release papers would be ready for me to collect on the morning of the 15th.

I visited the courthouse early in the morning and was handed my certificate of *libertad plena*, without a hint of an apology for the fact that it was now, according to their own calculations, four months, twenty-one days and twelve hours overdue. On the morning of the 16th, as the aircraft left the ground for the flight to Caracas, I vowed that this time I would definitely not be coming back to the island.

I spent a few days in San Cristóbal, putting all my bits and pieces in order, packing and saying farewell to people. Then, early on the morning of the 20th, I made my way out to San Antonio airport to begin the journey back to the UK, delighted that, against all odds, I was going to be home for Christmas.

Watching the Scottish countryside roll beneath the aircraft as we prepared to land at Glasgow airport on the afternoon of the 21st was wonderful, and I was filled with excitement at the thought that in the next few minutes I would be treading my native soil once more.

Robin was waiting for me when I entered the arrivals hall, and said simply, "You made it, then," as we shook hands. We both knew that there had been many times over the years when it seemed unlikely that I would in fact make it. It was wonderful to be reunited with someone who had proved himself to be a true friend during those difficult times.

It was also only when back in Britain that I finally discovered who was behind the cocaine smuggling plot. I had never met, or known anything about, the gang who financed and arranged the operation. Everything had been done through Mick, on a strictly need-to-know basis, and frankly, the less I knew, the better. But someone sent me a copy of a press release that had been issued by the National Crime Squad in England on November 10, 2005, which suggested that the organisers had come from West Derby in Liverpool, a city with an unenviable reputation for producing drug traffickers. The press release read:

WEST DERBY MAN JAILED FOR SIGNIFICANT COCAINE SEIZURE

A West Derby man who masterminded the attempted importation of £48 million worth of cocaine from South America into Europe has been jailed today for 28 years.

300 kilos of the cocaine was seized from a yacht moored at the Hilton Marina in the Venezuelan island of Margarita in 2000. The crew, including two British nationals, were all jailed in Venezuela.

Today, at Liverpool Crown Court, Edward Robert Jarvis, DoB 05/04/65, of Holly Grange, Sandfield Park, West Derby, was found guilty of conspiracy to supply cocaine and was sentenced to 28 years. He was also found guilty of an offence under the Misuse of Drugs Act and sentenced to 12 years to run concurrently. He was also sentenced to two years after pleading guilty to obtaining a UK passport by deception, again to run concurrently. His sentencing followed an investigation by the Chorley Branch of the National Crime Squad.

The court heard how in April 1998 JARVIS, using a false passport, rented a house in Zwanenburg in the Netherlands, which was subsequently raised by local police. 200 kilos of amphetamine, 238 kilos of cannabis, a sealing machine for wrapping drugs, a semi-automatic pistol and ammunition were found. The total estimated street value of all the drugs seized was just under £1m. Three UK nationals were arrested and sentenced to periods of imprisonment in the Netherlands.

Also discovered at the house was a UK passport with JARVIS's photo in – but under the name of Peter Jones. Examination of the passport showed JARVIS had travelled to Turkey and South America.

In 1999 JARVIS applied for and was subsequently issued with another false passport in the name of Andrew Rainford.

In October of that year an associate of JARVIS bought an ocean going British registered yacht from an innocent party for £31,000 in cash delivered in a Tesco's carrier bag. The associate then recruited two crewmen from Burnley and Hartlepool.

The 38-foot yacht was collected from Rhodes, Greece, and subsequently sailed through the Mediterranean, across the Atlantic to the Caribbean, ultimately stopping at the island of Margarita, Venezuela, in March 2000.

The yacht and its crew then waited for two months during which time JARVIS, using his alias Rainford, visited the island. He stayed in four different hotels whilst there, each time paying his bills in cash.

On two occasions JARVIS, again using his Rainford alias, wired money from Spain to the crewmen in Venezuela, who then began renting a large people carrier from a local company in Margarita.

In May 2000 the two crewmen were seen unloading large packages of a white substance from the vehicle onto the yacht. The Venezuelan National Guard boarded the yacht and arrested them. 300 kilos of cocaine was seized onboard.

Following further enquiries by the Venezuelan authorities a further consignment of 293 kilos of cocaine was seized and four Venezuelans and a Colombian arrested. It was apparent the second seizure was also destined for the yacht. The street value of all the drugs seized was in excess of £48 million.

The British crew, the Venezuelans and the Colombian were all sentenced to periods of imprisonment in Venezuela.

In October 2003, JARVIS was sentenced to four and a half years imprisonment at Preston Crown Court after pleading guilty to tax evasion, money laundering and passport offences, as a result of a separate investigation by the National Crime Squad.

A year later, on his first day of parole, JARVIS was arrested upon release from prison in relation to the events in the Netherlands and Venezuela, and obtaining a false passport by deception.

"JARVIS was the head of an organised crime enterprise and effectively played a supervisory role renting accommodation, vehicles, supplying cash to lesser players," said Branch Commander John Tyrer of the National Crime Squad.

"He is a career criminal who has travelled the world extensively, living a life of luxury without any apparent means of support. The drugs seized in Venezuela were sourced from Colombia and were ultimately destined to be distributed into Europe – including the UK. This was without doubt a significant world seizure.

"The National Crime Squad would like to express its gratitude to the Venezuelan authorities, Staffordshire police, the Crown Prosecution Service and police in Antigua, Gibraltar, Greece, Spain, the USA, Curacao, the Netherlands and Cuba for their assistance in this investigation."

Gerry Wareham, Branch Crown Prosecutor said: "Jarvis's prosecution by the Organised Crime Division of the CPS relied on a complex trail of evidence from around the world which was uncovered by the NCS and police forces at home and abroad. While Jarvis lived a life of luxury, the drugs he was importing were responsible for untold misery and crime. Global criminals impact on the entire international community and require a cooperative international response from criminal justice agencies. This case has hit back at them seizing a massive £48 million of cocaine intended for our society. This can be regarded as an example of the type of work that will be undertaken by the newly formed Organised Crime Division of the CPS."

None of these names meant anything to me. I had been utterly dispensable to these people, a commodity or business expense like the yacht *Pulse* or the hotel rooms we booked. The severity of the sentence – twenty-eight years – reflected how seriously the British courts viewed this particular plot, and I could only feel the greatest relief that I had not received a similar sentence in Venezuela, for it would surely have been the end of me.

I spent a couple of months staying with friends until I was able to rent a flat of my own, simply relishing the joy of freedom and experiencing everything as if for the first time. A few delightful days were spent rediscovering the Scottish mountains, reawakening muscles that had lain dormant for years. In January 2006, I was able to travel to Hartlepool, where I was delighted to renew acquaintance with friends who had remained in contact with me during my time in prison, and to thank them for their support over the years.

The search for work has, so far, proved difficult, although I am sure that something suitable will come up. I have completed a computer course, ensuring that I am up to date with current word processing, spreadsheet and database applications, and am now the proud owner of a European Computer Driving Licence. I am confident that, having survived the hardships of the past few years, the quest for employment will not prove to be insurmountable.

My friendship with Denis and Daisy has continued. We talk regularly by telephone, I have spent two long weekends visiting them, and they came up to Scotland to spend an Easter with me. They form a very important part of my life now, one of the few really positive things to have emerged from all that we have been through.

The preparation of this book has been a cathartic experience for me, allowing me to put into perspective some of the dreadful events of recent years. There were parts that were particularly painful to write, given the need to relive experiences that I would much prefer to forget, but that activity has in itself formed a necessary part of the healing process.

I have little idea as to what the future holds for me, but one advantage of having been to Hell and back is that there is now nothing that life can throw at me that can ever seem so bad.

Chavez And The Lovely Revolution

ONE OF THE positive things that came out of my enforced stay in Venezuela for five and a half years was the opportunity to observe at close hand the recent changes that have taken place in that country and that continue to take place at an increasing rate.

For much of the twentieth century, Venezuela, in common with most Latin American countries, lived under the shadow of the United States. Successive right-wing governments were content to play second fiddle to their rich neighbour in the north in exchange for the opportunity to amass huge personal fortunes. The country engaged in the no-win game of exporting raw materials from its vast mineral resources at bargain basement prices whilst importing finished products made with these same materials at premium rates. Meanwhile, the infrastructure of the country was allowed to decay and the plight of the poor worsened with each successive generation.

All that was to change when Hugo Rafael Chávez Frías burst onto the political scene. Born into a modest family, and raised by his beloved paternal grandmother in a small, earth-floored house deep in the heart of the countryside, he eventually joined the military as a means of escaping the poverty trap of his youth.

Hugo Chavez's officer-training year was the first to benefit from what seems in retrospect an extraordinary decision by the Venezuela military, to provide a university education to their cadets at the same time as they were receiving their military training. Thus the military High Command created a rod with which to beat their own backs, as the new breed of young officers, educated in such areas as international law, history and philosophy, were almost programmed to be malcontents, unhappy with the way things were done both in the military and in the country at large. As a precocious student, with a keen social awareness, Hugo Chavez was among the leaders of this group of dissidents, and by the time he had achieved the rank of lieutenant colonel, his dissatisfaction had grown to the extent that he led a military uprising against the government in February 1992, ending up imprisoned for two years after the uprising failed.

Resorting to the campaign trail following his release from prison, he struck such a chord with the common people that he was elected as President with a very convincing majority, assuming power in February 1999. Since then he has made huge efforts to bring about the reforms that he sees as being vitally necessary for the country, his self-styled *Revolución Bonita* (the Lovely Revolution), whilst simultaneously fighting a rearguard action against the old vested interests and the right-wing opposition parties, who enjoy tremendous financial and other support from their American allies.

Gifted with a formidable intellect, a tremendous capacity for work and being very widely read, Chavez is more than a match for them. As one of the frequently heard chants at his rallies has it, "Chavez has driven them nuts . . ." Each attempt by the opposition to sabotage his government has left him in a stronger position than before, and his efforts to help the poor have endeared him to the vast majority of the Venezuelan people.

Venezuela is in a process of rapid and profound change. In two years, one and a half million people of all ages were taught to read and write through a Chavez-inspired national programme. The tribes of indigenous people were taught to read and write in their native languages as well as Spanish. The country has now been officially declared by the UN as being free of illiteracy.

Teams of medics have now been working in the *barrios* for four years, providing medical treatment to people for whom such treatment was, in the past, an impossible dream. In recent years, these teams have begun to be equipped with modern, properly equipped diagnostic and treatment centres in which to carry out their work. Hundreds of thousands of Venezuelans have been flown to Cuba for cataract surgery, at no cost to themselves, in the so-called *Operación Milagro*, or Project Miracle.

The prisons continue to be a terrible indictment on Venezuelan government and society. In 2005, nearly 400 prisoners met a violent death and close to 600 were injured. Nearly 30,000 prisoners continue to live in conditions described by human rights organisations as inhuman. The Government is addressing the issue, and a working party is focused on the need to drastically improve the conditions in which prisoners are held. The intention is that new prisons will be built over the next few years to completely replace the old system, and that the new prisons will be properly run, by trained staff. It is a move that cannot come to soon if Venezuela wishes to consider itself a modern, dynamic democracy.

In recent years, Chavez and his government have been able to take advantage of the high oil prices to begin a transformation of the country's economy. Vast sums are now being diverted towards huge infrastructure projects, such as new road and rail systems, bridges and water purification plants. Perhaps more importantly, the materials for all these projects will be produced within the country, and a new "steel city" has recently been inaugurated to produce the steel that Venezuela needs, all of which would previously have been imported from abroad.

The problem of personal security remains a major issue, and one which will need to be addressed before Venezuela can hope to take advantage of its huge potential as a tourist destination. I sincerely hope that the towns, cities and transport networks can be made safe from the risk of theft and casual murder, as the country has some of the finest scenery in the world, and the vast majority of its people are warm, welcoming and generous.

As long as President Chavez is able to keep at bay the malevolent influence of the United States Government in the region, I believe that Venezuela will be transformed in a very positive manner over the next few years, and that the Chavez style of "twenty-first century socialism" will become the model not just for Latin America but for many developing regions across the world.

The most perfect government is that which produces the greatest possible amount of contentment, the greatest amount of social security, and the greatest amount of political stability.
Simón Bolívar
South American Liberator (1783–1830)